# Aquatic Productivity:

## an introduction to some basic aspects of biological oceanography and limnology

Cover photo is of inshore marine zoöplankton, collected in late spring at Woods Hole and preserved in formalin. The sample includes adult calanoid copepods, two arrow-worms, a subadult shrimp (probably *Crangon*), other shrimp larvae, and an adult amphipod (*Calliopius*). A key is provided in Figure 4·4C on page 65 [Photo by the author.]

# Aquatic Productivity:

## an introduction to some basic aspects of biological oceanography and limnology

## W. D. Russell-Hunter

*Syracuse University and The Marine Biological Laboratory, Woods Hole*

The Macmillan Company

Collier-Macmillan Limited, London

PERCONTARI AUDE

For **P. D. R-H.;** *may his descendants*
*bear these arms in a well-fed world.*

**The Macmillan Company**
866 Third Avenue, New York, New York 10022

**Collier-Macmillan Canada, Ltd., Toronto, Ontario**

Library of Congress catalog card number: 77–113935

PRINTING    456789    YEAR    3456789

*Nothing in nature stands alone* . . . —John Hunter, 1786

*La vie et la mort sont choses corrélatives* . . . *la vie ne saurait exister sur la terre, s'il n'y avait pas en même temps, non seulement la mort, mais la dissolution,* . . . —Louis Pasteur, 1865

# Preface

THIS BOOK is addressed to beginners in biology and to some nonbiologists. It presents only certain basic (or elementary) aspects of aquatic productivity, some understanding of which I believe to be fundamental both to *the survival of man* and to our comprehension of evolutionary processes. Some biologists—especially those already accustomed to think of ecological interactions in quantitative terms—will find much of it trite. However, as teachers they are unfortunately few, and the synoptic treatment attempted here can be defended as an essay to communicate the significance of recent studies in the energetics of organic productivity to a wider audience without training in mathematics and with little or no background of biology or chemistry. More widespread educational exposure to certain elementary aspects of biological oceanography and of freshwater biology is urgently needed in our western culture.

The purpose and bias of a book are rarely independent and this book is no exception. Consideration of organic productivity in aquatic environments has both applied and theoretical significance. With the increasing rates of human population expansion, marine and freshwater productivity will have to play an increasing part in world protein nutrition. Given appropriate levels of research and development, further improvements of existing fishing methods, in combination with entirely new kinds of exploitation of aquatic productivity, *can* provide a greatly increased supply of protein in the next decades. However, it is important to realize that organic productivity is *finite*: there is a limit on the trophic potential of the world (even allowing for the future development of human synthetic abilities), and thus a *real* biological limitation on future population growth in man. On the theoretical side, studies on bioenergetics in aquatic ecosystems are contributing significantly to a new and modified understanding of the processes of evolution.

Aquatic environments—particularly the seas and fresh waters of temperate zones—have been the subject of much ecological research in recent years. It is now possible to survey and discuss some fundamental aspects of aquatic productivity in a short book at a relatively elementary level. The basic biogeochemistry of organic cycles, and the peculiarities of biomass transfer (or energy flux) between organisms of different trophic levels, can readily be illustrated using marine and freshwater examples (which are relatively well understood). This is done in the initial chapters. The longer chapters (3 through 7) survey the seasonal and other basic factors controlling primary productivity and food-chains in the temperate oceans and then include a shorter consideration of the more unusual trophic conditions found in polar and tropical seas, and in lakes and rivers of various types. Chapters 8 through 11 consist of a closer examination of some aspects of biogeochemistry and of energy transfer, encompassing the importance of trophic ratios such as carbon:nitrogen, the prediction of optimal cropping levels for fisheries, and the significance of productivity studies to evolutionary biology. The *finite* nature of organic productivity is explored in an annotated series of simple computations in Chapters 12 and 13, and the future exploitation of the oceans in Chapters 14 and 15, with some recapitulation—in Chapter 16—of geopolitical implications. Admittedly, the coverage is far from exhaustive and some examples are "classic" rather than modern: this is an evangelical rather than a dogmatic book. Obviously a more rigorous survey of the subject matter would be required as part of the professional training of graduate biologists. That a simpler survey of the fundamentals of aquatic productivity can be usefully communicated to nonbiologists has already been proven with diverse groups: with a workers' educational extension program in Scotland, with staff officers of an élite armed service, and with small experimental tutorial groups of nonscientist students (potential honors freshmen at Syracuse University).

The subject matter has not always been in the realm of public ignorance. This is the field which Sir Alister Hardy called "scientific natural history" and H. G. Wells had earlier designated as an extension of human economics "to the whole world of life." It is of some interest that, in the early years of this century in the country schools of certain districts both in Scotland and in northern New England, there was taught "rural science" which involved a primitive quantification of agricultural, fishery, and human ecology. Only very recently—and in a few high schools of limited regions—has biological oceanography returned to school curricula. Some public education in aspects of organic productivity is urgently needed—if only to prevent politicians talking about "inexhaustible" natural resources (particularly those of human foodstuffs or of fossil fuels). The motivation of authors of books is necessarily mixed, and a background of Judaeo-Christian ethics is of surprisingly little help in analysis. Hindu academics can probably do much better: the dialogue of the Bhagavad Gita, for example, contains more on the analysis of mixed motives than does the entire Pentateuch. Rationally, the motives involved in preparing an introductory book should not include hope of professional esteem or of fiscal returns. In the present climate of science, any reputation for scholarship is usually diminished by publication of an elementary text, and more profitable returns come for unit time spent in research or even in teaching. Among the motives (and consequent biases) behind this book are a desire to communicate certain "human" matters outside a peer group of biologists, and a possibly anachronistic resentment at the present fragmentation of even elementary knowledge within most human cultures.

As C. P. Snow (now Lord Snow) pointed out more than a decade ago from his peculiarly promiscuous stance, the humanistic and scientific subcultures of education in the English-speaking world do not normally interact. Argument about this has continued—about causes, about extent, and about "cures"—though few dispute that there still exists an unfortunate separation, even in the more diffuse secondary education of the United States. There is also, as discussed by Snow, an educational gulf between pure science and technology in some fields, which is largely absent in German or Russian secondary and tertiary scientific education. The effects both of the major polarization, and of the minor one between pure and applied science, can often be exaggerated. Nevertheless, even the degree of both separations which the best general education allows (largely because the individual competencies of academics are confined to small subfields of the major disciplinary divisions) represents practical and intellectual loss to mankind. In the fields of ecology and bioenergetics discussed in this book, there has been an unusual degree of interaction between science and technology. The oustanding contributions from applied areas have included those of brewery management to statistical methods, practical agricultural genetics to statistical theory, both the life-insurance industry and practical fisheries research to predictive population dynamics, and agricultural animal husbandry to physiological energetics.

On the other hand and unfortunately, studies in organic productivity are *terrae incognitae* to most academics and teachers in the humanities, and to their "applied" fringe of social scientists and political theorists. This is tragic. Narrow interpretations of culture are inappropriate today. A valid culture for our species would needs involve considerable insight into our natural environment and clear appreciation of the finite extent of human artifacts within it, along with a real comprehension of the creative achievements in the past, and the aspirations for the future, of all kinds of men. A well-educated man should have a critical knowledge, not merely of the literature of one national group over a tiny historical period, not merely of that part of physics concerned with electron-energetics in semiconductors, but of these parts comprehended within a wider appreciation of, and pride in, our species. This book is a small attempt at a contribution to a truly humanistic culture—if its message is appreciated by a few teachers and even a single politician, then the sweat will have been worthwhile. A major source of bias therefore is that passionate (and, to some observers, occasionally pathetic) faith in education which is characteristic of Scots and Ashkenazim, and which provides a classic example of mixed motivation. The book also shows many, more minor, biases. Completed in a year of lunar landings, and in the face of a biology increasingly molecular in emphasis, it presents the view that, quite apart from their applied significance, certain aspects of aquatic ecology can be included among the exciting growing points of biology as a modern science. There is, perhaps, some overemphasis on "classic" marine examples from Scotland and from around Cape Cod: these reflect the limitations of one author's background but, for historical reasons in the development of biological oceanography, are less biased than might be supposed.

Examples used in sections of Chapters 6, 8, and 11, and in scattered paragraphs elsewhere, are based on field and laboratory work on the physiological ecology of molluscs by my associates and me, which work has been supported by a research grant (GM-11693) from the U.S. National Institutes of Health. Considerable parts of Chapter 12 (though with somewhat modified data in the computations), and small sections in Chapter 13 and elsewhere, are based on a group report on certain aspects of biological oceanography which resulted from discussion-meetings with Professor Edward C. Raney of Cornell University and Professor Wolf Vishniac of the University of Rochester, during the winter of 1963–64. This report was part of a series of projections of the 1985 era prepared for the United States Marine Corps (Navy contract # NOnr 4345–00). Although circumstances dictated that I should be the *rapporteur* of our discussions, the content of that group report—and thus of the derived material in this book—was truly mutual, and it is a very pleasant duty to acknowledge my indebtedness to Drs. Raney and Vishniac. In turn, the three of us are grateful to the Marine Corps for the initiation and financial support of what proved to be an intellectually enriching experience. Much of this book was written during a sabbatical leave from Syracuse University, and while using the superb library facilities of The Marine Biological Laboratory, Woods Hole. Had the unrivalled journal holdings of the latter been fully exploited, this would have been a better book.

I am grateful to all the individuals and organizations who helped with illustrations, and due acknowledgments are made in the appropriate captions. As with both books on invertebrates, my special gratitude is due to two associates: Dr. Douglas P. Wilson of the Plymouth Laboratory, in this case for some never-equalled photographs of living marine plankton, and Mr. Peter Loewer, whose skill has once again created a valuable series of line drawings out of my rough diagrams.

As regards the text, I am happy to thank my wife, Myra Russell-Hunter, for her support and active help at all stages of its preparation —without her, this book would never have been completed. I am most grateful to all the others who read the original manuscript and contributed helpful suggestions. These include Dr. H. Burr Steinbach (Director of The Marine Biological Laboratory, and Dean of Graduate Studies, Woods Hole Oceanographic Institution), Dr. Gordon A. Riley (Director of the Institute of Oceanography at Dalhousie University), Mr. William D. Eastman and Mrs. Elisabeth H. Belfer of The Macmillan Company, and three of my research associates, Dr. Martyn L. Apley of Brooklyn College, Miss Sandra E. Belanger, and Mr. R. Douglas Hunter. In particular, I wish to record my appreciation of the fact that a number of Dr. Riley's constructive criticisms have improved the earlier oceanographic chapters; although I recognize that, to any active professional oceanographer, my pedagogical devotion to certain simpler "classic" but still valid examples (including that of the Spring Diatom Increase in Loch Striven, Scotland, first investigated forty years ago) rather than to more modern ones involves the distressingly obsolete methodology of "old stuff." But this is merely one aspect of my unique responsibility (shared by none of those I have thanked) for those discussions in which uneven emphasis is obvious, and for all the errors that remain.

W. D. R-H.

# Contents

# Introduction: Productivity in evolution and in nutrition

WHEN THE PROPHET Isaiah, later echoed by the apostle Peter and many others, proclaimed ". . . all flesh is grass . . . ," presumably his primary intent was to emphasize the transitoriness of the bodily condition. However, the aphorism embodies the basic premise of all ecological studies on living communities: the ultimate source of all animal and human food is "grass" or the true green plants, which alone can incorporate solar energy. To live, grow, and multiply, all green plants require—besides sunlight—water, carbon dioxide, and certain mineral salts in solution, most notably phosphates and nitrates. Animals may feed directly on green plants, and be termed herbivores, or they may feed on other animals as carnivores. The latter's prey may in turn have fed on other animals, or on plants, but the ultimate source of food—or "fuel" for energy—must always be a light-absorbing plant. All living organisms require a source of potential energy to maintain themselves, to grow, and to reproduce their own kind. For all animals, this source has to be the contained chemical energy of food. In other words, to provide for the work done in movement, for the increased energy content of growth, and for the energy output of reproduction, every animal has to ingest preformed organic materials with high content of chemical energy (that is, compounds involving high-energy bonds whose breakdown or rearrangement can involve the liberation of energy). Only those plants possessing the green pigment chlorophyll can utilize radiant solar energy to create from simple inorganic substances *new* organic materials involving high-energy bonds. Of course, the process termed photosynthesis (involving the building of a simple sugar) is basic and follows the form:

$$6CO_2 + 6H_2O + \text{light energy} \rightarrow C_6H_{12}O_6 + 6O_2$$

This process of photosynthesis in plants—the conversion of carbon dioxide, water, and the kinetic energy of sunlight into free oxygen and sugar of high potential energy—is clearly an energy-binding *reduction*. In contrast, almost all the activities of animals (and respiration in plants) involve energy-releasing oxidations. The exceptions to this animal-plant dichotomy are scientifically intriguing, but involve only insignificant fractions of the energy flow through communities of living organisms. One example would be those few species of sulfur bacteria which obtain energy for their synthetic activities by the oxidation of hydrogen sulfide to elemental sulfur and thence to sulfates. Much more significant to organic cycles are those (essentially nongreen) plants, such as fungi, the majority of bacteria, and even those exceptional higher plants which are insectivorous, all of which have energy sources like those of animals. These sources are preformed organic materials obtained from the tissues of other organisms (whether living or dead) and thus ultimately again from green plants. These matters of energy content and energy transfer will be examined more closely in Chapter 9.

The reality of green plants as the only source of primary organic productivity is readily appreciated in the aquatic environments with which this book is principally concerned. This is particularly true of the shallower seas and the fresh waters of the temperate zones which have been the loci of much ecological research in recent years. The fertility of any body of natural water—whether salt or fresh—depends on the productivity of the green plants within it. In turn, this depends on the interaction of certain factors: first, the amount of energy gained by the body of water from solar radiation; secondly, the physical and chemical characteristics of the water itself, notably its content of certain dissolved nutrient salts; and, thirdly, the configuration and nature of the substratum in which, or over which, the body of water lies. All three involve the topographical setting, both geographical and geological. Of the four major green plant requirements mentioned above, in shallow seas and in temperate fresh waters, water and carbon dioxide are never in such short supply as to control the extent of plant productivity. The so-called limiting factors on primary production are, first, the available light-energy and, secondly, the availability of certain nutrient inorganic salts. Changes in primary production are regularly brought about by changes (including the seasonal ones) in available solar energy. Most result directly from changes in the amount of light penetrating through and impinging on the living cells of green plants, but some changes result indirectly by way of changes in water temperature. On the other hand, periods of intensive plant productivity in aquatic environments are often brought to an end by the complete exhaustion of an essential inorganic nutrient salt such as phosphate in the waters. Such limiting factors, and their seasonal influence, will be discussed in Chapter 3, and elsewhere.

## Productivity as biomass and energy

Consideration of even the simplest food-chain, for example, green plant eaten by herbivore eaten by carnivore, requires some measures for productivity and for the transfer of food energy. The most usual are biomass (or weight of organic materials in the living organism) and energy content (or calorific value). It would seem easy to assess these two measures in appropriate units, and to relate them to each other; but, in most natural communities, this simplicity is deceptive. However, a simple arithmetic relationship does lie behind most measures of biomass and calorific value; and, in well-studied fields like human nutrition, tables of "equivalence" can be drawn up. Most readers will have encountered the dieticians' sets of figures of calories per ounce (that is, energy content unit per biomass unit) of butter, lean beef, wholemeal bread, and so on. In many ecological problems involving food-chains, accurate measurement may not be easy, and equivalence may be more doubtful.

For almost all purposes, the crude definition of biomass as weight of living tissues, including organic materials ingested as food and not yet assimilated, must be further refined. Obviously, the live wet weight of a complex organism will vary with the amounts of watery fluids in its internal cavities, and in many higher animals there are rhythmic variations in the water content of the tissues themselves. Thus it is better to kill the organisms as rapidly as possible and then dry them to constant weight. Apart from difficulties arising from the loss of volatile substances during the drying process, dry weights of tissues of higher organisms are disproportionately affected by variations in the content of inorganic salts within the originally living tissues and by the proportions of skeletal materials. Thus we derive the measure of "ash-free dry weight" indirectly by subtracting the mass representing inorganic salts which remains after total combustion in a muffle furnace from the original whole tissue dry weight for the same specimen. Another—and relatively meaningful—method is to express biomass as total organic carbon content, usually employing methods of "wet oxidation" for the carbon determinations. Further understanding of the proportions of different organic materials involved in the biomass can be obtained by making parallel determinations of total organic nitrogen (see Chapters 8 and 13). Increasing sophistication of assessments of biomass could involve complete parallel series of analyses of fat, protein, and carbohydrate for all organisms at all their growth stages at all levels in the food-chain.

Many completely adequate ecological studies need only involve measures of biomass as dry weight or as total organic carbon. Such measures of biomass can be applied to individual organisms at different growth stages, to populations of a particular species, to all representatives of a particular taxonomic group of organisms, or to all organisms in a community summed together irrespective of systematic position. In almost all cases except the first, it would be usual to express the biomass per unit area or unit volume of the environment. The biomass of organisms on the sea bottom is commonly expressed as a total weight of organisms per square meter of the bottom. In the case of the drifting organisms of the open sea, the plankton, an assessment of biomass would usually be expressed in milligrams per cubic meter of seawater, although for some purposes (most notably in relation to the incidence of solar radiation), biomass can be expressed as the total weight of organisms under unit area of the sea surface (that is, in milligrams per square meter of illuminated surface). Determined at any one time, such estimates of biomass per unit area or per unit volume are measures of what is termed *standing crop*. It is very important to distinguish assessments of standing crop from those of biomass production, which are *rate* measures expressed in terms of increase of biomass per unit time.

One purpose of assessments of biomass is to provide estimates of the stored energy of the organic materials in the individual organisms or in the species or in the community. Absolute energy values can be computed from such measures of biomass, but such calorific values can also be determined empirically. By use of a bomb-calorimeter the calorific value of an organic specimen can be measured directly. The chemical-energy content in calories of any tissues or organisms is assessed by causing known weights of them to undergo complete combustion in an elaborately insulated metal container (or bomb), and by measuring in calories the quantity of heat produced within the bomb-calorimeter by their combustion. In almost all considerations of energetics in biological systems, heat units can conveniently be used. The interconvertibility of all known forms of energy is asserted in the First Law of Thermodynamics (or the principle of conservation of energy). As a result of the physical nature of heat energy (as random kinetic energy of molecules), the only complete energy transformations are those from other forms of energy—mechanical, magnetic, electrical, chemical, and so on—into heat energy. All such forms can be converted quantitatively into heat. The usual heat energy unit, the calorie or gram-calorie, is defined as the quantity of heat required to raise the temperature of one gram of water through one centigrade degree at 15°C. One thousand such small calories ($10^3$ cal) are equivalent to one large Calorie or one kilogram-calorie (Cal or kcal), which is better defined as the heat required to raise the temperature of one kilogram of water in a similar fashion. The megacalorie ($10^6$ cal or $10^3$ kcal), or the Therm of Armsby, is equivalent to one thousand kilocalories (kcal) or one million calories, and is used principally for assessments of fuels and occasionally for the nutritional demands of animals larger than cattle. Happily, these are the only heat units used in ecology. The equivalent unit on the avoirdupois (ounces-pounds) system, the British thermal unit (BTU), has been used only in a few nutritional studies of farm animals. Unfortunately, in measurements of the biomass of standing crops, pounds and acres are frequently used, particularly in fisheries statistics, and there are three different measures of mass called tons employed internationally. The energy content (in calories) is often used as a measure of a standing crop, but again in studies of productivity we are concerned with *rate* measures such as changes in calorific value per unit time. Thus the aquatic productivity of a sea or lake can be expressed in calories per square meter of surface per day, or per year.

No matter whether one measures as biomass or as energy units, the majority of food-chains involve production pyramids (of transfer of living mass, or of calorific content). In our simplest case, where a green plant species is consumed by a herbivore which is in turn consumed by a carnivore, the production of the green plant must be greatest, of the herbivore less, and of the carnivore least. In living communities, such pyramids of energy transfer are nearly universal, and their causes and consequences make up a considerable part of the study of organic productivity, and of this book. Before we pass to more detailed aspects of productivity in aquatic environments, it is worth outlining the importance of such studies both to applied biology and to theoretical biology. Of course, in the former they are concerned with the survival of man. In the latter, they are basic to any thorough analysis of the working of natural selection, as well as to any consideration of the nature and stability of ecosystems.

## Feeding the world

Whatever the food demands which result from increasing human populations, and those created by the industrialization of underdeveloped countries, it is already clear that there *are* food shortages—particularly of protein—in about half the world at present. Estimates prepared by WHO and FAO of the United Nations suggest that even to provide a reasonable level of nutrition for the world population of 1980 would require doubling of the 1965 production of foodstuffs. Marine, and to a limited extent freshwater, organic productivity will have to play an increasing part in protein production. The exploitation of this aquatic productivity for human food will involve some of the most critical research and development of the next twenty years. That part of fundamental research in biological oceanography and in freshwater and marine ecology which is concerned with organic productivity may well contribute the most important socioeconomic results of any "pure" research field in the immediate future.

When the likely future developments in human exploitation of the oceans are discussed, they fall into two broad categories. First, there are new technological developments (already being introduced) which constitute improvements of conventional techniques of fish-finding and of fish-cropping (see Chapter 14). Secondly, there are several unconventional methods (already technologically possible, but not tried on any great scale) which would amount to maritime "farming" (see Chapter 15). Apart from unconventional methods, entirely new resources represented by organisms not presently cropped may also be involved. Both the further development of existing fishing methods and any new exploitation by fish-farming involve legislative and international political questions such as the limits of the areas of ocean under national sovereignty and the effective control of international fisheries to allow the maximum output from each exploited fish stock.

There is one clear lesson from existing studies on aquatic productivity, which biologists must teach to the rest of mankind. It is that—quite apart from the practicalities of exploitation—there is a limit on the potential of the world's organic productivity to support an ever-increasing human population. Putting this in very crude terms, we are concerned with the relative amounts of organic material—from an immediate point of view particularly protein food—which can be gained from a *finite* amount of solar energy impinging on the Earth's surface. (See Chapter 13 for a quantitative assessment of this.) We *have to rely* on organisms to convert this solar energy into carbohydrates and thence into proteins. In any rational discussions of these matters, it can be regarded as the duty of all those with some biological education to impress upon economists and politicians this "lesson." Mankind *must* learn of the ultimately finite nature of organic productivity in the world (even including the future development of human synthetic abilities), and thus the *real* limitation on future population growth in our own species.

## Productivity and evolutionary change

Before we discuss the importance to theoretical biology of studies in aquatic productivity, it is worth noting that a strict dichotomy between applied and pure science is unrealistic in many aspects of bioenergetics. The case that basic or "pure" research always contributes eventually to advances in applied science and technology is often urged by academic scientists. That a reciprocal contribution has often proved true again illustrates the weakness of the dichotomy. There are several examples in the field of work on organic productivity which serve to illustrate the introduction into basic research work of methods or even concepts developed as the result of applied research. Practical investigation of problems of over-fishing has given rise to computational methods at least as valid as, and considerably more applicable to further problems than, those developed by theoretical workers on the dynamics of predator/prey relationships or by other biologists studying the same problems in cultures of flour beetles or other animals (see Chapters 9 and 10). Perhaps even more striking is the fact that much of the basic theory of bioenergetics, including concepts of nutritional and growth efficiencies, as well as many of the proven methods of investigation, were laid down by applied scientists working in agricultural research institutes and colleges, and not by "pure" academic biologists. In the 1920's and 1930's, men like F. B. Mumford and H. C. Sherman in the United States, and John Boyd Orr (now Lord Boyd-Orr) in Scotland, were directing research on animal nutrition which built on the earlier work of H. P. Armsby and others. That research revealed consequences for human nutrition which undoubtedly saved many lives in western Europe during the Second World War, but it also laid conceptual and methodological foundations for more modern pure research in ecological energetics. The same agricultural research also contributed an early—but still valuable—textbook in Samuel Brody's *Bioenergetics and Growth,* the first edition of which was published in 1945.

As for pure research, if we were to attempt to predict the fields of biology in which fundamentally important advances are likely to be made in the 1970's, three such areas stand out among the more likely ones. These fields are: first, the physicochemical nature of complex processes, including memory, in "higher" nervous systems; secondly, the molecular bases of developmental processes in relation to the transmission of genetic information; and, thirdly, the synthesis of studies in population genetics, physiological ecology, and population dynamics into a more predictive theory of evolution. Obviously, studies on the organic productivity of aquatic environments can contribute but little to the first two areas, but they could be of major significance to the third field. Our knowledge of, and theories about, the processes of natural selection stand in need of some revision, particularly as regards relative rates of evolutionary change and the plasticity of physiological response.

While it is undeniable that selection works on the genetic variability of species, it must only rarely occur that the raw materials are genetic differences in externally obvious characters (e.g., in color pattern or in setal numbers). I believe that they must more often be genetically controlled differences in metabolic efficiency, that is, in the efficiency of conversion of organic materials into fertile adults of the species concerned. Natural selection must be principally concerned with the relative efficiencies of genetic variants in passing on organic biomass (or fixed energy) to the next generation of each particular species. Two areas of study in aquatic biology can be of fundamental importance. They involve: attempts to produce "energy balance-sheets" for natural populations of aquatic animals, however difficult these may be to complete, even in relatively "closed" systems; and, secondly, assessments of the extent of infraspecific interpopulation physiological variation in naturally isolated series of populations of a species. Bodies of fresh water, spatially limited, and transitory in a geological time-scale, represent a uniquely set up series of natural experiments for the latter kind of evolutionary studies (see Chapter 11). Certain problems in the evolution of homeostasis in organisms, and in populations, may well receive partial explanation in terms of the bioenergetics of some aquatic systems. Aspects of further problems involved in the evolution of predator/prey relationships, and even more puzzlingly in the ostensible conservation which is seen in many herbivore/plant relationships, are most readily investigated in the organic economy of certain aquatic communities.

# Organic cycles and trophic levels

IN ALL COMMUNITIES of living organisms, the three principal kinds of organisms—which, for the moment, we can refer to simply as animals, plants, and bacteria—are clearly interdependent. Their relationships are trophic (that is, relating to nutrition) and characteristically make up the cyclical processes known as the organic cycle of productivity, the carbon cycle, the nitrogen cycle, or the trophic cycle of energy flow. Before more detailed consideration of such cycles, it is worth introducing a few more concepts and terms.

The assemblage of organisms which live together in a freshwater pond, or in a definable area of the sea, is termed a biotic community. The living community and the nonliving environment which interacts with it, in the exchanges of energy in various forms and of chemical substances, are together regarded as forming an ecosystem, which can be briefly defined as a biotic community *plus* its abiotic environment. As regards the energy relations of most ecosystems, there are three main categories of living organisms—plants, animals, and decomposers —represented, and it is now necessary to define these more strictly in functional terms based on their nutritional relationships.

Green plants are distinguished as autotrophic organisms, which alone are truly self-nourishing. They are able to absorb radiant light energy, utilizing chlorophyll to build up complex organic substances which incorporate considerable chemical energy in their bonds. These plants take in simple inorganic substances, including necessarily carbon dioxide and water, and their synthetic activities are in energy terms described as *endergonic*, that is, involving an increase in ordered energy. It is important to realize that the simple equation for the photosynthetic activities of autotrophs [$6CO_2 + 6H_2O + $ light energy $\rightarrow C_6H_{12}O_6 + $

$6O_2$] shows nothing of the elaborate series of stages by which the process is carried out. The complete biophysics of photosynthesis involves a few stages as yet incompletely understood, but it is possible to say that there are at least one hundred chemical steps involved in sequence in the production of a simple sugar from carbon dioxide and water, after the absorption of solar energy. Each of these steps involves energy exchanges under the control of a specific enzyme molecule. From the ecological point of view, however, we can still use the simple equation, and regard the amounts of energy involved as representing the overall "balance-sheet" for the various credit and debit energy transactions involved in photosynthesis (see also Chapter 9).

All other living organisms can be regarded as heterotrophic organisms which, on balance, gain energy for various purposes from the breakdown and rearrangement into simpler components of complex organic materials synthesized elsewhere. Such organisms require complex organic materials for their nutrition, and thus rely on the availability of preformed organic food of high energy content. By this functional definition, of course, heterotrophs encompass both animals and decomposers such as bacteria and fungi.

A few alternative terms are also useful. The autotrophic component of the ecosystem—the green plants—can be referred to as the producers. This is emphasized in many descriptions of ecosystems by referring to the chlorophyll-bearing energy-fixing organisms as the primary producers of the community. Of the heterotrophic parts of the community, the animal component can be termed consumers. The simplest trophic subdivision of the consumer category—into herbivores and carnivores—is obvious. The other heterotrophic organisms act as decomposers, sometimes as transformers, and are chiefly bacteria and fungi. Such organisms (often spoken of as saprophytic) break down the complex organic materials of dead plants, dead animals, and animal excreta and, while absorbing some of the products of decomposition for their own growth and other energy requirements, characteristically release simpler chemical substances such as soluble inorganic salts, which are then suitable for uptake by green plants.

A few terms relate to the spatial distribution of living communities of organisms in aquatic environments, including plankton, nekton, and benthos. The term plankton, "that which is made to wander or drift," emphasizes the passive nature of the drifting of these organisms in the open waters of the sea and of large lakes. Although mostly minute, rarely more than a few millimeters in length, many planktonic organisms are capable of considerable locomotion in an effective fashion, but in general utilize this capacity in vertical rather than in horizontal movements in the sea. The plankton, of course, includes both plants and animals. Such organisms contrast with those of the nekton, actively swimming organisms (all animals), most characteristically fishes but including also squid and a few other active invertebrates. The third major group, the benthos, consists of the bottom organisms, both plants and animals. Originally the term benthos referred only to deep-sea bottom-dwellers, but it is now more broadly applied and includes the bottom fauna and flora of the shores and shallow waters as well as those of greater depths. A general term for both plankton and nekton of the open sea is the pelagic fauna and flora. In the literature on aquatic ecology, two other terms are found: the neuston, consisting of those organisms associated with the water's surface, and the psammon, consisting of the minute organisms living in the interstitial water (typically between sand grains) at or near the water's edge. Although of considerable physiological and some evolutionary interest, these two groups of organisms are relatively unimportant in terms of productivity, and make up only a tiny fraction of the biomass of most aquatic environments. They will not enter much into our further discussions.

The photosynthesizing microörganisms of the plankton are referred to as the phytoplankton, the animals as the zoöplankton. The latter can usually be divided into the "permanent" animals of the plankton, which live and grow to maturity and breed as drifting organisms, and the "temporary" zoöplankton, larval stages of many benthic and nektonic animals which spend a short or long larval period in the plankton. These categories will be more fully discussed in Chapters 3, 4, and 5.

All early—and many continuing—investigations of the plankton used a relatively simple collecting device called a tow-net: essentially a small bag of fine silk mesh shaped like an elongated cone (see Figure 3·4A). The towing rope is attached to cord bridles which diverge onto the hoop, and the actual fabric which forms the fine sieve makes up the bulk of the surface of the cone. The hoop itself is usually attached to a band of stout canvas, and instead of the netting cone tapering completely to a point, another narrow tube of stout canvas to which a small jar can be attached is usual. Traditionally made of various grades of the silk "bolting cloth" which was used by flour-millers, plankton nets are now mostly made of nylon mesh. The finest mesh nets, with about 80 cross threads per centimeter, are required for the sampling of the finest phytoplankton. Coarser mesh, of about 25 threads to the centimeter, filters better for the capture of the more active zoöplankton. In spite of contrary attributions, such tow-nets were invented and first used in investigating the drifting life of the sea by John Vaughan Thompson in 1816. He was a British army surgeon and great amateur naturalist, who later (in 1833) first elucidated the peculiar life-history of barnacles. He anticipated much later work both in formal zoology and in ecology; for example, in the course of a memoir on crustacean larvae, published in 1828, he wrote, "The more minute and invisible inmates of the sea then, must constitute the food of oceanic fishes and birds." Vaughan Thompson was also the first to note that the optimum speed for successful tow-netting is low. For hydrodynamic reasons, at appropriate mesh-sizes, it is actually a little less than 2 nautical miles per hour. At faster speeds, the net simply pushes a mass of water ahead of it, and this prevents efficient sampling. Many plankton-feeding animals, such as basking sharks, habitually cruise along at speeds of 1.5–2.5 miles per hour (with their mouths open) while feeding.

## Organic cycles

There are several ways of viewing the interdependence of green plants, animals, and bacteria. As regards matter, for example, carbon and nitrogenous substances, the relationships are truly cyclical, while as regards energy the interdependence is more a one-way flow (see Figures 2·1 and 2·2).

There are three principal kinds of organisms, and thus three kinds of dependence. The dependence of all animals, as heterotrophic organisms, upon the synthetic abilities of green plants has already been

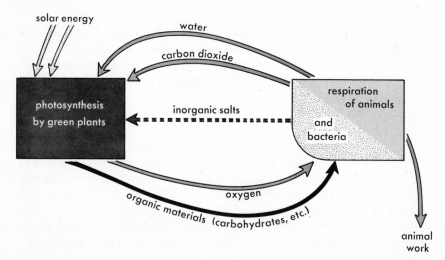

**Figure 2·1. The organic cycle** of carbon and water in a highly simplified community of autotrophic organisms (green plants) and heterotrophic organisms (animals and bacteria). For further explanation of the oversimplifications see text, and compare with Figure 8·1.

emphasized. The requirement for the bacteria and other decomposers is obviously a supply of dead tissues of plants and animals and their excreta, all of which can be broken down. The third type of dependence, that of green plants upon the decomposing activities of bacteria, is perhaps less obvious. The words of Louis Pasteur quoted at the preface of this book imply, in crude translation, ". . . life could not exist on earth . . . without not only death, but decomposition. . . ." The soluble inorganic salts of nitrogen, of phosphorus, of sulfur, and so on—often referred to as the nutrient salts or fertilizers of green plant growth—all become available only through the activities of the decomposers.

A highly simplified representation of the exchanges of carbon and water as components of biomass is presented in Figure $2 \cdot 1$, wherein all heterotrophic organisms (both typical animals and typical bacteria) are treated as a single component, exchanging with the autotrophic or green plant world. The external energy input is only to the plant side of the cycle; but, though energy output principally occurs from the heterotrophic side, it in fact occurs on both sides of the cycle. The so-called carbon cycle consists in the fact that carbohydrates and other products of plant synthetic activities pass from the autotrophic side of the cycle to the heterotrophic, along with the oxygen produced by the gas exchanges of photosynthesis. In contrast, carbon dioxide and water result from the respiratory or catabolic (breakdown) activities of the heterotrophs and both substances pass as input supplies to the autotrophic side. There are obviously many oversimplifications in this. For example, not all heterotrophic bacteria are aerobic, that is, normally using free oxygen in their metabolic activities and liberating carbon dioxide as such. Obviously, the rates of exchange on both sides of the cycle vary with different communities of organisms. Further, the proportionate amounts of carbon involved in the autotrophic biomass and in the heterotrophic biomass must also vary from time to time within any ecosystem. Of major importance in studies of aquatic productivity is the seasonal variation in the standing crop of green plant biomass, and hence of the carbon involved in that part of the cycle.

A similarly simplified pattern of the flow of energy through the living world is given in Figure $2 \cdot 2$. It is important to note that this generalized pattern forms a unidirectional flow, although cycles of energy exchange occur at many of the intermediate biological levels conveniently ignored in this figure. Such cycles, which in general terms are all concerned with the conservation of energy within living organization, are characteristic of all biological systems (from biochemical reactions catalyzed by enzymes, through the fecundity-controlling mechanisms of populations, to the interactions of the biotic components

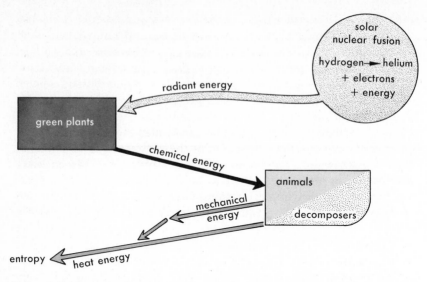

**Figure 2·2. The flow of energy** in the organic world. Note that this highly simplified pattern (which ignores the universal occurrence of partial recycling) forms a *unidirectional flow of energy* in contrast to the *cycling of matter* presented in Figure 2·1.

of ecosystems). It is almost trite to claim that such recycling of energy (with, as a corollary property of the systems, the capacity to form negative feedback controls stabilizing rates of change) can be regarded as diagnostic of biological organization at all levels. However, if we ignore this paramount characteristic of energy conservation in living systems for the moment, it is clear that the flow of energy through the biological world involves, overall, a constant degradation of energy and an irreversible flow. In very crude terms, the high-grade radiant energy of solar radiation becomes in part the medium-grade chemical energy of organic substances, and this in part provides for the mechanical energy involved in work done by organisms on their environment, and this (and much more from all stages) is dissipated as lower-grade heat energy into the environment, and finally becomes biologically useless as entropy (the theoretical condition of maximum randomness in a thermodynamic system or, crudely, the condition of maximum energetic "levelling down" to uniformity). There are important losses at each of these stages, so that only a small fraction of the energy originally used in endergonic processes (energy-absorbing syntheses) is available for the effective work of animals.

The energy in all biological systems has its origins in the sun. A nuclear-fusion conversion of hydrogen atoms into helium atoms and electrons releases energy initially in the form of gamma radiation.

Further reactions lead to the emission of much of this energy as quanta of light-energy or photons. The solar radiation which passes to Earth involves energy in the form of electromagnetic waves of photons. At the terrestrial end (see Figure 2·2) some of this energy is absorbed into biological systems, initially by the photons providing energy to move electrons to higher-energy orbitals around the nucleus of an atom. The biological molecules engaged in this energy absorption are said to have become "excited." In slightly different terms, the visible light is absorbed by the colored components of the plant cells, particularly and most importantly by chlorophyll. The details of the subsequent exchanges of energy between molecules which together result in the synthesis of new molecules of carbohydrate need not concern us here. However, it is important to note that much of the energy is conserved in a chemical form by the agency of a cyclical electron-transport chain used in the formation of ATP (adenosine triphosphate) from ADP (adenosine diphosphate) and phosphate. This process is termed cyclic photosynthetic phosphorylation. (See Figure 2·3, which shows the more general cyclic transfer of energy in all cells.) Of course, all green plants require energy for their living activities and obtain this by respiratory processes involving breakdown of the synthesized organic substances. Obviously, the net productivity of any green plant depends on the excess of its synthetic activities over the internal breakdown involving respiration. The exact proportions

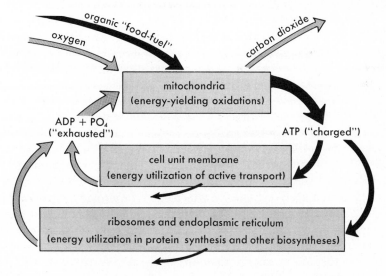

**Figure 2·3. The cyclic transfer of energy** within single cells: considerable energy conservation is achieved by electron-transport chains involving recycling of adenosine triphosphate (ATP) and adenosine diphosphate (ADP).

will vary with the age of the plant, the season of the year, and the time of day. Although the initial energy capture by green plants can only take place in daylight hours, some parts of the subsequent synthetic processes can be carried out in darkness. Some ecological aspects of the level of no growth (the compensation level), when the synthetic activities of a plant are exactly equaled by its respiratory breakdown, are discussed in Chapter 3.

As shown in Figure 2·2, the excess organic material synthesized by green plants goes into their growth and may become available as food for animals. This involves the passage of chemical energy to the heterotrophic organisms of the animal world. Here again, within living animals, we find energy-conserving cycles to be the rule. Figure 2·3 illustrates the cyclic transfer of energy within single cells by the use of ATP as the "charged" form of the energy-transporting system and ADP as the "exhausted" form. In spite of energy-conserving and cyclical processes, some proportion of the energy must pass to the environment from the animal as mechanical work, or as heat or other forms of energy leading to entropy. Further, there is loss to entropy at almost all stages of biological energy exchange; in machine terms, biological processes are not frictionless.

In considering energy flow in biological systems, whether through single cells or through ecological communities, it is important to realize one significant difference from the usual analogy with machines. Without any exceptions, all man-made pieces of machinery—even including theoretical constructions such as the ideal heat-engine of Nicolas Sadi Carnot, which is used as a standard of efficiency—would continue their physical existence as organized matter even if all energy flow through them ceased. If the energy flow through a biological system does not continue (to some extent), then the system is no longer a living one, and its components will pass almost immediately (if not prevented by human artifact) to dissolution, both by autolysis (self-digestion) and decay. Living systems are maintained by the continuous flow of energy through them. Indeed, despite the universal presence of energy-conserving cycles within living organisms, it is characteristic of them that sustained life is in metastable equilibrium with its surroundings and has to use energy, which could be termed "anti-entropic" energy, to prevent its dissolution. Further, the loss of some part of the energy involved to heat and to entropy would seem to be an essential feature of life itself.

If we turn from energy flow to more specific concern with the organic exchanges and interdependence of matter, then we return to clearly cyclical systems. These have been aptly termed the biogeochemical cycles. Although we will discuss some of these in more detail in Chapter 8, it is worth considering that of the element nitrogen in its

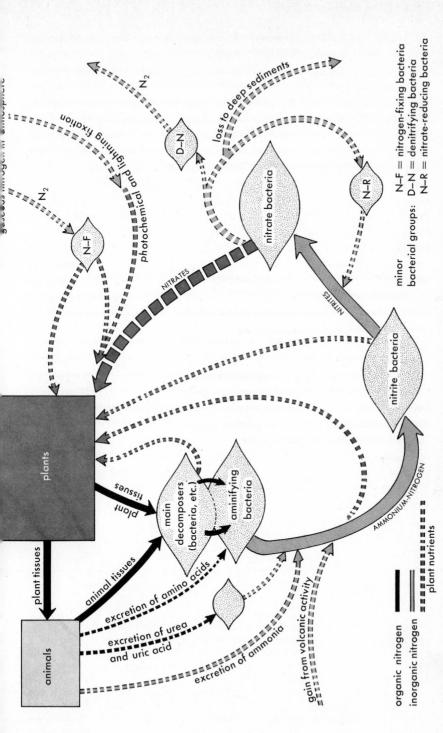

**Figure 2·4. The biogeochemical cycle of nitrogen compounds** in aquatic and other environments. As is the case with most "essential" elements, *inorganic salts* are taken up as nutrients by plants and transferred as organic compounds to animals and to decomposers, mostly bacteria. Sequential bacterial "oxidations" (see also Figure 8·2) are responsible for making the nutrients (in this case, largely nitrates) again available for the uptake, biosynthesis, and growth of plants.

17

combined forms here. In Figure 2·4, the cycle of organic nitrogenous substances is represented. Here again as with carbon, we have the organic nitrogen-containing substances first synthesized in plants and ingested by animals as part of their food. The dead parts of both plants and animals pass, along with the nitrogenous excretions of animals, to bacteria. These last gain energy from the breakdown of these substances, and such decomposition leads to the eventual liberation of such inorganic products of decay as nitrates, which are suitable mineral nutrient salts for uptake by green plants. The cycle is somewhat complicated by the existence of a few bacteria which are able to fix gaseous nitrogen from the atmosphere and add it to the cycle, and of other bacteria (termed denitrifying) whose metabolism involves the breakdown of nitrates and liberation of nitrogen to the air. Further, no normal bacteria utilize an input of amino acids and other organic residues and themselves liberate an output of nitrates. At least three functionally distinct groups of bacteria are involved in the sequential processes of this decay, and the penultimate products are nitrites, which must then be further oxidized by bacterial action before becoming available to green plants as nitrates.

The biogeochemical cycles of phosphorus and several other elements could be depicted similarly. In all of these cycles, organic compounds involving the elements are synthesized in plants and pass from them to animals, and thence (and also directly from plants) to bacteria. The activities of bacteria return the elements as phosphates and other nutrient salts suitable for uptake and for further biosynthesis to the water bathing the green plants. One of the seminal facts underlying all studies of aquatic productivity is that the smaller available quantities of most elements, such as nitrogen and phosphorus, involve organized life in more rapid cycling than is the case with carbon. We will return to this theme again.

**Figure 2·5. Stylized ecosystem of a large pond or small lake.** There are three principal groups of organisms (producers, consumers, and decomposers) organized in two principal food-chains. The first trophic level (primary producers) consists of the microscopic green plants of the phytoplankton for one food-chain and the marginal rooted plants and their epiphytes for the other. The corresponding second-trophic-level animals are filter-feeding zoöplankton and browsing benthic herbivores, respectively. The third and fourth trophic levels of carnivorous animals could lead to an old cannibalistic pike operating at both the fourth and fifth trophic levels. Compare this freshwater ecosystem with the stylized ocean ecosystem represented in Figure 4·1.

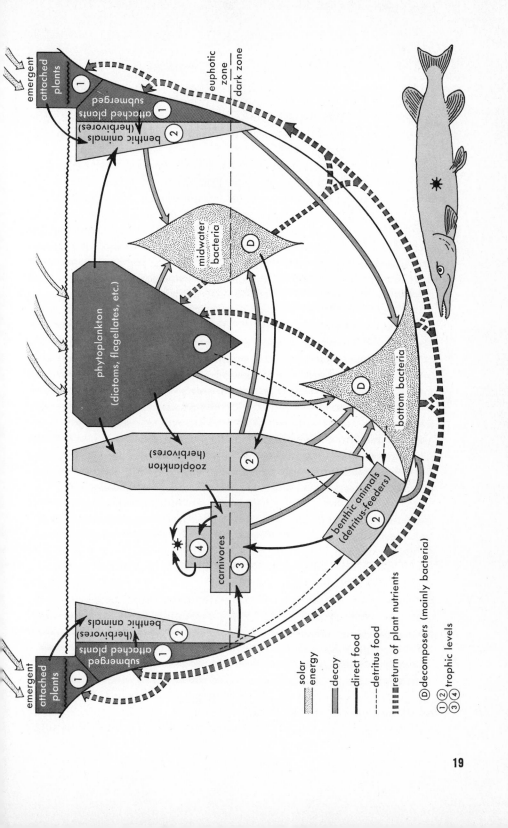

## Trophic levels

At this point, it is appropriate to turn from the somewhat theoretical discussion of geochemical and energy cycles "to the solid ground of Nature" (with Wordsworth) and consider the actual food-chains of a limited ecosystem. This can lead to a more detailed consideration of biomass pyramids and trophic levels.

The convenience, as nearly closed natural systems, of large ponds or small lakes has not escaped ecologists. Such bodies of water have provided sites for important research, ranging from the earliest studies in plant succession through the most recent use of radioactive tracers in following biogeochemical cycles, and they provide a starting micro-cosm for discussion in many textbooks of ecology. A stylized representation of such a small body of fresh water appears in Figure 2·5, wherein the three principal groups of organisms (producers, consumers, and decomposers) are shown. There are two main food-chains. One group of primary producers is made up of the rooted plants and their epiphytes, together forming the benthic vegetation of the margins of the lake. This vegetation is fed upon by herbivores, browsing animals of various sorts (in a small lake, mainly insect larvae, crustaceans, and molluscs), which in turn are fed upon by predaceous animals (probably mostly larger insect larvae and small fishes) which could be termed secondary consumers or primary carnivores. In turn, these might be fed upon by larger fast-swimming, predaceous fish such as the pike, and the diligent student of food-chains could term this fish a tertiary consumer or secondary carnivore. The other food-chain begins with the microscopic green plants of the phytoplankton. These primary producers are fed upon by the animals of the lake zoöplankton (mostly copepod and cladoceran Crustacea) as primary consumers. This zoöplankton is the food supply for small fishes and a few large preda-ceous insect larvae, and these in turn form the prey of the larger fishes. A large specimen of the pike is often cannibalistic, and so this second food-chain in our stylized ecosystem could end in a pike as a quaternary consumer or tertiary carnivore. Obviously, the terminology at the apex of the biomass pyramid, or the ends of the food-chains, becomes a little unwieldy. It is possible to designate the trophic, or nutritional, levels more simply: as first, second, third, and so on. The first trophic level involves all primary producers, whether rooted water plants, or micro-scopic diatoms, or other algae of the phytoplankton. The second trophic level includes both the zoöplankton and the browsers on benthic plants. Thus our old cannibalistic pike would probably operate at both the fourth and the fifth trophic levels.

Until about 1941, studies of the ecology of freshwater communities were largely concerned with description of the spatial interrelationships of the organisms, or with questions of the "biotic succession" in the larger species of plants. Around that time, the trophic-dynamic view of such communities was investigated and formalized by several workers, most notably Raymond L. Lindeman and G. Evelyn Hutchinson. Their work showed the analytic value of investigations of energy exchanges between trophic levels, and, in many ways, initiated the continuing investigations concerned with the "efficiencies" of food-chains in nature.

Of course, the existence of pyramids of numbers (and of biomass production) in communities of animals had been recognized much earlier. During the period from 1914 to 1918, the Danish marine biologist C. G. J. Petersen was publishing his classic studies on the faunal associations of the sea bottom in the eastern North Atlantic. Not only did he demonstrate the pyramids of production involved, but his applied conclusions on "crops of useful fish" are surprisingly modern in emphasis. Perhaps the most significant early formulation of the concept was that of Charles Elton in his book *Animal Ecology,* first published in 1927, a book which almost alone founded a new sub-discipline of biology. Recognizing this, many later workers have referred to the pyramids of numbers in animal communities as Eltonian pyramids. In its simplest form, such a pyramid of numbers is shown in Figure 2·6, which could represent the "standing crop" conditions in our model lake for the open water or planktonic food-chain in late spring. The reasons for this seasonal and geographical limitation will become apparent later. The animals at the base of the food-chain (second trophic level) are the most numerous, and there is a progressive decrease in numbers at each successive trophic level. Complications are introduced into this simple concept by the fact that most animal communities form food-webs rather than parallel series of discrete food-chains. We have already encountered this in our model lake: the old pike at the apex is not only ingesting food from at least two trophic levels but also food that originated in two distinct kinds of primary producers. Examples of more complex food-webs which can occur in natural circumstances are given in Figures 2·8 and 7·2. Other complications arise when numbers of individual organisms are counted. Obviously, pyramids of numbers will be modified by the sizes of the organisms involved. The broad base of the pyramid in Figure 2·6 results from the minute size of the diatoms and other single-celled plants in the lake phytoplankton. If we were concerned with an animal community where the primary producers were large trees, then, in terms of numbers, we might have a small number of individual primary producers supporting a large number of animals as browsing herbivores (that is, at the second trophic level). Only above this second trophic

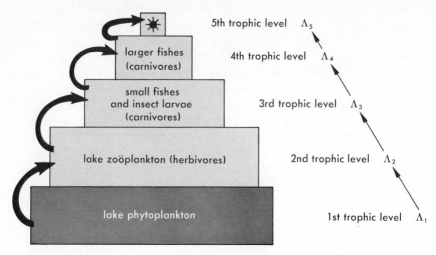

**Figure 2·6. The standing crop pyramid** (of numbers or of biomass in late spring) for the open water (or planktonic) food-chain of the model lake of Figure 2·5. There is progressive decrease (greatly underestimated in this diagram) in numbers (or in biomass) at each successive trophic level, and such community models are often referred to as Eltonian pyramids (see text).

level would an upright pyramid of animal numbers be recognized. Completely inverted pyramids of numbers occur in peculiar situations when the organisms at each successive trophic level are smaller than those they feed upon. This exceptional situation only occurs in nature in cases where a very large plant or animal nourishes a stock of parasites which in turn provide the food for a population of hyperparasites. Even in exceptional cases like this, if we turn from consideration of numbers of individual organisms to considerations of the amount of animal tissue produced at each level—or biomass production per unit time—then we can again represent the situation as an upright pyramid. In other words, the production of the hyperparasites is always smaller than that of the parasites on which they feed and so on.

In biomass terms, in any "stable" ecosystem, the weight produced per year of all predators at the fourth trophic level must always be much lower than that added annually at the third, which in turn must be less than that for the herbivorous animals of the second trophic level, whose total weight production in turn must be much lower than the weight of plant production in the community. As was noted by Elton, this has implications extending to the size and to the population densities of the organisms at different trophic levels. The probability is that predators will be successively larger than their prey, and there is near certainty that they will be less frequent per unit area (or unit volume) of the environment than these prey. If, in our model lake, we consider this question of size at each trophic level, it will be apparent that the kind of primary producer in any food-chain itself imposes some constraints on the feeding mechanisms, feeding behavior, and even size of the animals of the second trophic level (the herbivores). In our model, the browsers on the attached vegetation can be macrophages (ingesting large mouthfuls of plant food) and therefore can be moderately large animals. In an actual large pond or small lake, the individual biomasses of such browsers would probably lie in a range between grams and kilograms. On the other hand, the animals of the zoöplankton feeding directly on the green plants of the open water must necessarily be microphagous, probably actually filter-feeders, and —if permanent members of the plankton—are necessarily minute animals. In fact, zoöplankton organisms, both of the seas and of fresh waters, are commonly animals with individual biomass values appropriately measured in milligrams. We can see intuitively (though, as in Isaac Newton's case, quantitative proof may take rather more effort) that the number of stages intervening between the plants of the plankton and our apical old pike is likely to be greater than the number of stages from attached vegetation to his maw. Elton's generalization on size could be extended to encompass this aspect of food-chain length were it not for the important exception of some very large filter-feeding (and thus relatively microphagous) animals, including basking sharks and whales.

As regards the population densities appropriate to different trophic levels, here again we can intuitively accept the consequences in matters of human ecology. We must exclude from consideration those many cases where densely populated areas of the world are nourished by foodstuffs transported over long distances. However, a suitable contrast is provided between the rural population of south China, essentially vegetarian, and the "cowboys" of the cattle-raising areas of central Argentina. The density of the essentially second-trophic-level Chinese can be much greater than that of the third-trophic-level (with actually less primary production, and a very wasteful selectivity as carnivores) stock of gauchos. Of course, potential nutrition, and therefore population density, are not a matter of biomass alone, and for reasons of the carbon:nitrogen ($C:N$) ratio, which will be discussed later (see Chapter 8), a human population like the vegetarian Chinese could not exist at higher latitudes.

Biomass pyramids can be in part inverted if they are based on data gathered on the "standing crop" of each trophic level at a particular point in time. For example, the plankton-based community of our model lake would not have yielded the complete upright pyramid of Figure 2·6 if it had been based on numerical (or even biomass) data collected in midwinter, when the stock of phytoplankton can temporarily amount to a smaller biomass than that of the herbivorous zoöplankton. However, if we consider biomass production per unit time (or productivity) for each trophic level, then we again return to the pyramidal arrangement. Clearly, whatever is true of biomass production per unit time will also be true for any *rate* measurement such as organic carbon per year or rate of energy flow. If we accept the "how" of trophic pyramids as being nearly universal, we can turn to the "why" of this phenomenon.

To do so we have to consider the potential exchanges of a single trophic level with those above and below it, within the constraints of what is possible in terms of the nutritional physiology and general metabolism of the individual animals which make up the trophic level in question. This can be considered in terms of production of organic carbon biomass per unit time, as is illustrated in stylized form in Figure 2·7. Of the total productivity of the previous trophic level (in this case the plant as primary producer), only a fraction is ingested by the herbivore and some part of the carbon is egested as faeces, so that only a fraction of a fraction is assimilated. A considerable part of the assimilated organic carbon is broken down to provide energy for the activities of the animal—even including the energy expenditure of food intake— and only a fraction, the non-respired assimilation (N-R.A.), remains available for growth and increase in carbon biomass of the organism. Some variable fraction of this may be involved in growth of tissues which are of no nutritive value to the next trophic level (for example, the chitinous exoskeleton of many zoöplankton organisms), and so only a fraction of this is in turn available as a potential food supply for the predator of the next trophic level. Measurements have been made of the various ratios involved (for example, of carbon respired to N-R.A.). From these, along with surprisingly consistent results both from community ecology studies in the field and from the seductive "laboratory ecosystems" of predators and prey in culture (studied with greatest conceptual profit by workers like G. F. Gause and Lawrence B. Slobodkin), we can conclude that in most cases 10 per cent or less of the carbon biomass available for ingestion by one trophic level is in turn available for the next. In other words, in any closed community, each trophic level will have a biomass production per unit time, or productivity, about one order of magnitude less than the trophic level on which it feeds. Such questions of the relative efficiencies of energy transfer, including Slobodkin's concepts of food-chain efficiency and gross ecological efficiency, will be considered in detail in Chapter 9, and their applied significance in the control of human fisheries activities will be discussed in Chapter 10 and on pages 232 and 238.

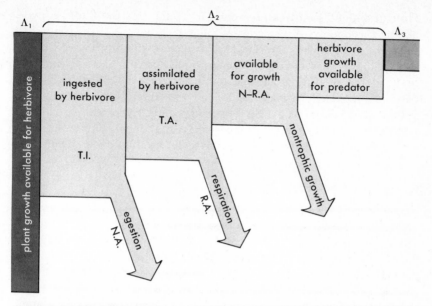

**Figure 2·7. The passage of organic carbon biomass** per unit time through a single trophic level. Of the productivity of the previous trophic level only a fraction forms the total ingested **(T.I.)**, and some part of that carbon is not assimilated **(N.A.)** and egested as faeces. Of the total assimilated **(T.A.)** a considerable part is broken down as respired assimilation **(R.A.)** for maintenance and other activities and only the non-respired assimilation **(N–R.A.)** remains available for increase in the carbon biomass of the animals by growth and reproduction. Only a fraction of this is in turn available to the next trophic level. Compare with Figure 9·2.

Hutchinson and Lindeman developed an elegant method of representing trophic-dynamic relationships in energy terms. The standing crop of any one trophic level has an energy content designated by a capital lambda ($\Lambda$). Subscripts are employed to indicate the several trophic levels: primary producers as $\Lambda_1$, herbivores as $\Lambda_2$, and so on, with the fifth trophic level being represented by $\Lambda_5$. At a time when the standing crops of several trophic levels form an Eltonian pyramid (that is, in the temporary condition of Figure 2·6), then $\Lambda_1$ is greater than $\Lambda_2$, which is greater than $\Lambda_3$, and so on. The contribution of energy per unit time from one trophic level to the next higher level (for example, from $\Lambda_2$ to $\Lambda_3$) is indicated by little lambda ($\lambda_3$ for our example). Using this terminology, we can represent the gross ecological efficiency, which we discussed above as being usually about 10 per cent or less, as:

$$\frac{\lambda_3 \times 100}{\lambda_2} \qquad \text{(for further explanation, see page 191)}$$

Hutchinson and Lindeman symbolically epitomized the Eltonian pyramid and its energy relationships as follows: $\lambda_0 > \lambda_1 > \lambda_2 > \lambda_3 > \lambda_4$. In this case, $\lambda_0$ represents the rate of solar energy entering the ecosystem. This synoptic view of trophic-dynamic relationships has continued to be valid for all further natural and laboratory ecosystems that have been investigated. In many of the ensuing discussions, the units involved in detailing exchanges between trophic levels will be those of transfer of biomass per unit time—and actual energy fluxes need not be computed. Normally, the two rate-scales are interconvertible.

## Trophic series and evolution

In his 1927 book, Elton noted that food-chains occurring in nature only rarely have more than five trophic levels. In spite of the fantastic chains (A eats B eats C eats D and so on to K, if not to Z) which are found throughout old-fashioned natural history books, this rather simple generalization remains true. Theoretical consideration of why the length of any food-chain is limited is easiest with an Eltonian predator chain, in which the predator at each trophic level is larger as well as rarer than its prey. The computation which follows is a completely hypothetical one for a series of predators which ingest whole prey, and was originally developed by Hutchinson, though different figures for both energy transfer and relative size are used here. We can take as a likely average figure a gross ecological efficiency of 8 per cent (that is, only 8 per cent of the energy passing into one trophic level can pass from it to the next). If we then assume that each predator has twice the linear dimensions of its prey (or 8 times the mass), the number of animals produced at any higher trophic level must be less than 1 per cent of the number at the trophic level immediately below (that is, each predator produced per year requires an annual production of more than 100 prey organisms). In other words, starting with the first link in the food-chain (i.e., the second trophic level), the third animal link will have an annual yield of 1/10,000 ($10^{-4}$) of the numbers of the first, and the fifth (sixth trophic level, which *does* occur in a few recorded cases) a yield of $10^{-8}$ that of the first. To put it another way, in a food-chain of six trophic levels, we have only five animal links, but the population increase of herbivores per unit time must be 100 million times the increase of "top carnivores" (of the sixth trophic level) over the same period. In nature, food-chains seldom involve repeated series of predators ingesting whole prey but, even so, food-chains of six or more links are relatively rare. Obviously, a food-chain of twenty animal links is totally impossible in any environment in terms of the herbivore numbers required to support it. This process of *amplificatio ad absurdum* can also be applied to the size of the animals in a similar theoretical food-chain of twenty-two trophic levels (or twenty animal levels above the primary consumer). Even if we start with a very small herbivore of mean diameter 1 mm and 1 mg mass, the "top carnivore" would weigh $1.15 \times 10^{12}$ kg (over $10^9$ tons, or the weight of about 2000 supertankers or giant ocean liners) and, since it is unlikely to be spherical, be at least 2 miles long (hardly a possible inhabitant of the planet Earth). Possibly the physiological limit in actual animal size is reached with the blue-whale of 150 tons and length 100 feet.

We have already implied a way in which the length of a food-chain, or the number of possible trophic levels in a community, can be affected by the growth changes of a carnivore. To return to the pike in our model pond, the growth of such a fish could easily involve a thirty-fold change in linear dimensions, and this would involve a progressive shift through at least three trophic levels. At each level the fish would be competing with other organisms which would normally become its prey later in life. The main effect is a blurring of the lower trophic levels in their contributions to the biomass growth of the ultimate predator. Potentially, this can permit some slight increase in the length of the food-chain and, in some cases, necessarily involves the occurrence of a limited amount of cannibalism.

A much more important effect of natural selection has been the evolution of new forms whose success has depended on a shortening of the food-chain and thus the exploitation of a more abundant trophic level. The most dramatic example of this concerns the whalebone whales which have evolved from the earlier stocks of toothed whales, as is attested by a wide variety of evidence. Except for the sperm whale, the toothed whales—such as dolphins, killer-whales, and bottle-nosed whales—are all relatively small and feed on larger fishes, cephalopods, and smaller whales, thus operating at about the fifth trophic level. In contrast, the whalebone whales—such as the right-whale, blue-whale, fin-whale, sei-whale, and the lesser rorqual—feed directly on the zoö-plankton and thus are mainly operating at the third trophic level. These latter forms have evolved by eliminating the "middle men" in exploiting the immense food resources directly available in the plankton. One can see how natural selection would tend to bring this about. If we have a predator working at the sixth trophic level, any increase in its predatory efficiency will always increase the possibility of the extermination of the fifth-trophic-level link in its food-chain. Should this occur, the animal will usually adapt itself temporarily or permanently to consuming the fourth-trophic-level link or will itself proceed to extinction. In the case of organisms as large as the whales, this can only lead to a shortening of the food-chain.

Similar evolution has occurred in other groups of animals. The

majority of the shark-like fishes, including most true sharks, are predaceous carnivores. However, the large basking sharks (*Cetorhinus*),
not uncommon in the North Atlantic, and the whale-shark (*Rhineodon*) of the Pacific, the world's largest true fish, are both slow-swim-
ming plankton-feeders which have evolved from the predaceous stock
by development of the gill-rakers into an efficient filtering screen and
loss of the usually diagnostic jaws and teeth of sharks. Obviously, a
compensating lengthening of the food-chain could occur if a new
carnivore preying on the species which had moved down one trophic

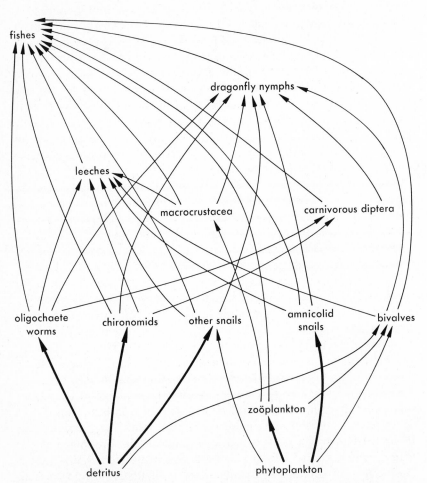

**Figure 2·8. Simplified food-web** for the biotic community in a mature river. Note
that animals at higher trophic levels are not restricted to a single prey species (and
its linear food-chain) but have a choice of several food organisms from at least two
trophic levels. [Adapted from data on the bottom fauna of the Mississippi River near
Keokuk, Iowa, in C. A. Carlson in *Ecology,* 49:162–169, 1968.]

level could be evolved. But for human development of the explosive harpoon about 1870, it is difficult to imagine any predator evolving which would be able to prey upon the blue-whale. As noted above, a larger imaginary predator would probably be mechanically impossible. It is also possible that some of the most typical crustacean microherbivores (second trophic level) have evolved from similar forms earlier operating in the sea as carnivores catching individual animal prey (see pages 64–68).

Before we leave this introductory consideration of organic cycles and trophic levels, it is worth noting again that their linear food-chains are relatively rare in nature. Almost all ecosystems involve, not a series of parallel independent food-chains, converging only in the higher trophic levels but, rather, food-webs. Some of these are illustrated in Figures 2·8 and 7·2, and a usual implication is that the animals at higher trophic levels are not restricted to a single prey-species in the trophic level immediately below it, but have instead a choice of prey, not only at that level but to a varying extent at lower trophic levels. There are both theoretical grounds and examples in nature which suggest that increasing complexity of the links in a food-web may create increased stability of the animal community as a whole. This aspect of complex food-webs will be discussed later (see pages 84 and 214).

# 3

# The seasons in
# temperate seas

MUCH SOCIOLOGY—and indeed much religious practice, including the pre-Christian festival taken over as Easter—has been founded upon the succession of the seasons as it is displayed in the land vegetation of the temperate regions of the world. In the seas of the same latitudes, a seasonal succession of diatoms takes place, which is less obvious, but of even greated ecological significance. In all but certain tropical areas of the oceans, the numbers of diatoms present in the waters vary greatly through the seasons and follow closely the same seasonal patterns of change year after year. Just as spring on land is marked by the regrowth of grass and trees, so in the sea a startling increase in phytoplankton production occurs in the spring and early summer. Typically, a sudden outburst of diatom growth occurs every year within a few days of its average occurrence for that locality, and this is best termed the spring diatom increase (SDI). It is often referred to as the "spring flowering" or "spring bloom," both of which are somewhat inappropriate terms for single-celled plants. The SDI depends on the reproductive capacity of the diatoms concerned, and under favorable conditions they can divide at a rate greater than once every 24 hours. The exponential increase in numbers which can result is the reason why areas of the sea may become green or brown with diatoms within a week. Repeated divisions build up the number of diatoms per unit volume of water to levels usually from 500 to 2000 times greater than their population densities through the winter in the same regions. In a few local areas, the increase in diatom numbers may reach 50,000 times. Such maxima of the SDI rarely persist for more than a few days, and in many cases the decline in numbers which follows is almost as dramatic as the rapid increase itself. A brief consideration of the structure and functioning of these minute plants will precede an account of some of the factors causing their dramatically sudden increase in the open sea in spring, and their almost as sudden disappearance.

## The phytoplankton

The primary producers in the marine plankton form a mixed population of photosynthesizing microörganisms of which diatoms (single-celled algae with tests of silica) are usually the most important. In addition, there are always extremely small naked green flagellates (termed $\mu$-flagellates) and, especially in temperate seas, numbers of the armored dinoflagellates. In some tropical oceans these latter are replaced by coccolithophores which have a calcareous test. Although this primary pasturage is made up of a mixed collection of many spe-

**Figure 3·1. Living diatoms from the marine phytoplankton,** mostly species of chain-forming diatoms of the genera *Chaetoceros* (with lateral spines), *Thalassiosira,* and *Lauderia.* Magnification is about 90 times. [Photo © Douglas P. Wilson.]

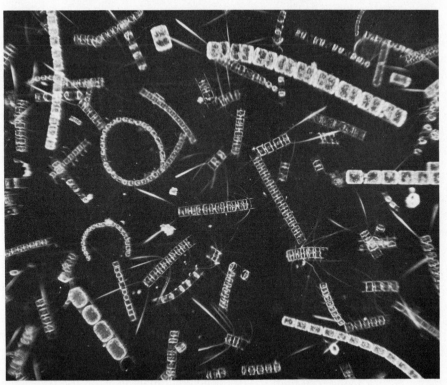

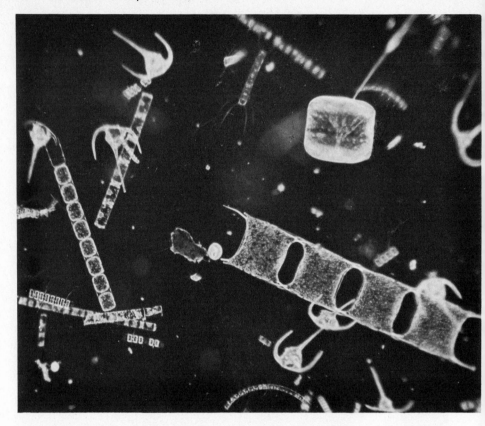

**Figure 3·2. Living phytoplankton** from the English Channel, including *Ceratium tripos* and related dinoflagellate species (anchor-like cells), as well as several diatom species. The single large barrel-like diatom cell is of *Coscinodiscus concinnus;* the chain of four large cells below it of *Biddulphia sinensis;* and the chains of smaller diatom cells include species of *Rhizosolenia, Stephanopyxis,* and *Chaetoceros.* Magnification is about 70 times. [Photo © Douglas P. Wilson.]

cies belonging to these four groups, it is characteristic that, in some parts of the oceans at specific seasons, more than 99 per cent of the actually photosynthesizing tissue will belong to a single species, which is usually a species of diatom. Living phytoplankton is illustrated in Figures 3·1 and 3·2, and both chains of diatom cells and individual dinoflagellates are shown. In many older books the phytoplankton is referred to as the nannoplankton in distinction from the animal forms of the macroplankton, now called the zoöplankton. Although this originally referred to the mesh-sizes of the nets used to catch the primary producers, it is worth noting because it emphasizes the minute size of these green plants. Most individual diatoms lie in the size range from 10 to 200 microns ($\mu$; 1 $\mu = 0.001$ mm). Dinoflagellates are commonly within the same size range, up to 100 $\mu$, while, as their name implies, the $\mu$-flagellates are much smaller, actually about 5 $\mu$.

Diatoms differ from other unicellular algae in having each cell body with its chloroplasts of brownish-green pigment enclosed by an external siliceous skeleton of hard glassy material. This is usually in the form of two parts which fit together like a miniature plastic pillbox, though in many, portions are drawn into long spines or other decorative extensions (see Figure 3·1). Viewed at the high magnifications of electron microscopy, the glassy wall of the box is actually an elaborate lattice-work with pores and channels perforating the secreted silica. The existence of this two-valved silica pillbox has an interesting consequence in the course of regular asexual reproduction of these diatoms, as illustrated in Figure 3·3. Each successive division of diatoms involves the formation of only one new valve in each daughter cell, and it is secreted to fit closely within the old one inherited from the parent. This process of repeated division forming new half-boxes within the old results in the average size of the diatoms so produced becoming smaller and smaller. After a certain number of such generations there is formed an auxospore which throws off its old valves, enlarges, and forms new valves about twice the linear dimensions of the discarded ones. In some diatom species, the formation of auxospores has a seasonal significance. Resting spores are also formed, but processes of sexual reproduction in diatoms are obscure and must be of rare occurrence. As regards the other members of the phytoplankton community, both dinoflagellates and $\mu$-flagellates are among those protistan organisms in which only certain species have green pigments and can photosynthesize, while others, though closely related are heterotrophic (lacking pigment), and still others may combine the modes of nutrition usually regarded as diagnostic of plants and animals. In considering primary producers along with the dominant diatoms we are mainly concerned with the chlorophyll-bearing dinoflagellates and $\mu$-flagellates.

Diatoms, and all other producer forms in the phytoplankton, have physiological requirements like all green plants. To grow and reproduce they require input in four main categories: water, carbon dioxide, sunlight, and certain inorganic nutrient salts. In the sea, water and carbon dioxide are readily available, and solar radiation and certain inorganic salts (notably the so-called nutrients, phosphates and nitrates) are the limiting factors for plant growth. In spite of the fact that the open sea, like all ecosystems, is under multifactorial control with extensive feedback systems, it is the existence of limiting factors which makes significant quantification possible, and even prediction

[A1]

[A2]

[A3]

[A4]

[B]

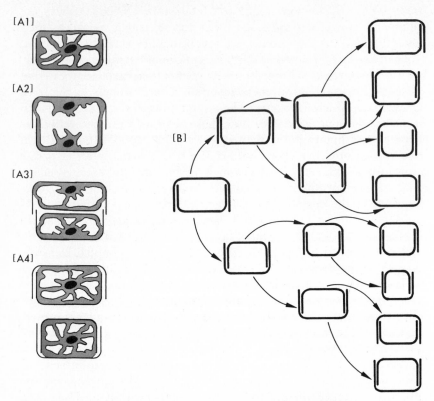

**Figure 3·3. Asexual reproduction in certain diatoms. A1–A4:** The process of cell division involves the formation of only one new siliceous valve (or half-box) in each daughter cell, the outer valve in both being inherited from the parent. **B:** Successive asexual divisions thus result in an obvious decrease in the *average* size of the diatom cells, and can only continue for a limited number of generations (see text).

reasonable. This will appear as we examine the seasonal changes in primary production.

The occurrence in the temperate oceans of the startling spring diatom increase (SDI) as part of an annual cycle of phytoplankton productivity is not really difficult to understand, if two groups of features in the physical environment and one additional biotic factor are clearly recognized. First, the light-energy required for photosynthesis is only available in the surface layers of the water. Secondly, when a body of water like an ocean is heated by solar radiation from the surface, a temperature stratification of the waters results. Another factor is biological and concerns the vertical distribution of bacteria and other decomposers in the marine environment.

# The euphotic zone

Both the phytoplankton and the attached plants are limited to the euphotic or lit zone of the sea, the extent of which varies with different physical and biological conditions. In the clearest oceanic waters, about 50 per cent of the light which penetrates the surface is transmitted to a depth of 18 meters, while about 10 per cent reaches depths of 45 meters. The oceans are less transparent inshore: coastal waters such as those off Cape Cod or in the English Channel would have 50 per cent of the light penetrating only to about 3.5 meters, and 10 per cent to 8 meters. Perhaps of more significance to green plants in the sea is the fact that 1 per cent of the subsurface light can extend to about 100 meters in the clearest waters of the open ocean, but only to about 17 meters in our typical coastal waters. Of course, a proportion of the solar radiation is lost with cloud cover, and some is always reflected back at the surface of the sea (this amounts to some 5 per cent of light striking the surface of a perfectly smooth sea or about 30 per cent when there is considerable wave-action). A further complication is introduced by the fact that the color components of the spectrum of sunlight are extinguished at different rates even in pure seawater. The red and orange components are reduced twofold within a few meters, and even at depths to which 80 per cent of the blue section of the spectrum remains, the yellow component will have been reduced to about 20 per cent and the violet to 50 per cent. The fact that it is the blue light which penetrates the greatest depths results in the clear deep blue appearance of the clearest oceanic waters, for example, in those tropical seas which in biological terms are relatively sterile.

Most natural waters, however, contain particulate material which alters the optical properties of the water. Some of this consists of dissolved materials and suspended particles, all of which reduce light transmission and have a wide variety of effects on spectral transmission. The minute organisms of the plankton themselves cause both a scattering of light and a loss of penetration, and these may particularly affect the blue wavelengths. The microörganisms of the plankton thus can modify their own environmental conditions, and a patch a few miles wide of a dense diatom outburst will cast a "shadow" on the deeper water layers beneath and thus curtail all other plant growth in those layers.

Although a great deal of sophisticated work in physical oceanography has been directed to measuring the available light-energy at different depths under all these different, possible conditions, and although we are now belatedly coming to know something about the utilization by phytoplankton of light of different wavelengths, it is

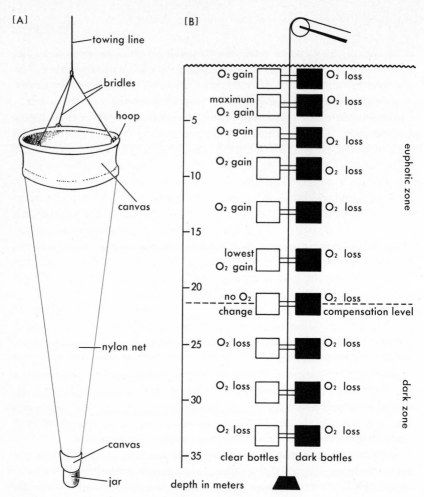

**Figure 3·4. A: A simple plankton net. B: Biological assay of the penetration of light** into the surface waters of the sea and assessment of primary productivity. At the beginning of each experiment, the pairs of bottles contain equivalent samples of the phytoplankton organisms and equal amounts of dissolved oxygen. After exposure for a definite time period, the chain of bottles is hoisted to the surface and the final oxygen concentrations determined for each bottle. Any gain in oxygen content in the clear bottles is proportional to the amount of photosynthesis carried out by the phytoplankton organisms less the oxygen consumed in their respiration (the *net production*). Decrease in oxygen content in the blackened bottles corresponds to the rate of respiration of the plants when no photosynthesis occurs. An assessment of the *gross production* of photosynthesis can be made by adding the gain in oxygen for an adequately illuminated clear bottle to the loss in oxygen in its blackened partner. The compensation level corresponds to the light intensity at which the synthetic activities of the plant cells are exactly balanced by their respiratory needs, and at greater depths there can be no net primary production.

still very difficult to use *physical* measurements of light penetration as a component in predictions of the productivity of the phytoplankton in particular areas of the sea. Various photoelectric cells provide efficient means of measuring the intensity of daylight at the surface of the sea, largely because the intensity of any one group of wavelengths is roughly proportional to the intensity of all the groups across the entire spectrum. However, photometer readings at any depth in the sea will not give a directly proportional comparison (and may be difficult to calibrate) because of the change in spectral composition with penetration which means that we are dealing with the unequal extinction of the originally unequal, but proportional, spectrum of daylight.

Happily, a method of "biological assay" of appropriate light penetration has been available for some forty-five years. Initially developed by the Norwegian marine biologist H. H. Gran, this elegantly simple method was first extensively employed about forty years ago in investigations in the Clyde in Scotland and in the Gulf of Maine. The assay method involves suspending glass flasks or bottles, containing samples of the phytoplankton population under investigation, at various depths beneath the surface of the sea (Figure 3·4B). The bottles are usually arranged in pairs, one of which is blackened to exclude all light. After exposure for a definite period of time, the chain of bottles is hoisted aboard the research vessel again and the oxygen content of the water in each culture bottle is determined. This allows an assessment of the metabolic condition of the contained plants at each depth, and in particular the relative amounts of photosynthesis and of respiration (Figure 3·5). The experiment begins with equal quantities of the phytoplankton organisms (= biomass of plants), and equal amounts of dissolved oxygen, in every bottle. As with all green plants, photosynthesis will add oxygen to the water in the closed bottle, whereas the respiratory (organic breakdown) activities of the plants will take up oxygen, thus reducing the concentration in the bottle. Any increase in oxygen concentration in the clear bottles will be proportional to the amount of photosynthesis which has taken place, minus the amount of oxygen consumed in respiration, and thus represents the net increase in biomass (or the growth) of the plants. The decrease in oxygen content within the blackened bottles corresponds to the rate of respiration in the absence of synthetic activities. For any specific depth covered by the experiment, an assessment of the total photosynthesis can be made by adding the gain in oxygen per unit in the clear bottles to the loss in oxygen per unit in the blackened bottles. If it were not for differences in temperature and other factors at the different depths, the respiration of the plants would remain approximately the same, while in greater depths with greater attenuation of the light the amount of photosynthesis would be reduced. For each plant species, there is a definite level in this reduction of light at which the rate of respiration first exceeds the rate of assimilation in photosynthesis (Figure 3·4B). This is known as the compensation level, or compensation light intensity. Essentially, this is the point at which the building activities of the diatom are exactly balanced by its respiratory needs, that is, the minimum intensity of illumination at which the plant cell can survive in nature (but, at the same time, an illumination too low for any increase as growth). In one of the earlier sets of experiments of this type, in Loch Striven in Scotland, Sheina M. Marshall and A. P. Orr used species of the diatom genera *Chaetoceros* and *Coscinosira,* determining the compensation level over an entire 24-hour cycle. It varied between 20 and 30 meters deep in summer and was usually less than 1.5 meters in winter. In general, the optimal photosynthetic activities took place within a range of a few meters, below which synthetic activities decreased with decreasing light penetration until the compensation level was reached. During the hours around noon in summer (at high sun angles), photosynthesis was inhibited to some extent by an excess of illumination close to the surface. Similar results from a series of experiments in the English Channel are shown in Figure 3·5, where the photosynthesis is plotted for different depths throughout the course of a summer's day. In this respect, it should be noted that all green plants "lie below the compensation level" during the hours of night and, if any green plant is to grow, its photosynthetic fixation during the day must be in excess of the material lost by its respiration (which continues throughout the 24 hours).

In general, the compensation level is at depths of from 5 to 35 meters in most sea areas. Different inshore coastal waters will have their respective compensation levels at midday at from 3 to 10 meters, while the open waters of the English Channel and the Gulf of Maine will show compensation levels of from 25 to 40 meters, and the clearest offshore waters in the tropics (which may actually show least biological productivity) can have compensation levels which at times approach depths of 100 meters. The compensation levels in lakes will be considered in Chapter 6.

In summary, then, to carry forward to our consideration of the changes in productivity with the seasons, almost all plant production in the sea takes place within a very limited vertical zone of surface waters, termed the euphotic zone. In other words, only a relatively small fraction of the volume of water in the oceans lies above the compensation level for the green plants of the phytoplankton, and thus *all* the primary productivity must occur within this small superficial fraction of the oceans. On the other hand, the heterotrophic activities of bacteria and of animals can occur *throughout* the immense oceanic

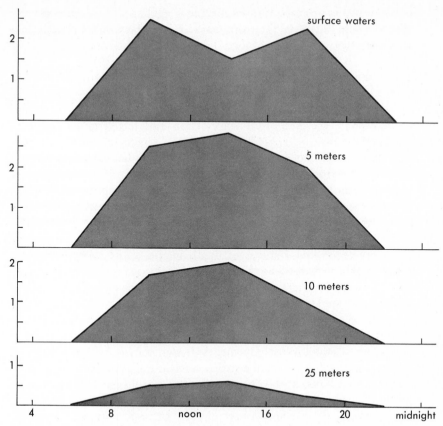

**Figure 3·5. Photosynthetic production** by the marine diatom *Coscinodiscus,* as assessed throughout a summer's day at different depths in the English Channel. Apparatus similar to that in Figure 3·4B was used, and the volume of oxygen evolved in milliliters per million diatom cells (vertical axes) is proportional to the net photosynthetic production at each depth and time. During the hours around noon the compensation level fell to a maximum depth of about 35 meters, and around the same time there was some inhibition of photosynthesis close to the surface (top polygon) by an excess of illumination. [Adapted from data of P. M. Jenkin in *J. Mar. Biol. Assoc. U.K.,* 22:301–342, 1937.]

volume. In particular, the great bulk of decomposition of organic materials by bacteria (see Chapter 8) occurs in waters below the euphotic zone and on the sea bottom.

## Temperature stratification

The second group of physical factors which define the seasonal course of plant productivity in the seas—and effectively limit the extent of all marine productivity—involves those concerned with the distribution of temperature in the sea. It is important to realize that the oceans, and even the larger lakes, of the world gain and lose heat only through their surfaces. Any exchange through lake or ocean bottom is negligible, and there is little or no heating due to chemical processes. It is also interesting to note that on the scale of the heat budget of a medium-sized lake or small arm of the sea, only a negligible heat gain to the medium will result from the heat losses of even a very rich fauna and flora. Finally, the gain from wave-action and the "friction" of tidal currents inshore—being a transformation of kinetic energy into heat—is again so small that it can be neglected. We are left therefore with all the heat loss from natural waters being through the surface, and all the heat gain resulting from solar radiation impinging on the surface. We can regard seawater as relatively opaque in its absorption of certain solar radiation. The energy received at the Earth's surface in the infra-red wavelengths (which represents a direct supply of heat) is largely absorbed in the first $\frac{1}{2}$ meter of depth in the sea and 98 per cent is absorbed at 2 meters below the surface. An obvious result of this is that, even in inshore waters, change in the sea surface temperatures with the seasons will show a considerable lag—often nearly two months—behind the corresponding changes on land in the same latitudes. In most temperate parts of the world, swimming in the sea is more pleasant in late fall than in early spring. As is well known, both this seasonal lag and the smaller range of temperatures in the sea affect the climate of islands and peninsulas. Spring flowers, shrubs, and trees bud in spring on Cape Cod at least four weeks later than those on the adjacent "mainland" of New England, but correspondingly, "summer" conditions persist in the land vegetation of the Cape long after fall has come to the hinterland. The time-lag in heating is most marked in waters of moderate depth over the continental shelf. In the northern hemisphere, the maximum radiation is received from the sun at the solstice in June, and most land surfaces reach their highest temperatures, with a slight lag, in July. The surface waters of the oceans mostly have their temperature maxima in August, but in deeper layers the temperature peak is even further delayed. At depths of about 80 meters or so on the continental shelf (or in medium-large lakes), the lag may be about five months and the temperature "seasons" almost reversed. As George L. Clarke once noted, for a worm living in the bottom mud under those circumstances, summer conditions might come in November! The lag can eventually cancel out any seasonal change. Off the Atlantic coast of North America in depths of more than 150 meters there are no measurable changes in temperature with the seasons. It should be realized that the great bulk of water in the oceans lies in such conditions: probably only 5 per cent of the oceans by volume undergoes any seasonal change in temperature.

Apart from the time-lag in heating, it is obvious that in deeper bodies of water the major changes in temperature occur only in the surface layers. This is largely explained by the facts that water is a poor conductor of heat and that temperature changes in water are accompanied by changes in density. It is sometimes difficult to appreciate how little heat conduction does occur in tranquil, unstirred waters. Perhaps a hypothetical example will help clarify this. The highland part of Loch Lomond (see Chapter 6) is a long, narrow, deep lake, a 12-mile-long trough with an average width of just over ½ mile and an average depth of over 300 feet with much water between 500 and 600 feet deep. If it were possible to prevent all wave-action and circulation in the trough and to cool all the water to 4°C (the temperature of maximum density), and then to heat the uppermost 2 feet of the water to 25°C, then it would take over 70 years for any of this heat to reach the bottom layers by the processes of conduction and radiation alone. The hypothetical calculations would be exactly similar for Cayuga Lake in the Finger Lakes of upstate New York, though in this case, 120

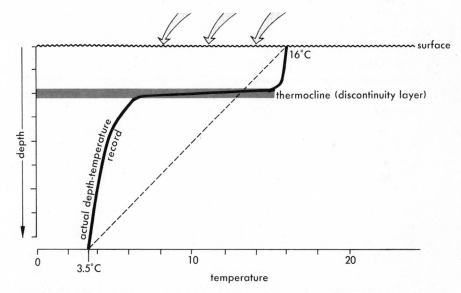

**Figure 3·6. The formation of a discontinuity layer or thermocline in the sea.** With the water surface warmed to 16°C in summer and the bottom water at 3.5°C, a simple temperature gradient might be expected to follow the broken line. In fact, the actual depth-temperature record shows the existence of a thermocline, or a limited discontinuity layer in which the temperature decreases rapidly with depth. The upper layers of warmed and less dense water are separated from the deeper layers of cold, denser water by the thermocline. Provided the heating from the surface continues, a thermocline will persist and become more marked as a discontinuity; and little or no exchange of water or solutes takes place through an established thermocline. See also Figures 6·6 and 6·7.

years would be required. In natural circumstances in the seas and in large lakes heat is transferred to lower levels largely by the actual circulation of water warmed by solar radiation in the surface layers.

In the polar oceans the temperature is low from the surface to the bottom. Elsewhere, one finds a vertical distribution of temperature which is closely related to that of density in the seas. The deepest waters underlying the temperate and tropical oceans are both cold and dense like those of polar seas. Actually, below 800 meters or so there is a constant temperature (in the North Atlantic usually between 2°C and 4°C) which is maintained all the year round. Such water is, of course, relatively dense. When the surface waters in the temperate parts of the world are warmed in the summer, the upper layer of warmed water becomes separated from the deep water by a transition or discontinuity layer within which the temperature decreases rapidly with depth. This discontinuity layer is the seasonal thermocline (see Figure 3·6). There are a number of complex reasons why, once established, a thermocline will persist and become even more marked as a discontinuity, provided the heating from the surface continues. These include the fact that the temperature gradient is also a density gradient and, as a result, any stirring by the wind which produces a circulation in the waters above the thermocline in a lake or a semienclosed sea fjord may produce a countercirculation below (see Figures 3·6 and 6·6) but no mixing. *Little or no exchange of water or of solutes takes place through an established thermocline.* Such a thermocline is always present in tropical seas. One occurs throughout the summer in waters in the middle, or temperate, latitudes, breaking down in winter when free mixing between the layers can occur. No thermocline can ever exist in polar sea areas. The physical significance of the thermocline as a discontinuity zone of extremely rapid density change is illustrated by the fact that organisms or artifacts of adjustable density, such as teleost fishes or submarines, can "rest" without expenditure of energy by lying on the thermocline. I was once impressed to see the depth-record of a rather badly discharged torpedo in a Scottish fjord which hit the thermocline at a low angle and then proceeded to bounce in a series of skips exactly like a flat stone skimmed by hand across the surface of the water. Some other aspects of thermocline formation will be discussed with regard to lakes in Chapter 6.

## The spring diatom increase

As we return to the seasonal changes in productivity, it is worth recapitulating the three causal features we have established. First, all plant productivity is necessarily in the surface layers of the euphotic zone. Secondly, the great bulk of bacterial decomposition occurs in the deeper waters of the seas. Thirdly, in temperate seas in summer, temperature stratification involves the formation of a thermocline as a physical barrier to water circulation at depths of about 15 meters.

Throughout most of the seas in temperate latitudes, the productivity of planktonic plants follows a very constant cycle, as illustrated in Figure 3·7, and we can examine the causes of this cycle in rather general terms. As a result of the breakdown of the thermocline in winter, there is an enriching of the surface layers with nutrient salts, so that in early spring the concentrations of phosphates and of nitrates in the superficial layers are higher than at any other time of the year. Thereafter, only when the available solar energy rises to an appropriate level

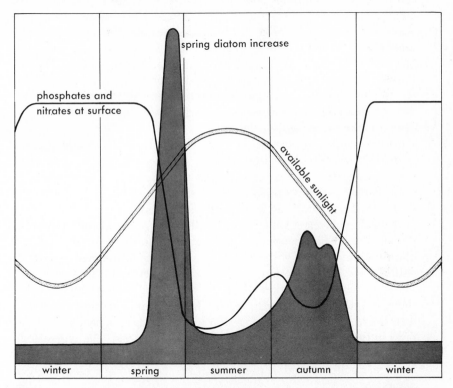

**Figure 3·7. The Spring Diatom Increase (SDI)** and other seasonal features of primary productivity in temperate seas. In the surface waters nutrient salts occur in greatest concentrations in winter, being depleted in late spring and remaining at low levels through most of the summer and autumn. In contrast, the availability of solar energy for diatoms and other phytoplankton is lowest in winter. In the stylized sequence shown here, the exponential plant growth of the **SDI** begins when a threshold level is reached in available energy and is ended by nutrient depletion. The less extensive (and less universal) diatom increase in autumn begins after a late-summer rise in available nutrients and ends as the available sunlight declines. For further explanation see text and Figures 3·5, 3·8, and 3·9.

does the outburst of the SDI occur. Although a complex of light and temperature effects is involved, one could claim that the SDI only begins after the compensation level for the diatoms concerned has extended to a depth sufficient to involve a "critical volume" of seawater for exponential growth of the diatom population to occur. At this time (see Figure 3·7), there is a heavy tax on the nutrient salts, and by late spring (the month of May in many areas studied) depletion of nutrients has gone so far that the plant cells no longer can afford the work necessary to take them up, and thus cease to grow and to multiply. The limiting factor involved in ending the SDI is thus nutrient depletion. Consideration of this factor alone can allow prediction of the end of the outburst, although two other factors are of some importance in certain natural circumstances. First, there can be increased grazing by a growing new generation of copepods and other herbivorous zoö-plankton. The increase in biomass at this second trophic level which occurs during the SDI brings about an ever-increasing rate of consumption of the plants, or an accelerated intensity of grazing. Secondly, the great increase in numbers of diatoms during the SDI will itself tend to decrease the transparency of the water and thus reduce the depth of the compensation level.

In the temperate open seas, plant productivity typically remains at a lower level throughout the summer. The occurrence of an autumn diatom increase is not so universal as that of the SDI. It appears to occur largely in those regions where decreased surface temperatures cause a breakdown of thermal stratification—and a return of nutrients to the surface layers—while there is still sufficient solar illumination for phytoplankton production. Thus, in contrast to the SDI, the autumn plant outburst begins with increased availability of nutrients and ends with decline in solar radiation. Then during winter again (see Figure 3·7), reduced illumination brings the compensation level high, so that there is little plant growth, while the continued mixing of deeper waters with those of the surface levels restores the nutrient concentrations in the surface waters to their high winter levels. The winter-long breakdown of the thermocline has been aptly compared to the ploughing of agricultural land in preparation for the growing season of green plants.

Some further aspects of the seasonal cycle of plankton diatom production will emerge if we consider in a little more detail the data available for one specific locality. Early studies on the marine seasons were carried out in Loch Striven, a fjord-like arm of the sea in the West of Scotland, by workers from the Marine Laboratory at Millport, notably A. P. Orr and Sheina M. Marshall. Loch Striven, like many other Scottish sea lochs, has a deep U-shaped cross-section with a shoaling

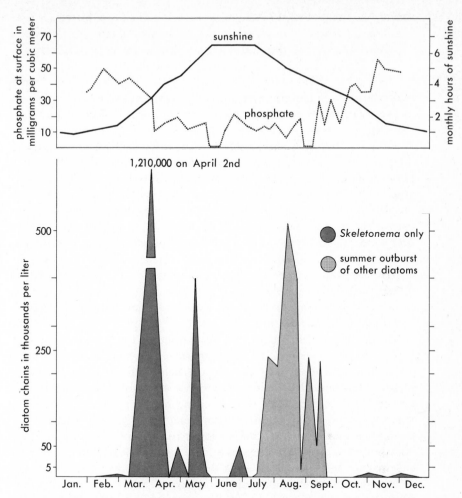

**Figure 3·8. Annual cycle of diatom production** in Loch Striven, Scotland. Monthly averages of hours of sunshine per day, and the concentration of phosphates in the surface waters of this fjord of the sea, are shown. The darker toned frequency polygons show the concentrations in the surface waters of the only important diatom in the **SDI**, *Skeletonema costatum*, and the lighter polygons those for the other diatom species of the late summer outburst. [From W. D. Russell Hunter in *Brit. Assoc. Handb.* (*Glasgow, 1958*), 5:97–118, 1958, using data taken from tables and graphs in Marshall and Orr, 1927.]

bar across the mouth, and thus it provides a most suitable, simple basin shape, almost completely isolated from the rest of the sea, for investigations of organic productivity. It is also relatively small, about 9 miles long with an average width of 1 mile, and its suitability is enhanced by the relatively low proportion of land drainage which it receives. In spring, the greatest part of the basic pasturage in Loch Striven is provided by chains of one species of planktonic diatom, *Skeletonema costatum*. Every year the SDI occurs in Loch Striven within about a week of March 20, and it is clearly due to a threshold being reached in the total available light (see Figure 3·8). The exceedingly rapid multiplication of diatoms uses up the nutrient salts available, for example, reducing the concentrations of dissolved phosphates found in the surface waters (see Figures 3·8 and 3·9). The concentrations of other nutrients follow essentially similar seasonal changes to those of phosphates. In other words, amounts of all nutrients sufficient to support a diatom increase are present throughout the winter. Thus, availability of solar energy is a true "limiting factor" (a concept first proposed by Justus von Liebig early last century; see the discussion on pages 54–57). Changes in the available light-energy, almost entirely directly—from the amount of light penetrating to and impinging on the diatom cells—but also to some extent indirectly by way of changes in water temperature, produce this spectacular outburst of diatoms regularly each spring in Loch Striven. Dissolved *organic* salts have never been clearly shown to exert any controlling influence on such diatom production in the sea (but see Chapter 8, page 173). In some other areas of the temperate oceans, the SDI is brought to an end by the complete exhaustion of nutrient salts. However, in Loch Striven, the increase seems to fall off each year before all the available phosphate is utilized. Other nutrients do not seem to be limiting in this situation. Of course, what we are saying here is simply that *Skeletonema* is a diatom whose nutrient uptake is simply not efficient enough to allow multiplication at levels of lower than 10 mg of phosphate per cubic meter of seawater. There is a considerable body of evidence from culture experiments that different diatom species have different ranges of tolerance as regards nutrients, and they clearly have very different compensation levels for light. During times of nutrient depletion, regular sequences of different diatom species may occur. The "shading" effect of increased numbers of *Skeletonema,* themselves affecting the compensation level, is probably not important in Loch Striven. The significance of grazing in these circumstances remains obscure. A near-classical theory that the accelerating rate of grazing was in part responsible for the decline of the SDI would imply that all—or a relatively large proportion—of the plant productivity was being made available at an unchanging rate for consumption by the zoöplankton. Several investigators have pointed out that considerable quantities of diatoms are destroyed, but not actually utilized, by grazing copepods. In fact, D. H. Cushing and H. F. Nicholson have recently claimed that in some conditions in the North Sea this destruction of plant cells provides a necessary immediate regeneration of available compounds of phosphorus, and thus maintains a rate of plant turnover higher than that which would occur if all diatom cells killed (and broken in grazing) were incorporated into copepod tissue. From a human view of ecology, overdestruction of a food resource beyond the limits of ingestion and assimilation would seem to be a most unlikely method of conservation of that resource!

In the surface waters of Loch Striven, after the end of the SDI (see Figure 3·8, there are usually several smaller maxima of *Skeletonema* and other diatoms in the late spring and again in the autumn. There is less regularly (but shown for one year in Figure 3·8) a summer diatom maximum in July or August, the time-course of which is less constant and the composition of which more varied. Other diatom species including those of *Nitzschia, Leptocylindrus, Eucampia, Chae-*

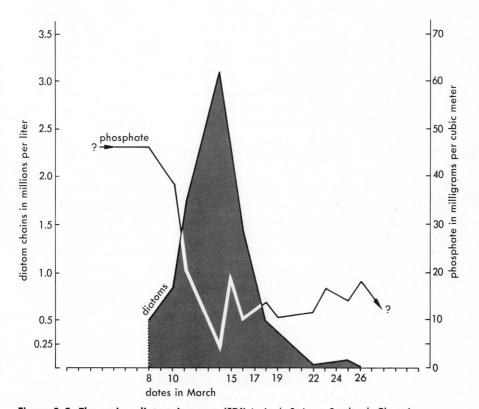

**Figure 3·9. The spring diatom increase (SDI)** in Loch Striven, Scotland. Changing concentrations of diatoms and of phosphates in the surface waters are shown for the spring period one year later than that in Figure 3·8. These seasonal changes follow a very constant cycle, and each year the **SDI** in this fjord occurs within about a week of March 20. [From W. D. Russell Hunter in *Brit. Assoc. Handb. (Glasgow, 1958)*, 5:97–118, 1958, using data taken from tables in Marshall and Orr, 1930.]

*toceros,* and *Rhizosolenia,* are involved; the increase of each diatom species begins in the surface waters and gradually spreads deeper, decreasing at the surface as it does so. In such summer conditions, the diatom of the SDI, *Skeletonema costatum,* is typically absent. Summer conditions end in Loch Striven in October, when the temperature stratification and distinct thermocline break down, and there follows general vertical mixing of the waters. The nutrient content of the surface waters is replenished from the concentrations built up in the bottom waters during the late summer and autumn by the bacterial decomposition of plant and animal material which has rained down there from the waters above during the course of spring and summer. Significantly, a small increase in *Skeletonema* often occurs in October.

In discussions of the SDI, and particularly of the factors which bring about its cessation, it is important to realize that throughout the outburst of *Skeletonema,* traces—amounting to less than 1/10,000 of the phytoplankton biomass—of many other species and genera have been present. Some of these are present as traces throughout the entire year, while others are involved in the less regularly occurring summer diatom maxima. In most localities 95 per cent of the SDI is made up of less than four species. (Some investigators have described a succession of dominant species.) All of this might tend to suggest that the *extent* in time of the outburst period of exponential increase for any single diatom species could be determined by physiological factors endogenous to the diatom population rather than directly by environmental factors. To nutrient depletion, grazing, and "self-shading" we probably have to add for many planktonic diatoms "physiological state" as a factor in the ending of the other outbursts, if not the SDI itself.

There are conditions under which an SDI occurs but which probably do not involve any nutrient depletion. The attached diatoms of the lower parts of the seashore live in conditions of continuous nutrient replenishment. Some personal observations made during one spring at Millport in Scotland are summarized in Figure 3·10. These concerned the diatoms forming the "scum flora" over boulders near the low-water mark (and also on nontoxic surfaces used in antifouling investigations), and they clearly show a succession of dominant forms during the period of the spring diatom increase. *Schizonema grevillei* and *S. ramosissima* were the first species in the sequence: they increased steadily in amount from the middle until the end of February. By mid-March *Rhabdonema adriaticum* had appeared in some quantity; on March 18, *Schizonema* spp. and *Rhabdonema* were present in approximately equal amounts, although the *Schizonema* were breaking up, whereas the *Rhabdonema* was healthy. The largest amounts of *Rhabdonema* occurred during the last week of March, but from the beginning of April onwards *Fragilaria striatula* and *F. oceanica* began to be important members of the community, reaching an equal abundance with *Rhabdonema* by April 10. At that time, *R. adriaticum* was in a less healthy condition than *Fragilaria* spp. The latter reached their peak during the last week of April and the first week of May. Their decline did not take place as rapidly as that of their predecessors, both species of *Fragilaria* persisting in moderate amounts for a further five weeks. As with planktonic diatoms, a significant feature of the sequence was that, throughout each "outburst," traces—in this case less than 1 per cent of the population—of other genera such as *Lycmophora, Achnanthes, Striatella, Grammatophora,* and *Melosira* were present. During this sequence, the only changing environmental factors were day-length and temperature (no compensation level is involved here), and it seems unlikely that these alone could determine the periods of dominance of each species. Studying the reproductive rates of diatom species in culture, H. W. Harvey showed that the rate of population increase could be dependent on the previous history of the diatom stock (on its rate of growth or physiological state before being introduced into the culture medium). In some natural successions of diatom

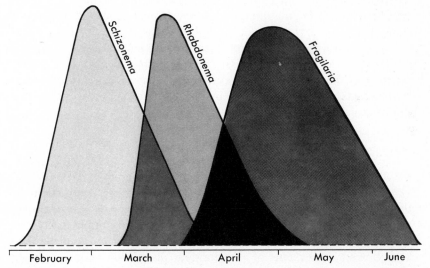

**Figure 3·10. Spring succession of diatom species** in the "scum flora" of the lower seashore near Millport in Scotland. Five species belonging to three genera—*Schizonema, Rhabdonema,* and *Fragilaria*—account for 99 per cent of the community throughout the period. Unlike the diatoms of the phytoplankton of the open sea, these forms live in conditions of continuous nutrient replenishment with day-length and water temperature as the only major changing factors in their environment. For further discussion, see text.

species, physiological factors endogenous to each diatom stock (possibly including latent periodicities) may be more important than immediate environmental changes.

The consequences of having a large number of diatom species represented only as potential propagules could have great energetic significance, and may be in part responsible for the complete exploitation each year of phosphates and other nutrients in those inshore waters where nutrient content and the physical variables, such as radiation, vary greatly from year to year. To use a physical metaphor, these inactive, nonreproducing, representatives of "rare" species must have a characteristic series of "half-lives." The ecological consequences have been more fully investigated in land plants, particularly with regard to the buried weed seeds of cultivated grasslands. If a favorable environment is created by some local disturbance of the grassland, there are almost inevitably some viable weed seeds available to colonize and exploit it. Such problems as succession of species and the physiological controls of apparently synchronous "outbursts" require further investigation in marine diatom populations.

It is obvious that the effects of a physiological periodicity latent in each diatom species can in many cases be superimposed upon the effects of physical and chemical changes in the environment on the productivity of the diatom population. However, it still remains a general truth that the low level of phytoplankton productivity in the winter months results from limitation of solar energy input, while the similarly low levels of productivity in the summer months in the open ocean result from limitation of nutrients. In the winter months, nutrients are sufficiently available; in the summer months, sunlight is sufficiently available.

## Primary production

Before the development of radioactive tracer techniques (see Chapter 12), three principal methods of estimating primary productivity in the sea had been employed. The first is the use (discussed above) of the rate of oxygen production as a measure of net productivity over a period (photosynthesis minus respiration). The second and the third both involve assessments of the standing plant crop at intervals: by direct counting of individual plant cells (or, less usefully, of chains of cells) after careful subsampling, or by assessment of the total chlorophyll complement of a measured volume of seawater. Under certain circumstances, the second and third methods of assessment of primary productivity yield significantly different results. The work of Gordon A. Riley and S. M. Conover showed this to be true during the annual cycle in Long Island Sound. In this area of the sea in some years, the

SDI is dominated by a species of *Thalassiosira,* while in others, the diatom of the SDI in the Clyde Sea Area, *Skeletonema costatum,* makes up the bulk of the outburst. The latter was dominant in the year illustrated in Figure 3·11, where phytoplankton cell numbers in millions and micrograms of chlorophyll per liter are both plotted as average values for the surface waters sampled over a number of stations in Long Island Sound. For the SDI, the cell counts, mainly of diatoms, and the chlorophyll analyses are closely comparable; while the productivity of late summer (particularly the months of August and September) is dominated by small forms not shown in the diatom counts and resulting in a marked disparity between the chlorophyll levels and the apparent cell numbers. More detailed examination of freshly collected water samples revealed that at these times of high chlorophyll content small naked flagellates and other minute *Chlorella*-like cells were present at many millions per liter. Other work in this area by J. H.

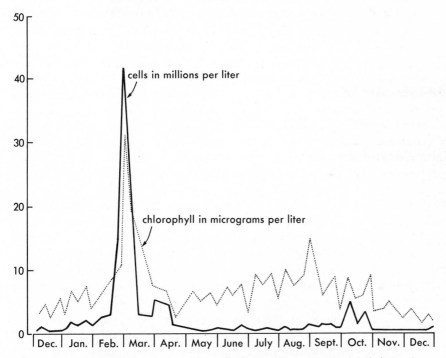

**Figure 3·11. Seasonal changes in phytoplankton** cell counts (mainly of diatoms) and in total chlorophyll concentrations in Long Island Sound. These two measures of primary productivity were closely comparable during the **SDI** when the diatom *Skeletonema costatum* was dominant, but differed greatly in August and September when "blooms" of small naked flagellates and other minute nannoplankton were responsible for much of the plant production. [Adapted from G. A. Riley in *Pap. Mar. Biol. Oceanogr., Deep Sea Res. Suppl.,* 3:224–238, 1955.]

Ryther demonstrated that "blooms" of these minute nannoplankton forms, instead of diatom outbursts, occurred under conditions of reduced salinity, high temperature, and relatively low nitrate concentrations.

When we try to assess natural primary productivity in the sea, our empirical estimates (using light and dark bottles), or theoretical calculations of the compensation level, must have been made over one or more complete 24-hour periods. The relative proportions of night, when only respiration takes place, and day, when both photosynthesis and respiration occur, are obviously important. As we noted earlier, at high angles of the sun (that is, at midday in temperate latitudes), optimum conditions for photosynthesis may not be in the most brightly illuminated surface waters but at a depth of a meter or so. At optimum light conditions, the so-called light saturation level for photosynthesis, synthetic activities involve a maximum of about fifteen times the amount of carbon involved in dark respiration for the same active plant cells. Above the saturation level, at higher intensities of illumination, photosynthesis is apparently partly inhibited, perhaps by photo-öxidation processes. Below the saturation level, the amount of photosynthesis is directly proportional to the light intensity, and thus declines with depth, as do physical measurements of light penetration. Obviously, if the ratio of photosynthesis to respiration reaches a maximum of 15:1 at optimum conditions of illumination, the ratio over any 24-hour period for any community of phytoplankton must always be less. The day-length and extent of the dark period, the maximum angle of the sun, and the atmospheric conditions all modify the actual ratio of photosynthesis to respiration. Further, in any phytoplankton community, a varying fraction of the plants is in suboptimum light conditions at all times. J. H. Ryther has made some revealing calculations of rates of photosynthesis and respiration, and their ratio expressed as percentage of respiratory loss, and these are shown in relation to different amounts of total solar radiation in Figure 3·12. The curve for photosynthesis and the straight line representing the daily amount of respiration cross at 100 calories per square centimeter per day, which thus can be regarded as the compensation level in terms of daily solar input for this theoretical plant community. It should be noted that this assumption that respiration remains constant under varying conditions of total illumination is certainly an over-simplification, because respiration is not totally independent of the extent of synthetic activities. In Figure 3·12, the difference between gross productivity and net productivity is expressed as the percentage respiratory loss and this ranges from 100 per cent at solar input values of less than the compensation level (100 calories per square centimeter

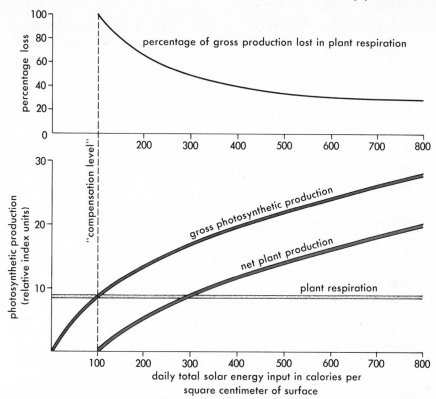

**Figure 3·12. The "compensation level" for phytoplankton.** Calculated values for gross and net photosynthesis and plant respiration are plotted in relation to different amounts of total solar radiation at the water's surface. Note that the percentage respiratory loss ranges from 100 per cent at this computed compensation level (here 100 calories per square centimeter per day) down to less than 28 per cent (with values for solar radiation corresponding to the longest days of middle latitudes with cloudless skies from dawn to dusk). [Modified from figures of J. H. Ryther in *Science,* 130:602–608, 1959.]

per day) down to less than 28 per cent on the longest days of middle latitudes under the best possible weather conditions (for example, on midsummer's day, June 21, at 45° North, with cloudless skies from dawn to dusk). Given these relationships, we can readily see how, at any single geographic locality in the middle latitudes, the potential compensation level will move lower and lower in the water column as the days lengthen in spring. Similarly, if a compensation level of, say, 6 meters is required for the appropriate amount of water to be involved to produce an SDI of a particular diatom species, we can readily see how, along a north-south coastline like the Atlantic seaboard, the SDI will appear to move steadily northward with the advancing year. In fact, "spring" as defined by the SDI reaches the highest latitudes of open waters in the Arctic in midsummer (and the corresponding waters of the Antarctic around December 21).

When we examine a variety of data on primary productivity in the temperate oceans, we find that in spite of the very great variations (largely produced by changing weather conditions) in productivity per day, the annual average net productivity per day is usually about one-tenth of the maximum net productivity observed for a single optimum day at that locality. Further discussion of the efficiency of primary productivity under different conditions will be found in Chapters 9 and 12.

## Limiting factors and predictive theory

It is worth examining the concept of "limiting factors" in a little more detail. Any living organism, to continue to exist in its environment, must be able to obtain certain basic requirements—both of matter and of energy—with some degree of continuity from that environment, in order to maintain itself, to grow in biomass, and to reproduce. The essential requirements differ for different kinds of organisms, but for the phytoplankton, like all green plants, they are light, water, carbon dioxide, and certain mineral salts in solution, especially phosphates and nitrates (and silicates for diatoms). The concept of limiting factors, often referred to as the "law of the minimum," was first developed by agricultural scientists concerned with the yield of crops, and can be stated rather simply. It is that the basic kind of energy or matter most closely approaching the critical minimum required will normally be the one whose quantitative availability determines and limits the extent of the productivity of the organism. As we have seen, for the marine phytoplankton—water and carbon dioxide being always available in excess of requirements—the actual limiting factors show a regular alternation between availability of the nutrient salts and that of appropriate levels of solar radiation. The first concise statement of the principle seems almost certainly to have been that made by Justus von Liebig around 1840, which has been known as his "law" ever since. Almost immediately, however, the concept was further exemplified and applied by pioneer agricultural scientists in several countries, including J.-B. Boussingault in France, J. B. Lawes in England, and William Anderson in Scotland. Their analytical work and experimental demonstrations could be said to have brought about the "second agricultural revolution" and, from about 1885 onwards, the rise of the "artificial" fertilizer industry. It also became increasingly clear that as regards the crop plants of land the limiting factors were often the so-called trace elements, such as soluble forms of boron and cobalt, which were only required in minute quantities. As early as the middle of last century, Lawes was also pointing out that all processes of agriculture intended to induce "artificially" a higher yield of food involve considerable expenditure of energy, whether in the manufacture and processing of fertilizers or in tilling or weed control. This surprisingly modern view of agricultural processes is close to that adopted later in this book in assessing the possible limitations on future exploitation of the oceans for human food.

Beginning in the later years of last century, further work in experimental agriculture has shown that the simple concept can be modified in many circumstances by factor interaction. For example, the abundance of some other substance can modify the rate of utilization of the limiting substance and thus modify the "limits" on productivity. Development of an analytic theory to deal with these multifactorial interactions had to wait until after the 1920's, when R. A. Fisher first developed methods of statistical calculation to deal with questions of prediction in genetic experiments. Such prediction is, of course, not deterministic, but stochastic (that is, involving random probabilities). Although these mathematical methods have now been employed for many years—even as "operational research" in industrial problems— the fundamental changes which they brought about in ideas about biological experimentation have not yet been universally accepted. A surprising number of biological scientists (though not ecologists) cling to the belief that the only acceptable method for experimentation invloves altering only one treatment or factor at a time.

About twenty years ago, Gordon A. Riley and his associates at Yale began to develop predictive forecasting of phytoplankton production. Their theoretical model involved a series of equations relating the quantity of phytoplankton to each of the potentially limiting factors in the physical and biological environment. For example, the more important physical variables are light, temperature, turbulence, the depth of the water, and the concentration of nutrient salts in the deeper waters. The most important biological factor, apart from the physiological limits on rates of phytoplankton multiplication, is the rate of grazing by the herbivores among the zoöplankton. The primary productivity can be directly related to the rate of photosynthesis minus the rate of respiration, modified, however, by the rates of grazing and of sinking to less well lit zones and the effects of turbulence. In turn, the rate of photosynthesis is largely limited by light, by phosphate concentration, and by temperature, while the rate of respiration (to be subtracted) is controlled only by temperature. Rates of grazing are difficult to assess, in part because of the apparent "exclusion" of zoöplankton from the regions of rapid plant growth, which will be discussed in the next chapter. The effects of turbulence are complex: a

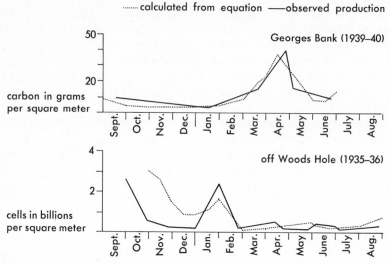

Figure 3·13. **Prediction of primary productivity in the sea.** Data on observed phytoplankton production in two well-studied areas are compared with theoretical seasonal changes as calculated using an equation which takes into account six environmental variables (solar radiation, transparency, depth to the thermocline, phosphate concentration, temperature, and intensity of zoöplankton grazing). In similar calculations, predicted values are usually within 25 per cent of the observed production. For further discussion, see text. [Adapted from G. A. Riley in *J. Fish. Res. Bd. Canada*, 10:211–223, 1953.]

low degree of turbulence will cause a reduction of productivity as a result of insufficient stirring of nutrient salts into the surface layers, and a high degree of turbulence will also cause a reduction of productivity, in this case by carrying plant cells down to depths below the compensation level and thus out of the zone of active growth and reproduction. Simultaneous solution of the several equations involved was eased in some models by the use of a simple but cumbrous procedure which allows one to obtain an approximate solution of any number of interrelated equations—the "relaxation" arithmetical method once used extensively in the computations of theoretical physics. In spite of the complexity of interrelationships among the various data used in the model, and despite some weaknesses in the mathematical assumptions on grazing, one of Riley's models with a basic equation involving certain physiological constants and six environmental factors (radiation, transparency, depth to the thermocline, phosphate concentration, temperature, and intensity of zoöplankton grazing) gave calculated predictions which were within 25 per cent of the observed phytoplankton productivity for a number of well-studied localities in temperate and subtropical seas. Two examples of the relationship between the observed seasonal cycle of phytoplankton and calculated predictions are shown in Figure 3·13.

The pasturage provided by the planktonic diatoms (and to some extent by dinoflagellates and $\mu$-flagellates) is primarily grazed by the animals of the zoöplankton. The most important "permanent" members are the copepod crustaceans such as *Calanus,* and there is also a wide variety of "temporary" planktonic larval forms which are growth stages of benthic animals and of fishes. Both the copepods and the larval stages show seasonal changes in occurrence, growth, and reproduction which fit them to best exploit the seasonal changes in primary productivity. The seasonal cycles of both permanent and temporary plankton animals will be discussed in the next chapter.

# 4

# Food-chains and productivity in temperate seas

THE CARBOHYDRATES, fats, and proteins synthesized in diatoms and passing to higher trophic levels are mostly first converted to animal tissues in crustaceans of the zoöplankton. In most parts of the world the copepods of the permanent zoöplankton are the most important, and, as with the plants, in many cases a single species predominates. As stressed earlier (see page 23), the fact that the phytoplankton consists of microscopic cells implies that the second trophic level in the plankton (the herbivores) must themselves be relatively small animals and inevitably microphagous filter-feeders. With certain important exceptions, the bulk of the herbivorous zoöplankton is made up of animals of between 0.5 and 5.0 mm in length, and there may well be reasons of energetic efficiencies for this size limitation. Throughout the temperate oceans, the dominant zoöplankton forms are usually cope-

**Figure 4·1. Stylized ocean ecosystem.** Producers, consumers, and decomposers are organized in similar trophic relationships to those of the model lake system in Figure 2·5. In the oceans, the fraction of primary production contributed by attached plants is minute compared to the immense productivity of the phytoplankton (the largest annual crop of green plants in the world). Thus the dominant fraction at the second trophic level consists of zoöplankton organisms feeding as microherbivores—in the open sea, often mainly calanoid copepods. These copepods are thus probably the most numerous animals in the world. Note the importance of detrital food-chains, and the distribution of the principal concentrations of bacteria below the levels of greatest plant production. The proportions of the stylized volumes do represent the approximate depth distributions of the organisms concerned in a portion of the ocean of moderate depth but are otherwise not strictly proportional (see discussion of this in text).

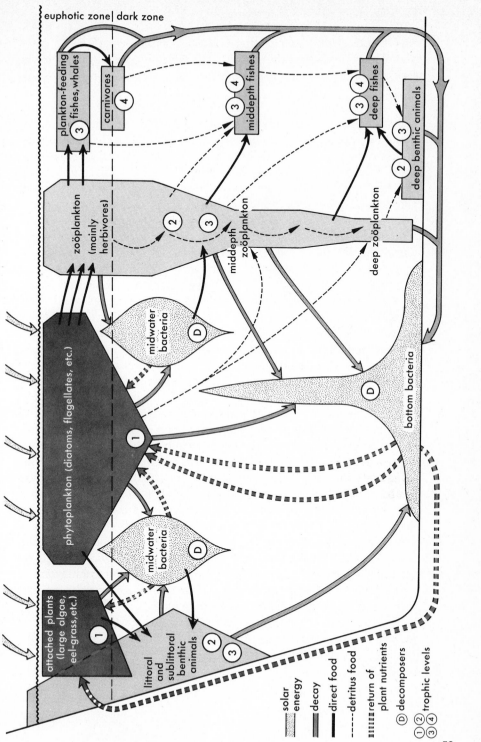

euphotic zone | dark zone

attached plants (large algae, eel-grass, etc.)

phytoplankton (diatoms, flagellates, etc.)

plankton-feeding fishes, whales

carnivores

middepth fishes

deep fishes

deep benthic animals

zoöplankton (mainly herbivores)

middepth zoöplankton

deep zoöplankton

midwater bacteria

midwater bacteria

bottom bacteria

littoral and sublittoral benthic animals

return of plant nutrients

solar energy

decay

direct food

detritus food

return of plant nutrients

Ⓓ decomposers

① ② ③ ④ trophic levels

59

pods of such genera as *Calanus, Acartia, Temora,* or *Metridia.* Such calanoid copepods are thus probably the most numerous animals in the world, since they are the most abundant of the microherbivores which feed directly on the largest crop of green plants in the world: the flagellates and diatoms of the marine phytoplankton. The single most abundant species—in terms both of numbers of individuals and of fraction of total animal biomass—is almost certainly *Calanus finmarchicus* or *Calanus helgolandicus* or a closely similar form. In Arctic and Antarctic waters, rather larger crustaceans, the shrimp-like euphausiids may also be important at the second trophic level. They are of moderate size (2–5 cm long), and are strictly deep-sea planktonic animals except in colder regions of the oceans. Calanoid copepods also occur in the high latitudes. In the tropics there is considerably greater variation in the dominant species of the zoöplankton, but again groups of calanoid species are important in some areas. All these crustaceans are, of course, members of the permanent zoöplankton (sometimes called the holoplankton) which spend their entire life-cycle as pelagic drifting animals. The zoöplankton of the open sea is rarely if ever dominated (even for a short time) by larval forms of the temporary zoöplankton (or meroplankton), although this is not the case in inshore waters.

The principal trophic categories in a model section of the sea are illustrated in Figure 4·1, with the energy exchanges of direct feeding and decay, and the cyclic return of plant nutrients, indicated. The stylized volumes do represent approximately the depth distribution of the organisms concerned, although they are not strictly proportional. The section is intended to represent a portion of the ocean of moderate depths; in the deepest parts of the oceans, the quantity of decomposing bacteria would be greatly attenuated in the middle and lower depths and only increase in bulk very close to the abyssal bottom. Further, it should be realized that while the relative volumes could represent the biomass of the various constituents at a single point in time, seasonal changes in the relative biomass of phytoplankton to zoöplankton, for example, could make hundredfold differences in this ratio alone. If we attempted to show the actual annual productivities for each group as volumes, then the disproportion between those for the primary producers and the animal groups would be such as to hinder visualization on the page. Similarly, for the oceans as a whole the proportion of attached plants to the phytoplankton would be very much smaller (compare this with Figure 2·5).

## Calanus **and its allies**

*Calanus* is found all over the North Atlantic: from the British Isles to the Gulf of Maine, and from east Greenland to the Azores. It is also found in the Mediterranean and in the South Atlantic and Antarctic. In the Pacific it is abundant off California and occurs off the west coast of South America, to the southeast of Australia and around New Zealand, and in the China Sea. In most of these areas it is *Calanus finmarchicus* or *Calanus helgolandicus* or a closely related form (there exists some systematic and taxonomic confusion) which is the dominant species. Even in waters where other copepods are numerically as abundant, *Calanus* may still constitute the most important fraction of the second trophic level. This is because *Calanus finmarchicus* (including here the closely allied forms) is a species, individuals of which are considerably larger than those of most other genera of copepods in the marine zoöplankton. A *Calanus* female is 4.0 mm long, the male is 3.6 mm, whereas species of *Acartia* average 1.1 mm, of *Temora* 1.5 mm, of *Metridia* 2.3 mm, and of *Pseudocalanus* 1.2 mm. The only cyclopoid genus of any abundance in the marine plankton, *Oithona,* has males averaging 0.6 mm and females 0.9 mm. In the Arctic, and in the deepest cold waters of Norwegian fjords and Scottish sea-lochs, there is a "giant" copepod genus, *Euchaeta,* with females of 8 mm and males of 7 mm in length, but these forms never reach great numerical abundance in the surface waters as does *Calanus*. (Some of these copepods are shown in Figures 4·3 and 4·7.)

Like all other crustaceans and insects, copepods are arthropods, with a jointed exoskeleton of chitin and epicuticle, and growing through a series of molt stages. As a group the copepods are relatively uniform in adult structure. The large head and six thoracic segments form the cigar-shaped body (or cephalothorax) behind which is a small jointed abdomen without appendages. As seen in Figures 4·5, 4·6, and 4·8, there are a large central eye and a pair of first antennae of great length (characteristically extended in Figures 4·2 and 4·6); the mouth-parts and first maxilliped are used in feeding, while the other five pairs of thoracic limbs are used for swimming. Two of the three most important orders of the copepods—Calanoida and Cyclopoida—are represented in the plankton, and they are distinguished by the biramous or uniramous nature of certain appendages, the position of the flexible joint of the trunk, and the type of egg-sacs (see Figure 4·8). Families and genera within these two orders are separated on relatively trivial anatomical features, and this stereotyped morphology is perhaps characteristic of animal groups where a highly successful pattern of functional machine has been successfully exploited.

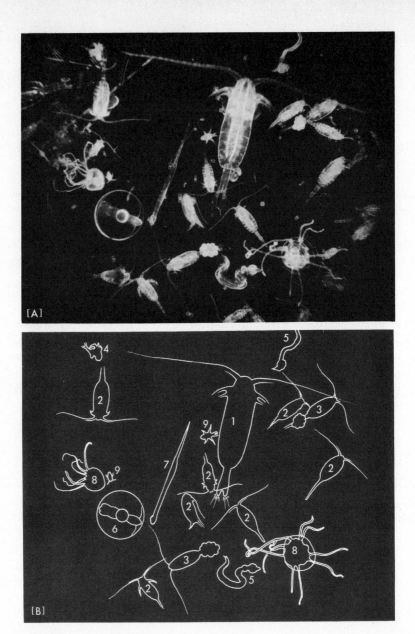

**Figure 4·2. A: Living zoöplankton from the English Channel. B:** Specimens of the following forms are represented in the key diagram: adult copepods, *Calanus* (1) and *Pseudocalanus* (2), including some females of the latter genus with eggs (3); a predaceous cladoceran, *Podon* (4); planktonic tunicates (primitive chordates), *Oikopleura* (5); a fish egg (6); a young arrow-worm, *Sagitta* (7); two different anthomedusan jellyfish (8); and copepod nauplius larvae (9). A few diatom chains are also visible, and magnification is approximately 12 times. [Photo © Douglas P. Wilson.]

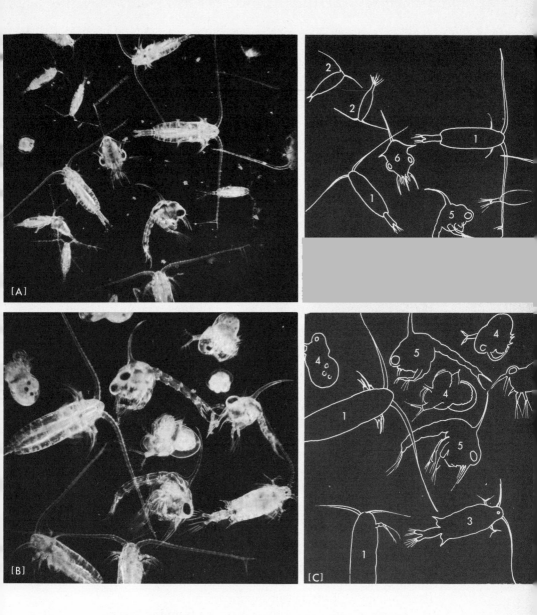

**Figure 4·3. A and B: More living zoöplankton,** almost entirely crustacean. **C:**
The key diagrams outline specimens of the following forms: adult copepods, *Calanus*
(1), *Acartia clausi* (2), and *Centropages* (3); predaceous cladocerans, *Podon* (4); and
zoea larvae of crab in side view (5) and from behind (6). Magnifications are approximately (**A**) 10 times and (**B**) 12 times. [Photos © Douglas P. Wilson.]

Locomotory and feeding functions are carried out in a similar fashion in both calanoid and cyclopoid copepods. They can swim smoothly by rhythmic beating of the trunk limbs or, particularly in forms like *Calanus,* by jerky strokes of their large first antennae. Many of them also use a sudden flexing of the body joint as an avoiding reaction. As in many other crustaceans, the thoracic limbs are multi-purpose: their beating serves for both propulsion and respiration, as well as helping create the swirling water currents of the feeding mechanism. The thoracic appendages are themselves the surfaces used in respiratory exchange and also create their own respiratory current. In several genera like *Cyclops,* the thoracic appendages are united transversely so that the four rami of each pair beat as one. Copepods can feed by seizing individual large particles or organisms in their mouthparts, but those of importance in the marine plankton also make extensive use of a filtering mechanism for suspension-feeding. As with the feeding mechanisms in other crustaceans, that in calanoid copepods was first elucidated by H. Graham Cannon. The actual quantitative performance of the filtering mechanism and of other feeding in *Calanus* has been most thoroughly investigated by A. P. Orr and Sheina M. Marshall at Millport in Scotland, along with many other aspects of physiology and ecology in this genus. When *Calanus* is swimming slowly, a series of vortices is created in the water (see Figures 4·5 and 4·6). These vortices bring small particles in toward the filter mechanism, which is of the single box type (and thus rather highly specialized when compared to the serial filtering units of more primitive crustaceans; see my earlier book, *A Biology of Higher Invertebrates*). In the case of the copepods, the box is formed of the head appendages: the mandibular palps, maxillules, maxillae, and maxillipeds all are involved, and all bear setae. In *Calanus* and most other forms, water is drawn in by lowered pressure created by an outward swing of the maxillipeds with their fringes of long setae. The volume of the box is then decreased and the water expelled by the maxillules being pushed forward, the expelled water passing through the sieve of the maxillary setae, which is illustrated in Figure 4·5A.

The particles thus filtered are removed from the "inside" of the sieve by being brushed forward by specialized long setae on the maxillipeds, or by the endites of the maxillules. This brushing directs the captured food particles between the mandibles and thence into the mouth. In most forms, including *Calanus,* the basket-like sieve of setae and the maxillae themselves are not moved during the filter-feeding process. However, in some species of *Acartia,* the setae of the maxillae can be spread apart and then drawn back together in a "clasping" movement. This is shown for the giant copepod, *Euchaeta,* in Figure 4·7A.

As developed in calanoid copepods, the filter-feeding mechanism is

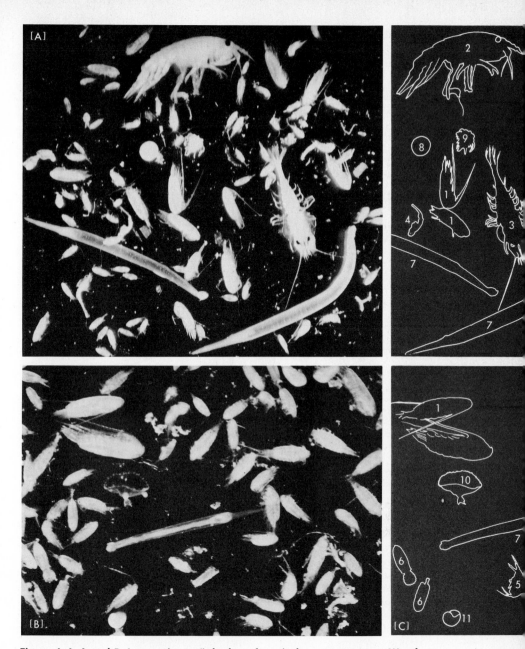

**Figure 4·4. A and B: Late spring zoöplankton from inshore waters near Woods Hole;** samples from tow-nettings preserved in formalin. **C:** The key diagrams outline specimens of the following forms: adult copepods, *Calanus* (1); an adult amphipod, *Calliopius* (2); a subadult shrimp, probably *Crangon* (3); younger "mysis-stage" larvae of a carid shrimp (4); smaller adult copepods (5); mostly unidentified but possibly including *Centropages* (6); adult arrow-worms, *Sagitta* (7); a fish egg (8); a free polyp head of the hydroid *Tubularia* (9); a leptomedusan jellyfish (10); and a late veliger larva of a gastropod withdrawn within its shell (11). Magnifications are approximately (**A**) 6 times and (**B**) 8 times. [Photos by the author; carids and *Calliopius* kindly identified by Dr. Eric L. Mills.]

65

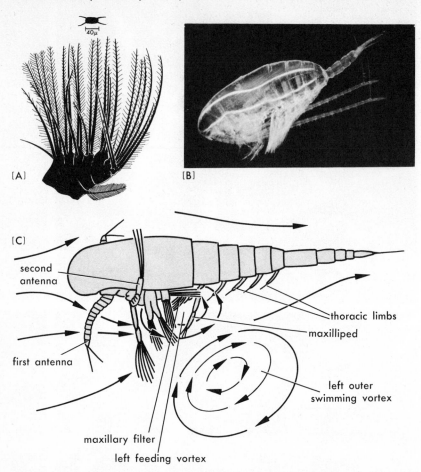

**Figure 4·5. Feeding in *Calanus*. A:** The filter formed by the setae of the second maxilla of *Calanus* with a food diatom *Chaetoceros*, drawn to the same scale. **B:** Lateral view of a living *Calanus*. **C:** Lateral diagram of the vortices created in swimming which bring food particles into the midline and through the maxillary filter. [From W. D. Russell-Hunter, *A Biology of Higher Invertebrates*, Macmillan, 1969. **A:** adapted from S. M. Marshall and A. P. Orr in *J. Mar. Biol. Assoc. U.K.*, 35:587–603, 1956. **B:** Photo © Douglas P Wilson. **C:** adapted from H. Graham Cannon in *Brit. J. Exp. Biol.*, 6:131–144, 1928.]

superbly efficient for the retention of food organisms in the size range of from 10 to 40 $\mu$. However, the same copepods also individually catch and digest diatoms of considerably greater size. Almost all the dominant forms of the phytoplankton can be utilized as food by copepods like *Calanus*. On occasion, the larger adult and subadult (copepodite) stages of *Calanus* and *Euchaeta* will catch and feed on some of the smaller *animals* of the plankton, including the young stages of the smaller copepods. Many investigators feel that the efficient mech-

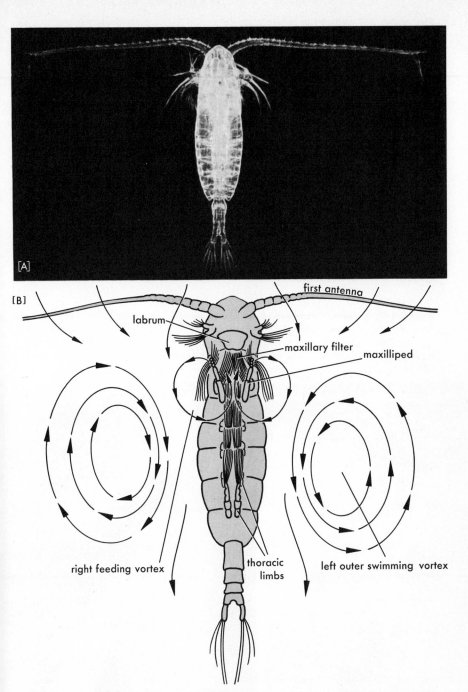

Figure 4·6. Feeding in *Calanus*. **A:** Dorsal view of a living *Calanus*. **B:** Ventral diagram of the vortices created in swimming which bring food particles into the midline and through the maxillary filter. [**A:** Photo © Douglas P. Wilson. **B:** adapted from H. Graham Cannon in *Brit. J. Exp. Biol.*, 6:131–144, 1928.]

anism of suspension-feeding in calanoids is probably a secondary development within the group, more primitive copepods in general being primarily raptorial. This does not necessarily imply that the "ancestral" copepods were other than herbivores, but it does suggest that their original food supply was limited to the larger diatoms of the phytoplankton, and that they were not able to browse effectively on the primary producers of all sizes as does *Calanus* today.

In both calanoid and cyclopoid copepods, the genital openings are developed on the seventh trunk segment behind the last pair of thoracic limbs. In many calanoid copepods, though not in *Calanus* itself, there is a single egg-sac, or better egg-mass, which is towed by the female below the abdomen (see Figures 4·3 and 4·7B). In *Calanus*, the female lays eggs in batches of about 50, with an interval of ten to fourteen days between each batch, and probably with a total egg production (if the female is well-nourished) of between 200 and 300

**Figure 4·7. A "giant" copepod,** *Euchaeta*, collected from deeper cold water in a Scottish fjord, Loch Fyne, and preserved in formalin. **A:** Head with mouth-parts spread for food capture. Compare the maxilla with that of *Calanus* in Figure 4·5. **B:** Three adult specimens, including one female with eggs. Magnifications are approximately (**A**) 14 times and (**B**) 4 times. [Photos by the author.]

[A]　　　　　　[B]

eggs. In a natural population of *Calanus,* egg production often takes place in a series of bursts, each lasting about a week, the bursts recurring at intervals of about two weeks. Levels of fecundity are almost entirely determined by the availability of food for the females, and this has obvious ecological consequences, some of which remain to be investigated in detail. However, it is already clear that in many parts of the world the peaks of calanoid egg production follow immediately upon each phytoplankton outburst.

## Copepod seasons

The growth stages, separated by molts, in the life-cycle of copepods are similar in all forms (see Figure 4·8). The egg hatches as a typical nauplius larva, which has three pairs of jointed limbs known by the names of the adult appendages into which they develop. Although these will become specialized head appendages—antennae and mandibles in the adult—they are unspecialized and used for both propulsion and food gathering in the nauplius (see Figure 4·8). The nauplius is followed by a metanauplius with four pairs of appendages, and these two forms together involve six successive molts. These are followed by a series of five molt stages called copepodites (see Figure 4·8), which resemble the adult but have initially only three pairs of biramous thoracic limbs and become progressively more like the adult forms. The final molt from the fifth copepodite stages results in adult males and females. In most calanoids, the molt to the adult usually involves the addition of two more pairs of trunk limbs, reduction of the second antennae and great enlargement of the first antennae or antennules, and the development of long, jointed rami on the furca of the telson. One of the most detailed studies of the seasonal aspects of life-cycle in *Calanus* was carried out by Drs. Marshall and Orr in Loch Striven. Seasonal variations in the numbers of adults, eggs, nauplii, and first to fifth copepodite stages in Loch Striven are illustrated in Figures 4·9 and 4·10. It can be seen that in this Scottish locality the annual populations of *Calanus* are made up of three successive broods. The whole cycle takes about two months in summer in Loch Striven, one month for development from egg to adult and up to one month for maturing the eggs. The overwintering stock in Loch Striven consists of fifth copepodites, and the slow development of this preadult stage means that the overwintering brood has a life-cycle lasting through seven or eight months.

Apart from the way in which the egg production and early development of individual broods are obviously fitted to the seasonal changes in plant productivity, we could claim that, for the temperate waters

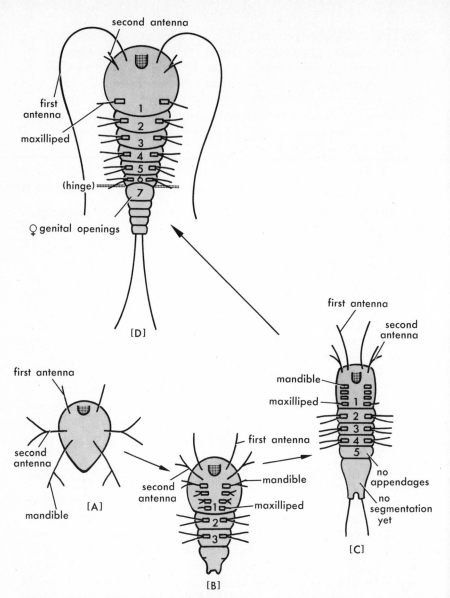

**Figure 4·8. Copepod larval development and adult organization. A:** Stylized
nauplius larva with three pairs of appendages. Although these will become specialized
head appendages—antennae and mandibles in the adult—they are unspecialized and
used both for propulsion and food-gathering in this larva. **B:** Stylized calanoid late
metanauplius with eight pairs of appendages including two pairs of thoracic limbs.
Workers on zoöplankton would designate this stage "nauplius VI." **C:** Stylized calanoid copepodite stage with three pairs of thoracic appendages and the fifth thoracic
segment already differentiated. **D:** Stylized adult calanoid copepod. Mouth-part appendages are omitted. Compare with Figures 4·5 and 4·6. [From W. D. Russell-Hunter,
*A Biology of Higher Invertebrates,* Macmillan, 1969.]

of the West of Scotland, a three-brood annual cycle is best fitted to exploit the growing season with greater trophic availability from March to September. Further, there are obvious physiological and ecological advantages to be gained from having a subadult form as the overwintering stage. It should also be noted (see Figures 4·9 and 4·10) that the adults resulting from the first and second broods are larger than those which result from the overwintering fifth copepodites, and that the fecundity of these overwintering females is lower than those from the first spring brood, which in turn is lower than that of the brood producing eggs in July. Thus the three generations suitably provide for a buildup in population numbers during the growing months at the latitude and in the conditions of Loch Striven.

At higher latitudes, the growing season is obviously shorter and, as we noted earlier, the phytoplankton outbursts are moved nearer to midsummer. Under these conditions—for example, in the waters of the east Greenland fjords—there is only one generation of *Calanus* in each year. Russian scientists, including B. G. Bogorov and B. P. Manteufel, found the same to be true in the abundant populations of *Calanus* in the higher latitudes of the Barents Sea. In the coastal waters of Norway, there is some variation with local conditions, but in general the life-cycle of *Calanus* is intermediate between those in Scotland and in Greenland: that is, there are two generations per year. Rather surprisingly, the two-generation pattern is also true for stocks of *Calanus* living in the open ocean in the Gulf of Maine and around Cape Cod. This may prove to be true for extensive waters in the central parts of the North Atlantic. Turning to warmer conditions, where the plant crop possibly provides better nourishment, we find four generations of *Calanus* per year occurring in parts of the North Sea and English Channel. It seems obvious that, if the same species of *Calanus* were physiologically able to extend into the subtropical waters of the central Atlantic, then the minimum generation time might apply throughout the year. In other words, the two months period required for life-cycle and egg maturation in Scottish stocks of *Calanus* in summer could become applicable throughout the year and an annual cycle of five, or even six, generations per year could result.

Throughout temperate seas, with a two-, three-, or four-generation pattern of life-cycle for *Calanus,* the biomass of copepods in summer is of the order of a hundred times that in the same locus in the winter months. In Loch Striven, concentrations of *Calanus* can give rise to a biomass, measured wet, of 100 mg per cubic meter of seawater at the summer peak value—that is to say, concentrations corresponding to 200 adult specimens of *Calanus* per cubic meter can be met with. To put this another way, if fished at the right time in most temperate seas, a 1-meter-diameter net towed for 15 minutes would yield about 2.5 mil-

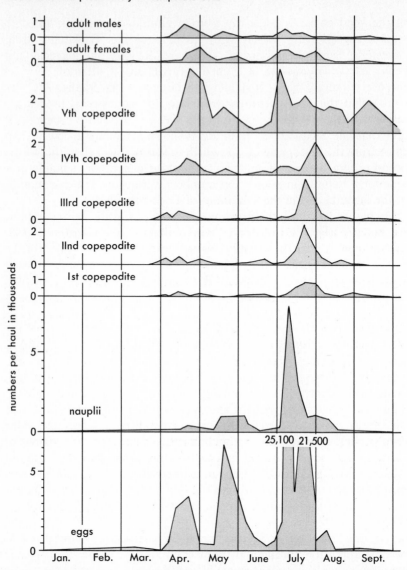

**Figure 4·9. Life-cycle of Calanus.** The frequency polygons show the numbers of each stage of *Calanus* (eggs, nauplii, Ist–Vth copepodites, and adult copepods) in plankton samples taken over nine months in Loch Striven in Scotland. [From W. D. Russell Hunter in *Brit. Assoc. Handb. (Glasgow, 1958)*, 5:97–118, 1958, after Marshall and Orr, 1958.]

lion specimens of adult *Calanus,* or about 1.5 gallons (U.S.) packed solid.

To recapitulate, the life-cycle of *Calanus* (and of several other copepods of the permanent zoöplankton) allows it to exploit the very

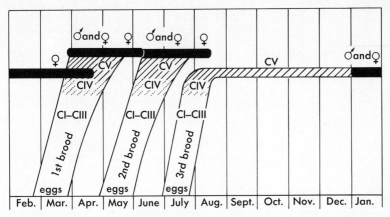

**Figure 4·10. Life-cycle of *Calanus*.** The diagram shows the annual succession of generations of *Calanus* in Loch Striven. The sizes of the stages are indicated by their positions in the vertical scale, with the eggs, copepodite stages and adults indicated for each of the three broods. Note that the overwintering generation has a life-cycle lasting through 8–9 months and that the overwintering stage for that brood is the Vth copepodite, or preadult stage. In *Calanus*, the number of generations per year is related to the climatic and trophic conditions of the environment: a single annual generation in the high Arctic (for example, in the waters of the east Greenland fjords), two generations per year in the coastal waters of Norway and in the Gulf of Maine, three generations in Scottish waters and off New Jersey, and four generations in warmer and richer conditions such as parts of the English Channel. [From W. D. Russell Hunter in *Brit. Assoc. Handb.* (*Glasgow, 1958*), 5:97–118, 1958, after Marshall and Orr, 1953.]

different seasonal patterns of plant productivity from the Mediterranean to the waters of the high Arctic off Greenland and in the Barents Sea, and also allows for the maximum possible buildup of animal biomass by the timing of the generations.

## Other holoplankton

Apart from the calanoid copepods, there are other animals of the permanent zoöplankton or holoplankton whose entire life-cycle is passed in a series of drifting pelagic forms. At least seven phyla of invertebrate animals are represented, and in many cases their reproduction and growth are seasonally patterned—like those of *Calanus*—to fit conditions of phytoplankton productivity.

Other crustaceans occur besides calanoids. A related group of copepods, more usually occurring in small bodies of fresh waters, the cyclopoids, is represented in the sea by a few species, only rarely and locally abundant, of such genera as *Oithona* and *Corycaeus*. Characteristically, they have a pair of true egg-sacs. The crustacean order Cladocera—representatives of which dominate the zoöplankton of

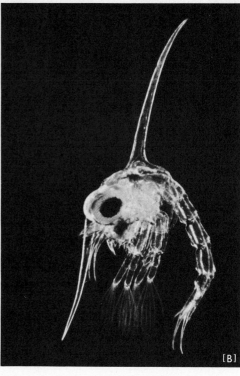

[A]　[B]

most lakes—has only a few minute marine species, mostly in the genera *Evadne* and *Podon*. Quite unlike the typical freshwater filter-feeders such as *Daphnia* and *Bosmina*, these minute marine cladocerans are raptorial carnivores. They show abundance in temporary patches in coastal waters under summer conditions (see Figures 4·3B and 4·13A). Minute bivalved crustaceans of the order Ostracoda are found in the plankton of the open oceans, but they are never a dominant component. Among the so-called higher Crustacea, the Malacostraca, which includes typical shrimps, lobsters, and crabs, there are a few holoplanktonic forms. The swiftly swimming opossum-shrimps are of moderate size (around 2 cm long) and include *Mysis* and its close relatives, which form extensive and dense flocks in shallow inshore waters over sand, but also include a few truly planktonic forms. Mysids have well-developed sense organs like predators, are excellent swimmers, and use both filter-feeding methods and raptorial capture in feeding. The typically inshore and littoral crustacean groups, Isopoda and Amphipoda (bottom-dwelling marine sow-bugs and sand-hoppers, respectively), have a few minor representatives in the plankton (see Figure 4·4). True shrimps and prawns are represented by species of such genera as *Ser-*

74

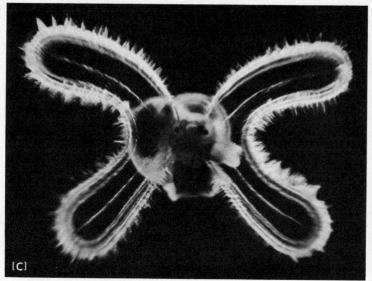

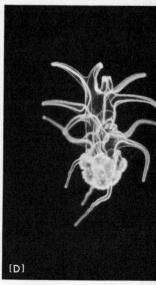

Figure 4·11. **Temporary zoöplankton:** living larval stages for four invertebrate phyla. **A:** Segmented post-trochosphere larva of the polychaete worm *Nepthys*. **B:** Second zoea larva of *Portunus puber* (velvet swimming crab). **C:** Veliger larva of the snail *Nassarius incrassatus*. **D:** Later brachiolaria larva of the starfish *Asterias*. In this lateral view, the radially symmetrical rudiment of the starfish body is beginning to form. Magnifications are approximately (**A**) 70 times, (**B**) 36 times, (**C**) 30 times and (**D**) 12 times. [Photos © Douglas P. Wilson.]

*gestes* (1.5–4 cm long), which are found mainly in the middepth and deep-ocean plankton—that is, below the euphotic zone. However, the most important group of malacostracans in the plankton is the order Euphausiacea. Species of such genera as *Euphausia* and *Meganycti-phanes* are shrimp-like animals of moderate size (2–6 cm long), and may be the dominant organisms in the zoöplankton of Arctic and Antarctic waters. They are filter-feeders operating at the second trophic level, and their feeding mechanism involves a conical basket which is formed by inwardly developed setae on six pairs of thoracic limbs. These are held stiffly as the animals swim along; water is scooped into the conical basket and filtered through the setae. There are minor variations in mesh-size and in the actual mechanism of ingestion. Some forms feed largely on detritus rather than on the phytoplankton directly (see pages 58 and 85). Euphausiids can occur in relatively dense swarms many miles in horizontal extent, as does *Euphausia superba* in Antarctic waters. In certain areas of the Arctic at certain seasons, and rather more continuously in the Antarctic, they form the principal food of whalebone whales, and as "krill," their swarms have long been known to, and sought by, whalemen.

Apart from arthropods, and the various single-celled prostistans not discussed here (although those many and various forms *without* chlorophyll must be considered members of the zoöplankton), six other phyla are represented. The phylum Cnidaria is represented by the many small jellyfish which, by suppression of certain attached stages or by other means, spend their entire life-cycle in the plankton (see Figure 4·12). The allied phylum, Ctenophora, consists almost entirely of marine planktonic forms. The ctenophores, or comb-jellies, when alive, are among the most beautiful of marine organisms (Figure 4·12B). Of a variety of sizes, from a few millimeters to many centimeters, they all move by the metachronal rowing of plates of fused cilia —the ctenes or comb-plates. They are carnivores, feeding avidly on forms like *Calanus,* and often competing to a measurable extent with

**Figure 4·12. Other living zoöplankton:** jellyfish and ctenophores. **A:** A hydrozoan jellyfish, *Gonionemus,* which is generally classified as a trachyline medusa, but which shows most of the features characteristic of the anthomedusae which are produced by certain hydroids. **B:** Specimens of *Pleurobrachia pileus,* a typical ctenophore from plankton in temperate waters of the Atlantic. Both cnidarian jellyfish and ctenophores are carnivorous and characteristically feed on the smaller crustaceans of the zoöplankton in competition with the young of several fish species. Magnifications are approximately (**A**) 6 times and (**B**) 1½ times. [Photos © Douglas P. Wilson.]

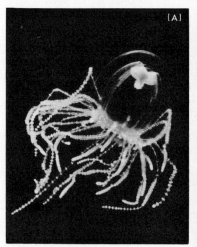
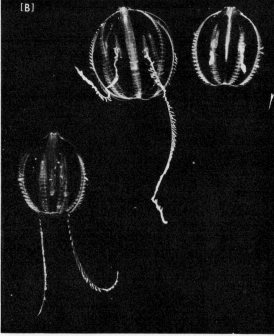

young fish for their food supply. Adult segmented worms (phylum Annelida are typically benthic animals, but a few, such as *Tomopteris,* are modified from the usual rag-worm organization, particularly by the development of swimming paddles, and pass their entire lifespan in the plankton. Similarly, the phylum Mollusca consists mainly in the snails and bivalves of the sea bottom and seashore (many of whose larvae are planktonic), but there are a few kinds of gastropods which live as adults in the plankton. Among these, the pteropods, or sea-butterflies, are modified snails with the middle parts of the foot drawn out into ciliated wing-like extensions on either side which are used for locomotion and also for collection of suspended food particles. In some forms, the typical snail shell is lost. In others it is less massive, and the beautiful little conical glassy cones of some tropical pteropods form distinctive deposits (the pteropod oozes) in certain parts of the ocean floor. The planktonic snails are not monophyletic; representatives of at least three different stocks within the class Gastropoda (phylum Mollusca) appear to have taken independently to pelagic life.

A characteristically planktonic phylum is the Chaetognatha, or arrow-worms. Although usually termed a minor phylum, with only sixty or so species, they can locally be among the commonest plank-tonic animals (see Figures 4·2 and 4·4). The majority of the species in the phylum are placed in one genus, *Sagitta.* They have transparent, torpedo-shaped bodies, unsegmented but showing bilateral symmetry. The mouth is surrounded by a group of grasping spines, and arrow-worms are predaceous on other members of the zoöplankton, which they pursue with surprisingly rapid, darting movements. They show patches of local abundance, often with significant effects on the whole marine economy; in some cases they destroy whole broods of eggs or young stages of certain of the commercially important fishes.

Specific forms of *Sagitta* are important as planktonic indicators of oceanic waters of different origins. Bodies of water which differ only very minutely in their physical and chemical characteristics are often distinguished by having, as biological indicators, specific arrow-worms. In many cases, these biological indicator species are more useful than microanalyses to oceanographers interested in the proportionate origins of bodies of oceanic water. A classical example of this is found in the temporal changes in the hydrography of the North Sea and English Channel. To summarize a fairly complicated relationship, the appear-ance of *Sagitta elegans* instead of *Sagitta setosa* is an indication of con-siderable influx of water from the northern Atlantic, and usually occurs in the North Sea in late summer and early fall of each year. Changes in micronutrients which accompany this influx of oceanic water are of great importance to the productivity of the area. Thus a series of census of *Sagitta* opens a real possibility of detailed prediction of the returns from herring fisheries in the area. Across the Atlantic, a similar situation was first described by Henry B. Bigelow for the Gulf of Maine. Variable offshoots from the "warm water river" of the Gulf Stream flow into this area, introducing species from the south, among them *Sagitta serratodentata* and *Sagitta maxima*. The varying numbers and survival times of these species of *Sagitta* in New England waters can thus afford a measure of the influx of masses of water from the Gulf Stream. In many other parts of the world, species of *Sagitta* are characteristic of distinctive water masses, and undoubtedly future predictive work on fisheries (see pages 101 and 261) will depend in part on sampling of arrow-worms.

Lastly, we have some representatives of the phylum Chordata in the permanent zoöplankton. Four groups of planktonic urochordates have evolved from the stocks of more typical sessile ascidians (the attached sea-squirts which have planktonic "tadpole" larvae). One of these, the Larvacea, has become specialized by the retention of an essential larval organization after the onset of maturity and the development of gonads. Thus, it is one of the classic examples of the evolutionary process which is termed neoteny. Species of such genera as *Oikopleura, Megalocercus,* and *Fritillaria* occur in the marine plankton in many parts of the world (see Figure 4·2). The biology of many forms is bizarre, involving the construction of an elaborate filter-feeding apparatus or house, a fine net for trapping nannoplankton for ingestion, and a coarse filter to protect the apparatus of nets and valves. The illustrated form *Oikopleura* lives within its "house," while *Fritillaria* lives outside the filtering apparatus during the feeding process. There is a simple life-cycle involving only sexual reproduction, and larvaceans live their entire life in the plankton. In the other three groups of planktonic chordates—*Pyrosoma,* salps, and doliolids—we have barrel-shaped forms like adult sea-squirts propelled by water currents created by muscle bands. The water current passing through a simplified group of gill slits within the "barrel" serves for feeding and respiration as well as locomotion (see Figure 4·13B). The entire life-cycle is spent in the plankton, but reproduction is complicated, involving both sexual and asexual phases. The individuals which develop from fertilized eggs—oözooids—differ greatly from the asexually produced blastozooids. In salps and doliolids there is regular alternation of these forms. Of these four urochordate groups, salps are the only ones ever important in the economy of the sea. They both compete with, and prey on, young fish and other elements of the zoöplankton. They appear irregularly, but in enormous numbers, in certain areas of the North Atlantic, and the years when salps occur represent very poor years for young fish. The

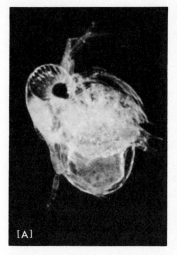
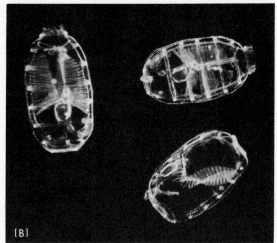

[A]

[B]

**Figure 4·13. More living "permanent" zoöplankton. A:** The small predaceous cladoceran *Podon intermedius,* showing the very characteristic single large compound eye. In some freshwater plankton communities the closely related genus *Polyphemus* occurs. **B:** Specimens of the barrel-shaped planktonic tunicate *Doliolum,* showing the propulsive muscle bands and the diagnostic pharyngeal gill slits. A fantastically complicated life-cycle (involving the alternation of asexual and sexual forms, a tadpole-like larva, and a complex process of stolonic budding of polymorphic zooids) is carried out entirely in the plankton of the open ocean. Magnifications are approximately (**A**) 40 times and (**B**) 16 times. [Photos © Douglas P. Wilson.]

underlying causes of "outbursts" of salps are inadequately understood.

## Larval forms and larval seasons

When we turn to the temporary members of the zoöplankton, we find representatives of every major phylum of the animal kingdom, and of the majority of minor phyla. It is this sheer diversity of larval representation that has allowed Alister C. Hardy to claim that the marine plankton encompasses an assemblage of animals more diverse and more comprehensive than is available in any other living community. The education of modern biologists at all levels unfortunately neglects the opportunities thus presented. Marine zoöplankton *can* be transported alive to inland teaching laboratories, and much more is to be gained than the important "exposure to animal diversity" with its necessary introduction to the methods and units of practical systematics. Apart from the many aspects of ecological interrelationships in the plankton still to be investigated, observational and simple experimental work on the mechanics of feeding and of locomotion, and on some of the array of adaptive devices exhibited, could be both original and profitable. The insects are the only major animal group not represented in the marine zoöplankton. The survey of larval types now attempted will necessarily be synoptic.

Sponges (phylum Porifera) are represented by a few flagellated larvae, actually little more than motile blastula stages for dispersal which probably take in little or no food during their brief planktonic phase. Of course, the Cnidaria are much more extensively represented. Not only are there larvae in the strict sense such as the planulae of a wide variety of hydroids, sea-anemones, and corals, but also there are the medusoid stages of the enormous number of hydroids. These minute motile jellyfish are not merely the dispersal stage but are actually the gonad-bearing sexual adults. (See Figures 4·2, 4·4, and 4·12A.) For example, in the case of many common hydroids, such as *Obelia* and *Bougainvillia,* the relatively massive and extensive colonies of hydroid represent a larval stage, benthic and attached, while the tiny fraction of their biomass released as planktonic medusae is adult. Other cnidarian larvae in the plankton include the ephyra stage of the larger jellyfish and the peculiar actinula larva, like a free-swimming juvenile hydroid individual, of *Tubularia* and its allies (see Figure 4·4). Flatworms (phylum Platyhelminthes) are represented in the plankton by a ciliated larva, as are the nemertine worms (phylum Rhynchocoela), and about seven minor phyla of benthic invertebrates. The major worm phylum, the Annelida, is represented by the archetypic trochosphere larva and by the later planktonic larvae with metameric segments being budded off (see Figure 4·11A). Several kinds of annelid worms also produce epitokes which are budded off, contain mature reproductive organs, and possess modified parapodia which allow for more efficient swimming. In a number of other cases whole adult worms metamorphose to a sexual swarming form which temporarily enters the plankton.

The various larval stages of bottom-dwelling crustaceans are also well represented. Some of these resemble the larvae of planktonic copepods: indeed, a typical nauplius larva occurs in the development of some species in almost all groups of crustaceans. At times, the plankton of temperate seas is dominated by the later larvae of barnacles (subclass Cirripedia), including the characteristic triangular metanauplius with horns and the penultimate stage before settlement, the cyprid larva. Some higher crustaceans have a nauplius larva, but many more show the typical zoea (see Figures 4·3 and 4·11B) which is succeeded in development by a presettlement stage, in higher crustaceans usually a megalopa. Mysids, shrimps, prawns, marine crayfish, lobsters, and crabs all have their own distinctive late larval stages (see Figure 4·4). Many of these have bizarre arrangements of long spines and flattened segments, which offer a high frictional resistance to the water, and they are relatively large, massive larvae. A great deal of work remains to be done on their equally bizarre behavior patterns, which must serve to take these penultimate dispersal stages into the appropriate habitats for settled life as adults.

The major phylum Mollusca is represented in the plankton by numerous ciliated larvae of a few rather stereotyped patterns. In a large number of more primitive molluscs, external fertilization in the sea gives rise to a trochophore larva with a characteristic ring of locomotory cilia. This is unlikely to represent shared ancestral recapitulation with the trochosphere of annelid worms; rather, it seems to reflect a parallel adaptational response to the immediate needs of larval life. In the marine snails, there is a later characteristic larva, the veliger, in which the trochophore ring has become developed into a typical wheel-shaped velum bearing long cilia (see Figure 4·11C). Still later a mantle rudiment appears and secretes a characteristic shell, and the minute shelled snail larvae may drift for a variable period in the plankton, before settling to the bottom to grow up as adult gastropods (see Figure 4·4B). In the Bivalvia, including clams, mussels, and oysters, the trocophore-like larva develops a bivalve shell, and this miniature and well-ciliated bivalve may drift, feeding, for some time in the plankton before it settles to the bottom and metamorphoses into a miniature of the adult form. This process of spatfall (settlement and metamorphosis) can be relatively synchronous through an extensive area of the sea, and for common littoral forms such as mussels, can involve a spectacular, simultaneous descent of myriads of tiny mussels on the seashore.

The totally marine phylum Echinodermata—starfish, sea-urchins, sea-cucumbers, and their allies—has diverse and characteristic planktonic larvae, and no other group of animals undergoes such complicated metamorphoses in the course of development. There are two main larval types (see Figure 4·11D), the plutei of brittle-stars and sea-urchins, and the bipinnaria or auricularia of starfish and sea-cucumbers. In all cases the body of the larva and particularly the larval lobes or arms (which are arranged in bilateral symmetry) bear bands of strong cilia which serve both for microphagous feeding and for locomotion. There is always a radical process of metamorphosis involving asymmetric rudiments in the larva, which rudiments give rise to the radially symmetrical adults just before settlement.

As already noted, primitive chordates are represented in the plankton by the "tadpole" stages of many benthic sea-squirts. In addition, the development stages of many fishes—both bottom-dwelling forms and pelagic members of the nekton—are temporary members of the plankton. The floating eggs of some fishes are planktonic, and newly hatched fry, both from these and from eggs laid on the bottom, are unable to migrate against water currents and are therefore also planktonic rather than nektonic. Some fish fry do not feed, being nourished by attached yolk-sacs (which also make them less dense), while others feed typically at the third trophic level, consuming large quantities of calanoid copepods and various small larvae (see Chapter 8).

This great diversity of larval forms is not present throughout the year in temperate seas. To speak teleologically, obviously the free-swimming fishes of the nekton, and the bottom-dwelling invertebrates of the benthos, are better able to exploit temporary fluctuations in basic marine productivity than are the animals whose entire life-cycle is spent in the plankton. In fact, the spawning of fishes, of starfish, and of clams, and the liberation of young larvae by barnacles and by various crabs each have a clearcut seasonal pattern. In many cases this is clearly arranged to allow the best utilization of a temporary food source, or to correspond to the best possible time in the oceanic seasons for success-ful settlement to the bottom. For the great majority of known larval life-cycles, we can readily perceive the adaptational advantages of spawning at a very specific time, but relatively little is known in detail about how such timed spawning is controlled in nature. In a small number of cases which have been investigated, including certain molluscs, the trigger for the onset of the breeding period is changing day-length. Spawning in other forms is clearly temperature-controlled. In still other cases, chemoreception of food organisms or of other appropriate environmental conditions has been implicated. Perhaps the simplest form of control is found where there is an apparent syn-chronization of spawning or of the release of larval stages from the parent which corresponds to the spring diatom increase (SDI). There is evidence for a number of benthic invertebrates of spawning or larval release occurring in the early spring in lower latitudes and progressively later northwards to take place in midsummer in the highest latitudes. Such synchrony of larval production and the SDI in the Arctic has particularly been elucidated by Gunnar Thorson. In at least one barnacle species, direct "chemical perception" of the SDI may be in-volved. Harold Barnes has demonstrated that substances present in the water of a concentrated suspension of *Skeletonema,* and probably re-sulting from the metabolic activities of the diatoms, have a marked effect in promoting the hatching of nauplii of the common barnacle *Balanus balanoides.* An extract of the bodies of adult barnacles had a similar stimulatory effect on naupliar production, but the effect of an extract of barnacle egg-masses was less marked. Barnes was also able to demonstrate that over several years at Millport in Scotland, local variations in the initiation and progress of the SDI could be correlated with hundredfold changes (within a few days) in the numbers of barnacle nauplii present in the plankton. Thus, besides the broad latitudinal synchrony of larval release with the peaks of primary productivity in the sea, there can also be local timing control (obviously not geophysical like changing day-length) which is involved in assuring optimal conditions for the relatively short larval life in such forms.

## More food-chains

While linear food-chains spanning a few trophic levels are undoubtedly easiest to comprehend and quantify, they exist but rarely in aquatic environments and probably never on land. We have already mentioned some examples involving the marine plankton which are, in some considerable fraction, linear. The herring is one of the most abundant of pelagic fishes, and commercially one of the most important crop fish for man. The food of young and adult herring in British waters has been fairly extensively investigated, by Alister C. Hardy and his associates in the North Sea, and by Shiena M. Marshall and A. P. Orr in the Clyde sea area. Young herring of the west coast of Scotland are involved in the simplest possible food-chain of three trophic levels:

$$Skeletonema \rightarrow Calanus \rightarrow \text{herring}$$

In the North Sea, Hardy found an additional level involved in the major flow of herring food. This involves the semiplanktonic sand-eels *Ammodytes,* whose diet is over 70 per cent *Calanus.* In turn, 40 per cent of the food collected by herring in these studies was *Ammodytes,* and only 21 per cent was *Calanus* taken directly. From our earlier discussions of trophic transfer (see pages 24 and 27), it is obvious that the ratio of direct to indirect contributions of *Calanus* to the nutrition of herring is not simply 1:2, but of the order of 1:35. To put it another way, the biomass of *Calanus* per unit time passing to the nutrition of this population of herring through *Ammodytes* is thirty-five times that which is directly ingested. Ignoring many complexities then, and considering only the bulk of the trophic transfer, we can depict this linear food chain as:

$$\text{diatoms} \rightarrow Calanus \rightarrow Ammodytes \rightarrow \text{herring}$$

Almost similar food-chains for another pelagic shoaling fish, the menhaden, have been revealed by the work of Gordon A. Riley and others in the coastal waters of New England. In one such case, smaller copepods of the genera *Temora* and *Acartia* replace *Calanus,* and in the primary pasturage, two dominant genera of diatoms compete with a success dependent on the temperature changes each season. This gives us the following food-chain:

$$\begin{matrix} Skeletonema & & Temora & & \\ \text{or} & \rightarrow & \text{and} & \rightarrow Ammodytes \rightarrow \text{menhaden} \\ Thalassiosira & & Acartia & & \end{matrix}$$

To the north, off the Atlantic coast of Canada, we again have regions with the simplest food-chain of diatoms, *Calanus,* and herring.

The trophic relationships of natural aquatic communities are usually much more complex for two principal reasons. First is the tendency, already noted, of animals at the higher trophic levels to exploit a number of alternative food organisms, not necessarily all of the same trophic level, the resulting multiplicity of relationships forming a food-web. A relatively simple food-web is depicted in Figure 4·14, which represents the feeding relationships of the herring in the North Sea, as elucidated by Alister C. Hardy. The energetic consequences of the existence of complex food-webs are enormous and still require much field and theoretical investigation. For the herring of Figure 4·14, the risks of starvation—and possible population extinction—are obviouly lessened by the existence of alternative food organisms and (for reasons already discussed; see pages 24 and 27) more especially by its ability to switch its feeding to a lower trophic level. An increase in direct feeding on *Calanus,* with a corresponding decrease in feeding on *Ammodytes,* involves a shortening of the food-chain, and thus (from the point of view of the herring) an increased efficiency in the exploitation of the original diatom crop. It would appear that the Scots herring of the Clyde—and the coast of Nova Scotia—have more permanently adopted this thrifty or parsimonious shift of feeding to a lower trophic level. There is more general significance in the occurrence of complex food-webs. From a wide variety of field observations on communities of organisms, we can make the generalization that increased complexity of food-webs results in increased stability of the community as a whole. In other words, increase in number of alternative links is favorably modifying the risks of extinction, not merely for one species like the herring but for all the organisms in the biotic community—at least, for all those animal species at higher trophic levels. The negative aspect of this generalization has been carefully and extensively documented by Charles Elton in his studies of the *unstable* ecological situations which can follow invasions of previously stable communities by animals or plants but without concurrent introduction of their more usual predators and parasites. Although empirically well-recognized, this aspect of community stability being based to some extent on the degree of complexity of food-webs has not yet been satisfactorily explained in

terms of a rigorous predictive model, in spite of continued efforts by
several distinguished theoretical ecologists (see also Chapter 11).

The second feature which complicates the trophic relationships
within aquatic communities was illustrated in Figure 4·1. So far we
have only discussed the *direct* feeding of a carnivore on living herbivores, and of herbivores on living green plant cells. However, for many
marine animals, the most important food source is *detritus,* the partially
broken-down tissues of dead—or even partially digested—plants and
animals. In the open waters of the oceans, much of the organic material
produced in the superficial levels falls as a continuous "rain" of dead

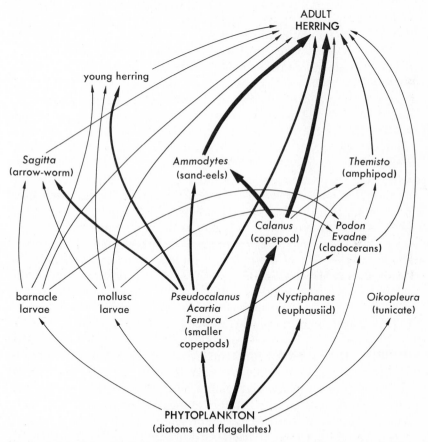

**Figure 4·14. A food-web for certain populations of herring in the North Sea.**
The major linear food chain runs: diatoms → *Calanus* → *Ammodytes* → herring; but
note the alternative food organisms and capacity to switch feeding to lower trophic
levels. [Modified from A. C. Hardy in *Fish. Invest. London, IInd Series, 7(#3)*:1–53,
1924.]

or dying bodies, or fragments of bodies, from organisms, both of the plankton and of the nekton. In inshore waters, some terrestrial organic materials are added to the larger masses of detritus resulting from the death and partial breakdown of benthic plants and animals. Indeed, in many areas of coastal shallows, and in estuaries, the primary productivity of the local phytoplankton can be quantitatively of less importance to the nutrition of the local fauna than is the detritus resulting from the breakdown of larger attached plants, such as species of the marshgrass *Spartina,* in the tidal zone, and the eel-grass *Zostera,* in the shallower waters of the sublittoral. It is significant that there are relatively few herbivores which browse directly on living *Zostera,* and almost none that can graze on healthy, living *Spartina.* Over large areas of coastal waters and the shallower seas, the dominant animals of benthic communities are often second-trophic-level consumers, but living as detritus-feeders, dependent on the productivity of underwater beds of *Zostera* or detritus of *Spartina* washed out of intertidal flats and salt marshes. However, even the detrital "rain" of the open ocean is important in the economy of the sea (see again Figure 4·1). The euphotic or lit zone occupies only a tiny fraction of the ocean's volume (see pages 38 and 228), and the ultimate green plant food source of all marine animals—whether direct herbivores or detritus-feeders, or their predators—must lie within its limits. But there are large numbers of animals in the oceans in intermediate depths and considerable numbers even in the greatest depths. It has often been pointed out that, in the oceans, the hypothetical Eltonian pyramid of biomass and of numbers is present in a form with some concrete reality in space—*but it is inverted.* The largest production of any trophic level is that of the plants in the uppermost sunlit layers. The direct grazers of the zoöplankton—of which less biomass is produced per year—occur here and in the layers immediately deeper. Animals of the third and fourth trophic levels occur even deeper but amount to a progressively smaller annual production. To this extent, the food-chains and food-webs can be considered as directed downwards, with the higher trophic levels represented by the smaller production of the inverted pyramid's apex. We can make some generalizations about the natural history of the animals found at different depths in the oceans. First, filter-feeding animals, whether of the zoöplankton or the benthos, which feed directly on the live plants of the phytoplankton, cannot extend much deeper in the open ocean or on the sea bottom than the local average depth for the compensation level of those plants. Secondly, all benthic suspension-feeders living below those depths, whether true filter-feeders or not, must feed on detritus. Thirdly, such bottom-dwelling detritus-feeders will decrease in numbers with increasing depth. The amount of detrital food of suitable size reaching the bottom diminishes with depth, although considerable quantities of finer particulate organic matter have recently been shown to occur at great depths. In general, larger plant and animal detritus originating in the euphotic zone is disintegrated through autolysis or bacterial decomposition—or simply eaten by animals in the intermediate depths—before it can ever reach the deep-sea bottom. Fourthly, the largest nektonic animals will occur in the surface waters and intermediate depths. Fifthly, the free-swimming animals of the greater depths—the bathypelagic forms— will tend to be animals of intermediate size, neither very small nor very large. Perhaps this last natural history generalization requires more explanation. In crude terms, there is too little food at these depths to support really large animals, and there is little small particulate food *suitable* for the support of small pelagic animals. Available food, whether alive or dead, comes in rare units of moderate size. The necessarily intermediate-sized swimming animals of the depths of the ocean must, as Alister C. Hardy has put it, "be capable of taking large mouthfuls at relatively long intervals." In fact, the bizarre assemblage of deep-sea fishes already known are mostly less than 20 cm long, have extraordinarily immense mouths and jaws, propelled by seemingly emaciated bodies, but with greatly distensible guts. Their trophic adaptations seem to resemble those of constrictor snakes.

## Food-chain tracers

Perhaps more characteristic of the *direct* food-chains than of the *detritus* chains are the occurrences of organic substances of moderate complexity which can be used as natural "tracers." Essentially, these are molecules which can only be synthesized *de novo* by certain primary producers in the phytoplankton. To a varying extent, they may be nutritional necessities to animals in the higher trophic levels. Perhaps the classic example of this is still incompletely understood. It concerns vitamins $D_2$ and $D_3$, whose antirachitic importance reflects their catalysis of several processes of calcium metabolism in higher animals. The D vitamins are formed by the action of ultraviolet light upon certain sterols which are found in both plants and animals. In the oceans, their production must be limited, not merely to the euphotic zone but, since the ultraviolet wavelengths are very rapidly absorbed, to the first few meters below the sea surface. However, as is well known, the liver oils of such bottom-dwelling fishes as the cod and the halibut are fantastically rich in the D vitamins. A major part of the food supply of such fishes—the benthic bivalves and crustaceans—has a very low content of these substances, and indeed of their sterol precursors. Vitamin D must reach the cod and halibut by way of a food-chain from the surface waters. Certainly for vitamin $D_2$ (calciferol), formed by the ultraviolet irradiation of green plant ergosterol, the food-chain must run:

$$\text{phytoplankton} \rightarrow \text{copepods} \rightarrow \text{capelin} \rightarrow \begin{array}{c} \text{cod} \\ \text{or} \\ \text{halibut} \end{array} \rightarrow \text{man}$$

Somewhat surprisingly, the vitamin D content of the lipids of *Calanus* is low on average. Further, George L. Clarke has suggested that such a food-chain is too long and tenuous to account for the large quantities of vitamin D in the fish liver oils. To date, however, no other ecological source is known. It is worth mentioning that, although prolonged exposure to sunlight is fatal to most copepods, including *Calanus,* at some times of the year they flock in brilliant sunshine immediately below the surface. It has been suggested that these temporary periods when their fats could be irradiated by ultraviolet could be significant. The trophic relations of vitamin A in the sea are similar. Again we have synthesis in plants, and again we have surprisingly large quantities in the livers and in certain other internal organs of whales. In this case, one of the possible intermediate links in the food-chain, krill (euphausiids such as *Meganyctiphanes* and *Thysanoessa*), is very rich in vitamin A, while *Calanus* is poor though very rich in total carotenoids which could include the provitamin.

Trophic exchanges of other vitamins in the open sea have been little investigated as yet. Vitamin $B_1$ (thiamine) cannot be synthesized by animals, and again must be formed in the lighted levels of the ocean. It is almost certain that every marine animal must take in $B_1$, since thiamine is a necessary precursor of a coenzyme in the universal citric acid cycle of oxidative metabolism. Empirically, it has been demonstrated in the aseptic culture of filter-feeding crustaceans by Luigi Provasoli and his colleagues that thiamine is among the essential requirements for growth and maturation. Under natural conditions in the sea, some fishes and large invertebrates may obtain their thiamine requirement as a result of synthesis by the bacterial flora of their own guts, but others, including most small zoöplankton organisms, must ingest a source. Similarly, vitamin $B_{12}$ (cyanocobalamin) was recently shown by C. B. Cowey to be present in zoöplankton at about twice the concentration by weight as in phytoplankton samples from the same localities. In this case, too, it is still not known whether these animals obtain their requirements direct from the phytoplankton or from bacterial flora in their guts. Again, the latter is less likely in the smallest copepods. Both the vitamin cyanocobalamin itself and the essential coenzymes derived from it contain the element cobalt unusually bonded to carbon. Cobalt has long been known as one of the so-called trace elements required for green plant growth and, although toxic in excess, in relatively tiny quantities its salts have been used in agriculture to achieve spectacular correction of the symptoms of mineral deficiency in both crop plants and animals. The universal importance of vitamin $B_{12}$ to all cellular organisms has been stressed by recent discoveries of the importance of its coenzymes in the synthesis of nucleic acids. Ecologically, there is some further importance in a series of observations which demonstrate a further requirement for this or for similar cobalt-containing substances in nitrogen-fixing plants and microörganisms.

There are, of course, many other organic substances which cannot be synthesized by higher animals. These include the polyunsaturated fatty acids. Once again these must originate in the primary producers of the lit zone of the sea. The most characteristic of them in most marine invertebrates, in fishes, and in whales are those of $C_{20}$ and $C_{22}$ chain length (eicosapentaenoic and docosahexaenoic fatty acids) which are members of the alpha-linolenic series. Both are found in relatively large quantities in *Calanus* and in krill, and, when ingested by various fishes or whales of the third trophic level, apparently pass intact and are incorporated into the larger animals. In most diatoms which have been studied, the predominant polyunsaturates seem to be those of chain length $C_{16}$ (with $C_{20}$, $C_{18}$, and $C_{22}$ as smaller fractions of the total fatty acids). In many common planktonic diatoms, such as *Skeletonema,* the fatty-acid composition of the individual cells changes with age, and the unsaturated acids of chain length $C_{20}$ and $C_{22}$ decrease markedly in old diatom cells. It is probable that some members of the zoöplankton—calanoid copepods and euphausiids—can form the $C_{20}$ and $C_{22}$ acids by chain elongation from $C_{16}$ and $C_{18}$ unsaturates. Clearly, they cannot carry out *de novo* synthesis of polyunsaturates. Incorporation intact from food remains important, and recent work by my colleague George G. Holz and his associates has demonstrated that certain primary producers are important sources of $C_{20}$ and $C_{22}$ polyunsaturates. They grew eight species of dinoflagellates, coccolithophores, and small flagellates in axenic cultures totally free of fatty acids, and demonstrated the synthesis of large fractions of $C_{20}$ and $C_{22}$ unsaturates. Thus a significant part of the polyunsaturated-fatty-acid content in larger fishes and whales could be made up of molecules derived from such primary producers and passed intact along the food-chains.

## Pelagic animal productivity

The greater part of the formation of new animal protein from plant food each year occurs in the marine zoöplankton. We shall discuss some methods of computing the total amounts involved in Chapters 12 and 13, but for the moment, we can take it that the marine production of new animal protein is at least five times the annual production on land, and at least three-quarters of the marine protein productivity at the second trophic level occurs in the zoöplankton. As we have already noted, this enormous crop of zoöplankton is in turn the direct food of such fishes as herring, mackerel, and menhaden, and also of the largest true fishes and largest mammals. Besides providing for such direct feeding the zoöplankton is an important indirect food source of many other commercial fishes, including: tuna, swordfish, haddock, cod, halibut, sole, plaice, and many others.

Where direct feeding occurs, enormous numbers of zoöplankton organisms are involved. For example, a sample of young herring (only averaging 18 cm long) collected near Millport in the Clyde contained an average number of 2000 specimens of *Calanus* in each gut. The consumption of *Calanus* per day by herring of this size must amount to more than twice this number because, although the time spent in the passage through the gut of a herring varies greatly, it is usually considerably less than 12 hours. The gut contents of adult herring vary somewhat more widely, since they are less continuous feeders, but one can find, in the guts of nonshoaling herring, numbers of about 70,000 specimens of *Calanus* being digested at one time. Young specimens of herring, mackerel, and menhaden are certainly not continuous filter-feeders; they dart about within, and on the fringes of, concentrations of zoöplankton, snatching at individual copepods and ingesting them singly. There is some controversy about the extent to which larger specimens of these pelagic fishes actually do filter their zoöplankton food *without* selection. It is not without interest that the filtering structures of some sizes of menhaden and anchoveta are capable of retaining the larger diatoms from the phytoplankton as well as small crustaceans, and there is evidence that such menhaden and anchoveta do feed in part at the second trophic level.

At this point, it is worth turning aside briefly to consider man's trophic relationship with certain menhaden shoals of the eastern seaboard of the United States. In this area of the sea, as elsewhere, the largest stock of living animal proteins consists of the calanoid copepods of the zoöplankton. These are consumed by menhaden, among other fish species. A multimillion dollar fishing and processing enterprise catches menhaden and turns them into fish-meal. Although at present (1968–69) suffering a relative recession, this industry has in recent years involved the use of light aircraft for spotting menhaden shoals and, besides many catching vessels, the use of small "bulk-cargo" ships like miniature tankers to transport the fish crop to the meal-processing factories. Although this fish-meal, and the even larger amounts now originating in Peruvian fisheries, is perfectly suitable for human nutrition, and would be a suitable supplement to diets in those many tropical countries where protein deficiencies already occur, it is not so used (see also pages 100 and 250). Instead, the fish-meal is used to supplement the diet of swine and broiler fowl by being incorporated in the feeding stuffs of "intensive" agriculture. By thus inserting an additional intervening trophic level into this food-chain of human nutrition, man achieves a remarkably inefficient and energetically indirect utilization of these marine proteins, and, in fact, may incorporate less than 1/10,000 of the original protein. The geopolitical consequences of such misuse of protein are immense, and some aspects of this will be discussed later (see Chapters 8 and 13).

If we turn to the larger animals which feed directly on the zoöplankton, including the basking sharks and whales, there can be no doubt that the process of feeding is simply filtration of large volumes of water, usually indiscriminate and often continuous. The two largest fishes in the world are the basking shark (*Cetorhinus*) which occurs in the North Atlantic and can reach lengths of 40 feet, though it is more usually between 20 and 30 feet in length, and the whale-shark (*Rhineodon*) of warmer seas which, though a stout-bodied fish, can reach a length of 55 feet. Their filtering apparatus consists of an elaboration of the protective gill-rakers found in all shark-like fishes, and in the basking shark these fine, comb-like bristles are arranged to give a mesh-size of about 0.7 mm, most suitable for catching calanoid copepods. Basking sharks habitually swim along with their mouths open; water passing in flows through the mesh of the gill-rakers before passing out through the greatly expanded gill slits behind the head. When feeding, basking sharks swim slowly, at speeds of about 1.5–2 nautical miles per hour and, as we have already noticed, for hydrodynamic reasons this is about the most efficient speed at which to pass water through such a filter. At such times in the summer when there are rich concentrations of *Calanus* in Scottish coastal waters, one commonly sees the large dorsal fins of these basking sharks as they cruise slowly along just under the surface in the regions of greatest concentration of copepods. Watching basking sharks collect plankton, as I have done on a number of occasions in lower Loch Fyne and at Carradale, one is impressed by the fact that when two basking sharks (or more rarely three) swim in company they invariably keep at a set distance and angle apart, rather like several mine-sweeping vessels working in echelon. It looks as if they were carefully remaining as close to each other as possible consistent with avoiding filtering any water twice. The "quartering" activities of even a single basking shark as it works over a particular bit of sea give the same impression of controlled efficiency. It is well nigh impossible to estimate the numbers of zoöplankton organisms which are ingested in this way, though calculations suggest that a medium-sized basking shark filters about 200,000 tons of water per hour. I once assisted at the rough dissection (with fire-axes and woodsman's saw) of a basking shark about 25 feet long from the Clyde. It had been killed accidentally by a ferry steamer while feeding, and its distended stomach (capacity estimated at 145 gallons) was packed with a semisolid mass which, when the wall was accidentally punctured, poured out like concentrated tomato soup. This bright red paste was actually an almost pure mass of *Calanus* undergoing the first stages of peptic digestion. It is of interest to note that basking sharks have to shed their worn-out gill-rakers each year and grow a new set of these bristles. In Scottish waters they do this—living on the bottom without planktonic food the while—in October and November, precisely at the time when the plankton crop is poorest. It is probable that the largest true fish, the whale-shark *Rhineodon,* lives and feeds in the same fashion. However, little is known about its biology, though Thor Heyerdahl gives a vivid account of one seen at close quarters during the Pacific voyage of the Kon-Tiki.

Although whalebone whales also feed by somewhat indiscriminate filtration, this is not quite such a continuous process as it is in these giant sharks. Unlike their predaceous relatives, the dolphins and killer-whales, the whalebone whales have teeth only during their embryonic development. Instead, hanging down from the sides of the upper jaw is a series of horny plates—the baleen or whalebone—whose inner edges are fringed out into vast numbers of stiff fibers, the whole presenting the appearance of a gigantic series of huge drooping moustaches hanging from the roof of the whale's mouth. Filtration is accomplished by opening the mouth and taking enormous gulps of seawater with its contained plankton, then forcing the water sideways through these enormous moustaches by an upward pumping movement of the gigantic tongue against the palate. The deposit of plankton thus collected on the inner fringes is apparently wiped off by a further movement of the tongue and then swallowed. The largest mammal in the world—indeed probably the largest animal that ever has existed—is a whalebone whale, the blue-whale, which reaches lengths of 100 feet and weights of about 150 tons. The fin-whale or common rorqual of the North Atlantic is somewhat smaller, reaching 80 feet in length, but for it we have an estimate of the amount of water filtered in each swallowing cycle. The mouth and distensible throat can have a capacity in excess of 1500 gallons (about 7 tons), and the plankton can be filtered from this volume of water in a cycle lasting only a few seconds. Apart from differences in size, different species of whalebone whales differ in the mesh-sizes of their baleen, and in the speeds at which they propel their filtering apparatus through the water. One medium-sized whale, the sei-whale, about 50 feet in length as an adult, has a relatively fine sieve of baleen fibers, and in consequence moves slowly and shows a close correspondence to the abundance of calanoid copepods. On the other hand, the lesser rorqual (usually about 25 feet long) swims more rapidly and takes some fish such as the herring in addition to the plankton, thus taking food at the fourth trophic level to a greater extent than any other whalebone whale.

Finally, it is interesting to note the implications of the size range of whalebone whales. They include the world's largest animals, but no whalebone whale is as small as the smaller toothed whales: the dolphins and porpoises. There is obviously a minimum size below which the baleen filtering mechanism ceases to be efficient. There are other aspects of size in whales where the physical and mechanical results of the surface:volume relationships are important. Even among the smallest toothed whales, there is no dolphin smaller than 4 feet (1.2 meters) long. Whales are warm-blooded mammals and lose heat from their surfaces below the minimum size; a hypothetical miniature dolphin would have too large a surface in proportion to its volume (or mass), and thus the loss of heat per unit mass would be too great. However, perhaps the principal reason for the great size of the larger whalebone whales is found in the importance of surface:volume ratios to swimming. Swimming effort is largely expended against surface resistance, which proportionately decreases with increasing size; on the other hand, the power output of whale muscle will be proportional to its mass and thus increase relatively with size. In other words, the larger the whale, the faster it can swim. It is not appropriate to discuss here certain mechanical paradoxes about the swimming of small whales, but there are authentic records of a 90-foot blue-whale attaining a speed of 20 knots for short bursts, and calculations reveal that about 520 horsepower is required at such times. In this, as in the trophic matters we have discussed, the whalebone whales represent an extremely efficient pattern of animal machine, and (in the absence of any efficient predators until Sven Foyn invented the explosive harpoon) blue-whales and the various species of rorquals lived as highly successful animals until after 1865 (but see Chapter 10).

# 5

# Polar, tropical, and inshore seas

THE PRECEDING TWO CHAPTERS have been largely concerned with conditions in the open ocean and offshore waters in temperate latitudes. As already adumbrated, the nature and level of productivity are markedly different in both polar waters and tropical waters, and also in such inshore waters as semienclosed bays and estuaries. Certain aspects of productivity in these three groups of marine environments will be discussed in turn.

## Arctic and Antarctic seas

The seas in high latitudes have a single summer period of zoöplankton abundance, and this implies certain peculiarities of physiology and of development in the life-cycles of the animals concerned. There have been a series of detailed investigations of productivity in the Barents Sea (that part of the Arctic ocean lying north and east of the North Cape of Norway) by Russian marine biologists, including B. G. Bogorov and B. P. Manteufel. At latitudes of about 72° North, there is a permanent night for about four months of the winter, and correspondingly over two months with the sun continuously above the horizon (24-hour-long days). At such latitudes in the Barents Sea there is a peak of diatom productivity in May with some reduction in June followed by a further increase in July. There is only one peak period of mass development of zoöplankton. In June there is a great increase in the biomass of *Calanus* and of juvenile euphausiids. Relatively high zoöplankton numbers continue until the onset of the winter night in late October. As mentioned earlier (see page 71), *Calanus* in such conditions has a simple annual life-cycle, and in the Barents Sea almost all the growth and most of the development stages are passed in the month of June. The later copepodite stages found towards the end of this period of mass development are bright red in color. This color seems to be associated with the presence of colored fats in the oil-sac, but whether it depends on the presence in the diatoms or other food of specifically colored fats is not yet known. The red *Calanus* are fed upon by a local stock of herring which do most of their growing in July and August, accumulating fat reserves which are steadily used up during the long Arctic winter so that there is a period after February and before the next year's zoöplankton increase when growth is completely stopped, the fat reserves are exhausted, and the herring are literally starving. As already noted, the copepod productivity of the short Arctic season is exploited by whalebone whales such as the sei-whale. In slightly lower Arctic latitudes, in the Davis Strait west of Greenland, the great Norwegian marine biologist Johan Hjort was able to demonstrate a close correlation between the local density of young euphausiids and the commercial capture of whales, including blue-whales, common rorqual, and sei-whales. These species of whales also occur in the Antarctic, and there a similar correlation with local concentrations of krill is found. Along with the humpback-whale, these three whales visit the highest latitudes only at the times of maximum zoöplankton productivity and migrate toward the equator to breed during their hemisphere's winter. For the four species, there seems to be little interchange of individuals between the stocks of the Arctic and those of the Antarctic, but no characteristic differences between the stocks have been found and they are regarded as four interbreeding species, worldwide in distribution. The remarkable growth rates of blue-whales and rorquals are sustained by this migration through temperate and boreal seas at their times of maximum zoöplankton production. The gestation period in the blue-whale is eleven months, and the blue-whale calf is born at a length of about 23 feet. The calf (twins are rare) is suckled by the mother for about six months (the mammary glands are muscularized and milk is pumped into the calf as the whales swim along), and at the time of weaning, the calf has reached a length of about 52 feet. By two years of age it can be up to 75 feet long. Less than three and a half years of foetal growth, suckling, and juvenile filter-feeding build up 60 tons or so of young blue-whale. This gives some idea of the richness of the krill and *Calanus* swarms as food supply, and of the capacity and efficiency of the maternal filtration mechanism and rates of incorporation.

The migrations of the plankton-feeding whales are equaled by those of such seabirds as the petrels, which move toward higher latitudes through spring and early summer, always remaining in the region of maximum copepod production, and so one species moves northward off our Atlantic seaboard a little after the northward movement of the spring diatom increase (SDI). Even more remarkable is the migration of the Arctic tern, which feeds on euphausiids and young fish, and contrives by its migrations to be in the high Arctic at the time of maximum production of such forms and, six months later, to be in the high latitudes of the Antarctic feeding on the same food. Arctic terns are typically working in the north temperate latitudes in late spring when maximum zoöplankton production is found.

In general, trophic conditions are richer in the Antarctic than in the Arctic. One major cause of this is the submarine topography of the waters surrounding the Antarctic land mass. All around the continent, but particularly to the south of the Atlantic, there are ascending currents of water which bring to the surface waters off Antarctica waters originating at great depths in lower latitudes. To some extent this process constitutes continuous injection of nutrient-rich waters into the Antarctic, and it enhances the high productivity of the short summer season. The phytoplankton increase of the Antarctic is characterized in most regions by a few species of relatively large diatoms and thus corresponds closely to conditions during the SDI in temperate seas. In contrast, much of phytoplankton production over large areas of the Arctic consists of nannoplankton organisms and has some resemblances to primary production in the nutrient-poor regions of tropical seas. In both polar seas, photosynthetic dinoflagellates are important, often making up the bulk of the phytoplankton after the initial outburst that occurs when the day-length approaches 20 hours or more.

A characteristic feature of all polar waters away from coasts and without permanent ice cover is that a thermocline is never established, although a nonthermal but stable stratification is found in many areas where reduced salinities near the surface create a similar discontinuity of density. In other regions, including the Barents Sea, the surface waters freely mix with and are *never* cut off from the deeper nutrient-rich waters. In the Barents, there are relatively high quantities of phosphates in the surface waters throughout the year, except for a few midsummer weeks following the major phytoplankton increase in May. In general, productivity in the high latitudes of both the Arctic and the Antarctic is more usually limited by available sunlight, and less usually by availability of nutrients for the primary producers.

In summary, conditions in polar seas are such that some of the greatest concentrations of plankton found in the oceans occur for a short time in their summer season. The number of species in the zoöplankton is always lower than in warmer latitudes, and for many species of copepods and other forms the individual size of polar representatives is greater than elsewhere. It is remarkable that, as regards both plankton and benthic organisms, the Antarctic has more than twice the number of species found in corresponding situations in the Arctic. Perhaps one explanation of this is revealed by the fact that the Antarctic populations share more species with the ocean depths of lower latitudes. It seems that the deep-water current systems favor exchanges with the surface waters of the Antarctic over those with the Arctic, though this remains an incomplete explanation of the species distribution. Again to recapitulate, in polar waters there is no productivity throughout most of the year, and an outburst of exceedingly high productivity in their short summer season, though this involves only a small number of animal forms.

## Tropical seas

Perhaps surprisingly, almost all areas of open ocean in the tropics show a relatively low productivity. The only important exceptions occur in limited areas where there are continuous or transient *upwelling* water movements. Most areas of the tropical oceans are relatively barren. Of the usual limiting factors, obviously lack of solar radiation cannot be important. Throughout the year, the solar energy per day penetrating the surface waters may be several times the critical values for temperate seas at the time of the SDI. As noted earlier (see page 35), tropical waters are particularly transparent and wavelengths suitable for photosynthesis can penetrate to depths double those in the temperate open ocean and up to eight times those in turbid inshore waters. Thus the compensation level for most phytoplankton lies deep, and remains so throughout the year, in tropical seas. On the other hand, except for a few special localities, there is a permanent thermocline. Thus the surface waters can be nutrient-poor throughout the year. Estimates of nutrient salt concentrations in water samples collected at a series of positions running down the center of the Atlantic are significant. The total nitrate concentration in the surface waters for 20° of latitude on either side of the equator is usually about 1/100 of the winter concentrations in the least fertile temperate seas. Phosphate levels in the same region often lie below the limit of detection (less than 1/100 the winter levels in temperate seas), and the only phosphate-rich waters within the tropics lie at depths below 150 meters, the richest concentrations being found in dense cold water at depths between 600 and 1000 meters.

As a result of these features of the physicochemical environment, there are normally no dramatic increases in phytoplankton production in tropical seas. Instead, primary productivity is typically low but continuous, and forms such as $\mu$-flagellates and coccolithophores are particularly important. One striking exception occurs in the Indian ocean where the changes induced by the monsoon result in a "seasonal" pattern of productivity. Although the maximum level of plant production for any one day in the tropics is considerably lower than the peak of primary production in temperate or polar seas, the gross production per year is rarely much lower than the temperate annual figures. For most tropical sea areas which have been studied sufficiently, annual average figures for primary production would lie between 50 and 80 per cent of the corresponding values for the open waters of temperate seas, though considerably below the figures for the most productive inshore waters.

As might be expected, given such primary pasturage, there are no clearcut seasonal cycles in the zoöplankton of the tropics. Thus the standing-crop biomass of zoöplankton never attains the levels which it can temporarily attain in summer in temperate and polar seas. On the other hand, the variety of species in the permanent zoöplankton is much greater than elsewhere, and in tropical waters we never encounter the "nearly pure culture of *Calanus*" characteristic of some colder seas. Some very approximate figures for the total number of species in certain permanent planktonic groups can be compiled. For chaetognaths, north temperate waters would have a maximum of 5 species, while tropical and subtropical waters would have 19 species; for ctenophores, the numbers would be 5 and 65, and for copepods, about 21 and over 500 species, respectively. However, no species is abundant and in most areas of the tropical oceans there are no shoals of pelagic plankton-feeding fish, and whalebone whales cannot gain weight in most parts of the tropics.

As with tropical plankton, so there is no direct relation between total productivity and the level of species diversity found in bottom faunas. The diversity of benthic animals to be found immediately below low tide level in the tropics is almost always obviously greater than in corresponding temperate shallow waters. Based on assessments of the standing crop of benthic biomass, however, productivity in some shallow temperate seas can be much higher. However, if the less obvious animals of the inshore meiofaunas (the smallest marine benthic metazoans, usually under 0.5 mm, and including some animals of the psammon; see page 11) of tropical seas are included in the assessment, the faunas are found to be remarkably close to those of temperate waters in both diversity and productivity. Thanks to the recent development of new bottom-sampling methods, workers like Howard L. Sanders and Robert R. Hessler are demonstrating an unsuspectedly high species diversity in deep-sea benthic faunas. Earlier studies of the animal communities of the deep-sea bottom with conventional dredges and bottom-trawls apparently could not give a valid indication of diversity because of the very great likelihood of partial or complete sample loss during the long haul to the surface. One striking feature is that very great faunal diversity may occur in those regions of the deep-sea bottom which lie directly under relatively sterile tropical waters. Sanders has concluded that the best explanation for the high level of diversity in the deep sea is the great stability of that environment over long periods of time. The hypothesis that levels of species diversity may be independent of productivity levels, and more closely reflect the extent in time of each relatively constant environment, is even more readily supported by the faunal conditions to be found in lakes (see pages 111 and 219).

There are certain exceptions to the generally low level of fertility in tropical seas, and two of these—regions of upwelling and coral reefs— are of some fundamental interest. Because of the world's pattern of prevailing winds and their effects on the surface currents of the oceans, upwelling is mostly found in certain regions of the western coasts of the continents. For example, north of the equator a prevailing wind from the north-northwest blowing nearly parallel to the west coast of a continent will cause an offshore movement of surface waters away to the southwest. This water will be replaced by an upwelling of colder, denser water, which may be rich in nutrient salts. This process actually occurs off southern California and the Atlantic coast of Morocco. Upwelling also occurs south of the equator (with a mirror-image pattern of currents) and is strikingly important along the coasts of southwestern Africa and Peru. Where such upwelling occurs in tropical and subtropical waters, we have the injection of nutrient-rich waters into a well-lit but otherwise unfertile region of the sea. As a result we have local regions of enhanced primary productivity, increased zoöplankton crop, and important commercial fisheries. The two major regions of upwelling north of the equator mentioned above gave rise to the commercially important tuna and sardine fisheries conducted from California and Portugal, respectively. South of the equator, the upwelling off southwestern Africa was responsible for the once important whaling conducted from Walvis Bay, and fisheries for shoaling pelagic fish are now being developed in that area. The Peruvian upwelling is responsible for the vast shoals of anchoveta. In the 1960's these have become the basis of the world's largest fishery, conducted off the coasts of Peru and northern Chile. It has now (1968) achieved an annual catch of over 10 million tons and thus surpasses in volume the entire annual landings in Europe from North Atlantic and Arctic fisheries (see pages 241 and 261). As was the case with menhaden, almost the entire catch is converted to animal feeding stuffs in fish-meal factories. Less than 10 per cent of this enormous crop is used for direct human feeding—in Japan; the rest of the output of fish-meal and oil goes to the countries of western Europe and to the United States (about 25 per cent to the United States, and the biggest single fraction to Great Britain), where it forms a large part of the basis of intensive production of broiler fowls and swine. Apart from the energetic inefficiency of this (see page 91 and 250), there is geopolitical significance in a world where considerable protein deficiencies already occur. A survey conducted in 1963 suggested that 29 per cent of the population in Latin America was then undernourished, particularly as regards protein. Undoubtedly, the percentage has increased since that date, but hardly any of the fish crop from the Humboldt upwelling off the Pacific coast of South America is being used to alleviate the condition. Similarly, the productivity of the Benguela current off southwestern Africa is not presently used to modify the 38 per cent level of malnutrition in that continent. To any humane member of this single human species, such exploitation of a protein resource by the technologically advanced countries constitutes— even more than the foreign exploitation of mineral resources such as oil and copper—one of the worst aspects of commercial neocolonialism (see also Chapters 8 and 13). Historically, the exploitation of Peruvian waters for the benefit of western Europe was significant more than a century ago, though in an even more indirect fashion. The sea area of the Humboldt current had long supported vast populations of fish-eating seabirds (cormorants, boobies, and pelicans) and their droppings accumulating in the arid conditions of a desert coast built up enormous deposits of guano. These deposits were shipped to western Europe, largely between 1840 and 1880 and, used as fertilizers, helped support the more intensive agriculture which nourished the expanding and more urbanized populations of the industrial revolution in the countries concerned.

Apart from the regions of upwelling, the other zones of high productivity in the tropics are associated with coral reefs. Some authorities believe that certain coral reefs are among the ecosystems of highest gross organic productivity. Since the productivity around coral atolls in the central Pacific is many times that of the relatively infertile tropical ocean which surrounds them, Eugene P. Odum has compared them to "oases in a desert." Apart from a local "black body" effect resulting from having the photosynthetic organisms of the reef close to the tropically illuminated surface, much of the high productivity appears to depend upon efficient and very local recirculation of nutrients. In other words, on and around the reef, little of each year's primary production of organic matter drops into deep water and is lost, as happens elsewhere in the tropical oceans. Some authorities also emphasize the occurrence of symbiosis between the various producer and consumer components of the reef. Fish are in local abundance on and around the reef, and the great bulk of the decomposers concerned in the system are also local in the shallow waters created by the coral growth.

Turning again to more general aspects, we note that productivity in the tropical oceans is largely limited by the availability of nutrient salts. To some extent this contrasts with polar seas where the limited weeks of suitable sunlight limit productivity to one short summer season. Appreciation of these two distinct limiting factors in tropical and in polar seas helps us understand the way in which alternation of these factors controls the progress of the biological seasons in the temperate oceans.

## Productivity in inshore waters

Shallow coastal waters and semienclosed areas of the sea can be characterized as sometimes more productive, and always more variable in productivity, than the waters of the open ocean in the same latitudes. These features are shown in two bodies of water which have received disproportionate attention from biological oceanographers: the English Channel and Long Island Sound. In both areas, the primary productivity and the animal production based upon it can vary markedly from year to year. The principal diatom increase in Long Island Sound occurs in late winter, and in some years the dominant diatom is *Skeletonema costatum,* while in other years the bulk of the increase is made up by a larger species of *Thalassiosira.* It seems that *Skeletonema* is favored by slightly higher water temperatures, and minor weather differences may have accounted for the dominance of *Skeletonema* in 1953 and 1955 with *Thalassiosira* dominant in 1954. As the studies of Gordon A. Riley and his associates revealed, the zoöplankton population in the Sound shows characteristically a large but rapidly fluctuating crop in spring and summer with vast differences from year to year. The most important copepods are two congeneric species, *Acartia clausii* and *Acartia tonsa,* and these species, with slightly different feeding efficiencies and preferred temperatures, alternate in a pattern of seasonal succession. Compared with other planktonic copepods, both species of *Acartia* are relatively inefficient feeders with high requirements in metabolic maintenance. They can probably only dominate the zoöplankton in such areas as Long Island Sound where the waters are sufficiently brackish to exclude more efficient oceanic forms such as *Calanus, Metridia,* and *Temora.* Similar variation in primary productivity is found in the English Channel, and this has long been studied by scientists from the Plymouth Laboratory. The indicator species of *Sagitta* already discussed (see pages 77 and 261) are here important. Increased numbers of *Sagitta elegans* characterize a greater influx of Atlantic water, richer in phosphates and other nutrient salts. Thus, in any year, greater eastern extension into the English Channel of water with *Sagitta elegans* will imply greater primary productivity in the area and ultimately greater fish production.

Although we will discuss some aspects of water pollution elsewhere (see pages 105 and 149), it is worth noting that small quantities of raw or partially treated sewage can have merely a fertilizing effect on a river or an area of shallow sea. Parts of southern Long Island Sound and the North Sea opposite the Thames estuary probably have increased organic productivity as a result of urban sewage discharge. These cases are exceptional: most human pollution implies locally decreased aquatic productivity.

Of course, a large part of the animal production of inshore waters involves the relatively larger biomass of benthic invertebrates and of the demersal fishes which feed upon them. In any coastal or inshore area, it is always difficult to assess the extent to which the large stocks of bottom-dwelling bivalves and crustaceans are maintained directly by feeding on the plankton, or are sustained by a detritus food-chain. As noted earlier, it is in these circumstances that the primary production of such *attached* plants as *Zostera* and *Spartina* becomes important. However, most bottom-dwelling fishes and benthic invertebrates have young stages which live as members of the temporary zoöplankton, and thus are affected by seasonal and year-to-year variations in phytoplankton production which are characteristic of inshore waters.

In shallow coastal waters, the bottom frequently supports a rich fauna, the benthic animals alone often amounting to a standing-crop biomass in excess of 100 grams of living tissue (mainly bivalve molluscs, annelid worms, and crustaceans) in each square meter of mud bottom. In these circumstances we have some of the fast local cycles of nutrient salts and rapid turnover of detritus mentioned previously as being characteristic of coral reefs. When we examine the dominant organisms of this large biomass, however—for example, the relatively long-lived bivalves—we find marked differences in the relative proportions of different age-groups. A typical bivalve population in shallow water or on tidal flats may be made up almost entirely of one-year-old, four-year-old, and six-year-old clams, with the two-, three-, and five-year groups hardly represented at all. For example, a population of the deposit-feeding bivalve *Tellina tenuis* at Millport in Scotland was sampled each year for twenty-five years. This survey showed that in only four of these years could the spatfall of young *Tellina* out of plankton be regarded as successful, and the young bivalves settling in each of these successful years made up the bulk of the population for several years after. This is also markedly the case in populations of the commercially important cockle (*Cardium edule*) in European waters, in many stocks of which a particular year-group may remain dominant for ten years or more.

Similar predominance of one age-group is well known in populations of several commercially important fishes living in shallow or inshore

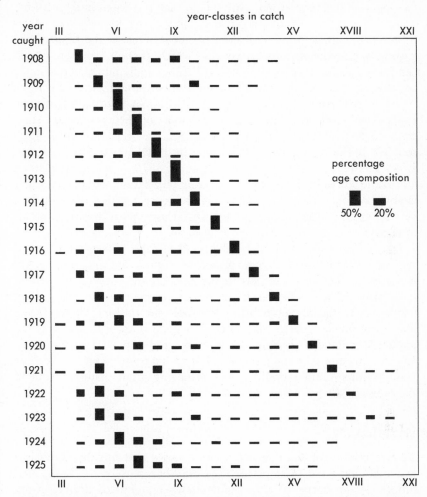

**Figure 5·1. Age composition of Norwegian spring herring catches.** Note that over the entire eighteen years shown in the histograms, only four year-classes were at all dominant: those born in 1904 remained dominant into the 1920's, those from 1910 were temporarily important, and those from 1913 and 1918 contributed significantly over periods of five years or more. These Norwegian herring are relatively long-lived and it is obvious that in this particular stock, successful survival of a year-class is an exception occurring somewhat infrequently. [Based on various publications of Johan Hjort and Einar Lea, especially adapted from Lea in *Rapports et Procès-Verbaux Cons. Explor. Mer, 65*:100–117, 1930.]

waters. On average, only in one year in every four does the breeding of haddock in Scottish waters result in a marked replenishment of numbers in the population. Annual fluctuations in inshore plankton conditions also affect the survival of the young of fishes which as adults live a more pelagic offshore existence. One of the best-studied cases concerns the Norwegian herring, which, though a pelagic plankton-feeder, is a relatively long-lived fish: individuals occasionally survive for over twenty years. The age composition of the catch in the Norwegian herring fishery was studied by Johan Hjort and his associates over a long period of years, and some of their results are summarized in Figure 5·1. It can be seen that over the years from 1909 to 1920 a single year-class, that born in 1904, remained dominant. Later dominant year-classes were those of 1910 (very temporarily), 1913, and 1918. In this particular herring population, a good year-class is obviously the exception, and the catches over a period of a quarter-century were dominated by the fish year-classes born in only three or four years.

In all these cases, both of bivalves and of fishes, there is an annual breeding season and we have no reason to suppose that the reproductive activities of the adult animals in the populations vary to any extent from year to year. The variations in age-groups seem to result from conditions in the plankton being favorable for the developing young of each particular species only in certain years. That is to say, it is not annual fluctuations in numbers of eggs produced that matter, it is annual variations in the number of larval fish surviving to become young adults, or in larval bivalves achieving a successful spatfall in the right place.

## Estuarine productivity

To the animals of tidal mudflats in estuaries and in other brackish-water habitats, the phytoplankton is only one part of the basic food supply. Water-borne detritus from elsewhere, detritus derived from crops of attached plants such as the marsh-grasses, species of *Spartina,* and the local crops of attached diatoms and microscopic algae are all important. The total productivity can be high and can support dense animal populations, particularly of benthic invertebrates.

The most obvious characteristic of all estuaries is the existence of a phasic mixing of waters: of inland, usually fresh, waters with those of the sea. Much physiological interest, and some evolutionary significance, attaches to the fact that all organisms living in estuaries must not only be capable of living in lowered salinities, when compared with true marine organisms, but must also be capable of withstanding considerable osmotic fluctuations. These occur not only over periods of hours within each tidal cycle but also over periods of months corresponding to seasonal fluctuations in the runoff of fresh waters. Much important work in physiological ecology has been concerned with the responses of estuarine organisms to such stresses and with their capacities for acclimation. However, the water-mixing characteristic of estuaries also has importance with regard to total productivity. The hydrodynamics of this mixing is complex, and only beginning to be understood, but it can be crudely summarized. Owing to density differences, and the reduced velocities of water movement where the two kinds of waters meet in estuaries, suspended material may become concentrated in measurable turbidity maxima in midestuary. To put it another way, the length of time that suspended materials remain in the estuarine zone after being brought in by the moving fresh water of a stream from the land or by the tidal currents from the open sea is significantly longer than would be the case at the slowest possible rate of transport without sedimentation in a simple flow system like a mature river. (It should be remembered that, with particles of the dimensions of detritus, a twofold increase in current velocity can mean a sixfold increase in the size of particles transported, and that the density partition between the salt water thrust in by the tides along the bottom of the estuary and the fresher waters flowing over it from the land can be just as abrupt as that in a thermocline, and of considerably greater magnitude.) The resulting turbidity maxima, which can be seen from the air as discolored zones in many large estuaries, are of great biological importance. To some extent, dissolved materials are also involved and many estuaries thus form "nutrient traps" where much higher concentrations of inorganic salts are held in circulation than in either the contributing river or the open sea. However, in all but the largest estuaries, the high turbidity works against there being any phytoplankton crop proportional to this local nutrient concentration, although those algal cells which live *attached* to surfaces and on the mudbanks exposed with each tide may show extremely high productivity under these nutrient-rich conditions. The unspectacular planktonic primary production is far outweighed by the amounts of suspended organic detritus—both autochthonous and allochthonous—in the estuarine waters. The total organic material per unit volume of estuarine water may be from five to ten times the content of rich marine systems such as the English Channel or Long Island Sound.

Such hydrological features of estuaries, which bring about the accumulation and subsequent retention of both suspended detritus and dissolved nutrients, can be very important factors in cases of human pollution of estuaries. Small quantities of raw sewage or similar organic wastes, if discharged in great dilution, may have merely a fertilizing effect on a river or area of coastal sea. In estuaries, however, pollution matter can be very persistent and show accumulation: the sewage of many estuarine towns goes downstream with the ebb tide, but much of it returns upstream with the flow.

As regards more natural sources of organic detritus, the length of time spent in recirculation within the estuary may be of great importance in allowing time for bacterial decomposition and proportionate change. This can involve not only complete decomposition, which provides increased nutrient salts for green plants, but also partial decomposition, which renders such plant materials as detritus from *Spartina* more suitable for animal nutrition. Studies by Eugene P. Odum and his associates in a salt-marsh estuary in Georgia have shown that the buildup of microbial populations on detritus consisting of dead fragments of leaves and stems of *Spartina* results in an increase in protein content from 6 per cent of the ash-free dry weight of the detritus to 24 per cent, thus providing a better food supply for detritus-feeding animals.

In the majority of estuaries the most important detritus-feeding benthic animals are molluscs, mainly bivalves. A general feature of the benthic ecology is the occurrence in each estuary of relatively few species (in contrast to the faunas of open, marine shores), but these being species numerically abundant as individuals. Many British estuarine habitats have a macrofauna of only four or five species, and large bivalves such as the cockle *Cardium* can occur at densities of up to 400 per square meter, while two smaller bivalves, *Scrobicularia plana* and *Macoma balthica,* can occur at 1100 and 6000 per square meter, respectively, in the estuary of the Exe in England. There, 60–70 per cent of the biomass consisted of these two bivalve species alone. The small prosobranch snail *Hydrobia ulvae* can exist in almost pure culture on estuarine sandflats, commonly reaching densities of 20,000 per square meter. Some years ago, my wife and I attempted a census of a population living on a tidal sandflat in the Clyde estuary. Our estimate for an area of less than 2.5 square miles of tidal sands was of $3 \times 10^{10}$ individuals, and observations on the behavioral changes in *Hydrobia* during the tidal cycle make it likely that the whole of this population is potentially panmictic. From an evolutionary point of view, such an enormous population is in complete contrast to the classic cases of isolated populations of small mammals or poorly flying birds on oceanic islands (where there may be no more than a few hundreds of interbreeding individuals of the species).

There are obviously several reasons why bivalve molluscs are among the most successful estuarine benthic animals in exploiting the accumulations of detritus food. Not only are the ciliary collection and sorting mechanisms of bivalves particularly well suited to collecting the finer detritus suspended in the water, or the settled detritus from the mud-water interface, but the same siphonal arrangements used for collection of food allow these bivalves to live within largely anaerobic bottom deposits while taking in better-oxygenated water from above. In the reducing mud of a tidal flat in an estuary, one can often find a thin halo of oxygenated deposit (often lighter in color) surrounding each individual bivalve. It has also been stressed by several physiologists that bivalves are uniquely equipped to close themselves off completely from the environment at times when conditions are temporarily unfavorable. This is probably of considerable importance to those bivalves of limited osmoregulatory capacity which are yet able to live in estuaries. Presumably such bivalves can remain closed for whole phases of the tidal cycle when the medium surrounding them is relatively dilute, opening for feeding and other activities only during those phases when they are bathed in almost pure seawater. Apart from such bivalves as clams and oysters, other animals feed directly on the rich accumulations of detritus in estuaries. They include penaeid shrimps, such as the commercial "pink shrimp" of the Atlantic seaboard, and young stages of such fishes as menhaden, mullet, and pompano, which live as adults further offshore (see Chapter 15).

At the next trophic level, feeding on the benthic bivalves and crustaceans of estuaries, there are some characteristic estuarine flatfish. These may occur in enormous numbers in suitable estuaries and (a matter of considerable interest to man as an exploiter of fish stocks) can show extraordinarily high growth rates in the rich conditions of unpolluted estuaries. Such flatfish include plaice, *Pleuronectes platessa,* and the European flounder, *Platichthys flesus.* The so-called summer flounder (*Paralichthys*) and the winter flounder (*Pseudopleuronectes*) of the coastal areas of New England are migratory species and do not show the fantastic growth rates of the more permanently estuarine species. Significantly, it is with plaice and flounder that some of the most successful experiments in fish-farming of coastal waters have yet been carried out. Of course, certain techniques of oyster-rearing and clam-raising almost amount to farming, and these are also carried out in estuarine or similar coastal conditions. Some aspects of future farming of the edge of the sea will be further discussed in Chapter 15.

# 6

# Productivity in lakes

THE CONCEPT OF the small lake as a closed microcosm has proved attractive to a long line of naturalists. More recently, as a model system, the lake microcosm has been utilized by several of the founders of modern theoretical ecology. In the first quarter of this century, E. A. Birge and C. Juday and their associates in the United States and Sir John Murray (of *Challenger* fame) and his team in Scotland surveyed large numbers of lakes and provided the hydrographic data which have allowed different systems of lake classification (both trophic and thermal) to be evolved. Successive stages of the interpretation of such lacustrine studies involved the development of the concepts of hydrarch succession—and even of the ecosystem itself—by European workers such as J. R. Matthews, August Theinemann, W. H. Pearsall, and A. G. Tansley, and later led to the first interpretations of trophic relationships in quantitative energetic terms which are associated with the names of G. Evelyn Hutchinson and Raymond L. Lindeman and were discussed earlier (see pages 21 and 25). On the pedagogical side, several authors—but perhaps most notably Eugene P. Odum in his two books on fundamental aspects of synecology—have utilized a model large pond or small lake as a convenient starting point in setting out the principles of ecology. More modestly, an idealized small lake dominated by a single giant pike was employed earlier in this book (see Chapter 2 and Figure 2·5) in our presentation of the concepts of trophic levels.

Lake models have pragmatic value, but the substantive diversity of lakes and of lake waters is immense. The sea presents a uniform and constant environment when compared with the enormous variations found in lakes, and this has led to extensive efforts to catalog the diversity and to create a comprehensible classification of lake types.

Lakes vary in size. Large ponds begin to be termed lakes when they extend to an acre or so; and, at the other end of the scale, there are probably fifteen lakes in the world with surface areas in excess of 15,000 square kilometers—a size range of over five orders of magnitude. Geographically, the productivity of lakes varies with latitude and altitude. The shapes and relative depths of lakes vary, and a most important effect on productivity is that the availability of solar energy is determined by bathymetric characteristics of the lake basin, such as the surface:volume ratio. The content of dissolved inorganic salts varies: for example, the content of dissolved calcium can vary 200-fold, and the ratio of calcium to sodium more than 50-fold (this ratio varies little in the oceans, calcium as a percentage of sodium remaining about 3.82 for most seawaters). There is also considerable variation in the availability of plant nutrient salts, and this has given rise to the most widely accepted biological classification of lakes, that of eutrophy/ oligotrophy. Lakes termed eutrophic are those whose waters are relatively rich in plant nutrients (such as phosphates and nitrates), usually have much rapidly decaying organic mud on the lake bottom, and usually show reduced oxygen tensions in their waters in summer. Oligotrophic lakes are those whose waters are always low in plant nutrients, usually highly oxygenated, and have relatively small amounts of slowly decaying organic material in their bottom deposits. In relation to the most important bathymetric consideration (that of their surface: volume ratios), eutrophic lakes are usually relatively shallow with gently sloping banks supporting wide belts of littoral vegetation; oligotrophic lakes are mostly deep, with steep rock sides. It is obvious that, in a eutrophic lake, the plankton will be richer and the entire annual turnover of organic material—and the resultant total faunal productivity—much greater than those in oligotrophic conditions. The trophic classification of lakes will be considered more fully below (see pages 116–124), after some brief discussion of the spatial and temporal extent of lake waters.

## Limits of lakes

Compared with the oceans, the world extent of lakes is not great. The world's total area of inland waters is approximately $5 \times 10^6$ square kilometers, in contrast to the oceans' $36 \times 10^7$ square kilometers, which is equal to about 70.8 per cent of the surface of the Earth. Relatively speaking, even the largest of the world's lakes are of relatively small area, and inland waters in general lack the geographic continuity of environment afforded by the sea. Lake Superior has the largest surface area of any body of fresh water—83,300 square kilometers; and there are probably only fourteen other freshwater lakes in the world with superficial areas greater than 15,000 square kilometers. Further, there are only a few hundreds of lakes (which can be tabulated in some tens of book pages) with areas greater than 50 square kilometers (or 19·3 square miles). The majority of lakes are smaller, and yet there are very many of them. It has been estimated that Sweden alone has more than 100,000 lakes, and the number for Canada must exceed ten times this figure.

Of perhaps even greater biological significance than the spatial limits of lakes are the corresponding limits in time. The environment afforded by fresh water usually lacks the permanence of that of land or sea, and most bodies of fresh water are relatively transitory in a geological time-scale. Most of the larger lakes of the world have existed as such for only some thousands of years; for example, the great lakes of North America mostly have ages of less than 8000 years, while Loch Lomond in Scotland has existed for 11,000 years. At the end of last century, the great Swiss limnologist F. A. Forel made some calculations of the likely future lifetimes of certain large lakes. The "life expectancy" of the Lake of Geneva was relatively high, but could only amount to some 40,000 years. The majority of the world's large lakes will cease to exist in less than 20,000 years. Smaller lakes and large ponds are even more transitory, with maximum lifetimes of some hundreds of years. With this we enter the time-scales of recent human history. In America and Europe, the publications of many local natural history societies record, over a generation or two, the gradual disappearance of many small lakes and ponds and the changes of flora and fauna accompanying the process. The botanical aspects of the evolution into dry land of small bodies of fresh water have been thoroughly investigated since the broad principles of hydrarch succession were first eluciated by J. R. Matthews and W. H. Pearsall in Scotland and the English Lake District, respectively. In spite of the enormous number of lakes at the present time in Scandinavia, which we noted above, more former lake beds can be detected on the land surface in such countries as Sweden and Finland than the number of extant lakes, and this enormous number of "fossil lakes" can only reflect part of the number of lakes in these areas which have become filled or drained by sediment deposition, by erosion of outlets, or by biological means within the relatively short period of time since the last glaciation. To sum up this matter of the transience of most freshwater environments, the duration of most lakes is of the order of $10^3$–$10^4$ years, and of ponds of $10^2$ years, whereas a relatively constant environment may persist on the land surfaces surrounding these inland waters for up to $10^6$ years, and in the sea for many times as long. The majority of populations of freshwater animals and plants live in bodies of water considerably smaller than a medium-sized lake such as Loch Lomond, these bodies having a much more transitory history. There are a small number of exceptional lakes, including Lake Baikal in Russia, Lake Tanganyika, Lake Ochrida in the Balkans, and certain lakes in Celebes, which can be termed "ancient" lakes having existed for periods of from $10^5$ to $10^6$ years, and whose faunas are both more diverse and more bizarre than those found in more usual freshwater habitats. More generally, the evolution of the faunas of normal fresh waters has differed markedly from the process of evolution in similar animals living in the sea or on land. As I have discussed elsewhere, this results from the transience of freshwater environments and the high degree of small-scale, short-term isolation which can occur within them (see also Chapter 11).

Apart from questions of the level of productivity, there are major differences between large lakes on the one hand and large ponds and small lakes on the other as regards the *nature* of the primary and secondary productivity. These differences arise from two sets of causes. Direct effects of physicochemical variations typify the first group of causal factors, with the smallest ponds showing the biggest variations in physical factors, diurnally and seasonally, while large lakes present a more stable physicochemical environment closely comparable to the sea. A second group of causal factors, which arise from the different scale of the topography, indirectly affect total productivity by modifying the proportions of primary production carried out in the plankton on the one hand and in attached macroscopic plants on the other. In large lakes, the proportion of open, deep water to shallows which can support rooted vegetation is high, and the greater part of the primary production is carried out—as in the sea—by the diatoms and other single-celled green plants of the open water. In contrast, in a small lake or large pond, the proportion of open water is small, and the primary grazing provided by the phytoplankton amounts to only a fraction of the biomass per year built up by the higher plants and attached algae of the shallow margins. Obviously, this affects the relative numbers of animals at the second trophic level, that is, the primary herbivores. In a large lake, the animals of the zoöplankton (capable of filter-feeding on the minute plants of the plankton) will have a similar importance to their position in the marine economy. In a smaller lake, the zoöplankton can make up only a minute fraction of the biomass of the second trophic level, the great bulk of that level being browsing animals, capable of feeding on higher plants directly, or on the detritus derived from them, or on the *Aufwuchs* which can encrust them. As is the case in certain estuarine environments, the *Aufwuchs* or attached organisms—bacterial, plant, and animal—forming the "fouling" scum which encrusts all suitable surfaces in the euphotic zone, but especially the stems and leaves of rooted plants, is a major component of the primary food supply. As one might expect, recycling of nutrients can occur relatively rapidly in the plankton community, but usually requires at least one complete annual cycle of seasons in the community associated wtih the marginal vegetation. This, and the general absence of supporting tissues from the phytoplankton (in contrast particularly to the cellulose and lignin of the emergent vegetation), result in marked differences in the distribution of bacteria and other decomposing organisms in different sizes of lakes. As Raymond L. Lindeman pointed out in his classic paper on trophic principles, the food-cycle relationships in a medium-sized lake are essentially bicyclic—one cycle involving macrophytic producers, the other the phytoplankton. Some other aspects of productivity which contrast with the monocyclic economy of the sea are worth brief consideration before we review questions of trophic classification and seasonal cycles.

The marginal attached vegetation—both microscopic diatoms and filamentous algae and large, rooted "higher" vegetation—is obviously restricted to those marginal waters of the lake which are shallower and above the compensation level for each type of plant. Thus, while this major part of the basic pasturage is limited, like the phytoplankton, to the euphotic zone, it is further characterized by a series of vertical zones in which different plant types are dominant. In a small lake with a shallow basin shape, these zones will form concentric bands of different plants surrounding the open water. In some, more eutrophic, small lakes, the turbidity of the water is so great that the compensation level for most attached plants lies at a depth of only 1 meter or so, and in such cases the marginal zone is narrowed and its subdivisions obscured. It is in medium-sized lakes, where the marginal vegetation still contributes a significant part of the primary production, that we can most clearly see the zonation of the attached plants. For example, in Loch Lomond in Scotland, the compensation level for the attached plants is about 4 meters at most seasons of the year (a few diatom species and other single-celled green plants, including blue-green algae, can live and grow at greater depths, utilizing light of longer wavelength). Most of the larger attached plants also require soft-bottom substrata for rooting. The potential phytal zone, or marginal zone of attached vegetation, in Loch Lomond is mapped in Figure 6·1, and there is an obvious difference between the wide, shallow "lowland" section of the lake and its deep "highland" part (see also Figures 6·4 and 6·5 and further discussion on page 125). In the lowland section of the lake, the potential phytal zone over mud, sand, and gravel shallows may be hundreds of meters wide. On the steep-to, eroded rock surfaces of the highland lake, the zone may be less than a meter in horizontal width, or on the smoother rock faces, be nonexistent. However, in the lowland part of Loch Lomond, not all shallow water, suitable in

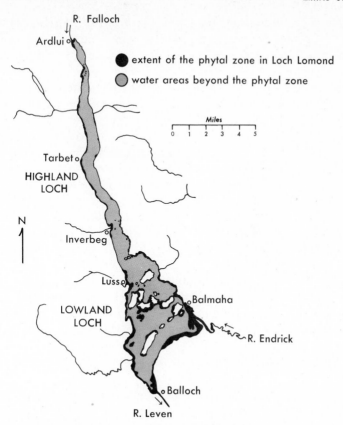

R. Falloch

Ardlui o

● extent of the phytal zone in Loch Lomond

◐ water areas beyond the phytal zone

Miles
0  1  2  3  4  5

Tarbet o

HIGHLAND
LOCH

N

Inverbeg

Luss

LOWLAND
LOCH

o Balmaha

R. Endrick

o Balloch

R. Leven

**Figure 6·1. Map of Loch Lomond, Scotland,** to show the extent of the potential phytal zone. The compensation level for attached plants is at a depth of about 4 meters for much of the year, and thus the zone shallow enough to permit the growth of rooted green plants is fairly extensive (up to hundreds of meters wide) around the lowland loch and its islands, but very narrow or nonexistent around the highland loch. For further discussion, see text. [From W. D. Russell Hunter in *Brit. Assoc. Handb.* (Glasgow, 1958), 5:97–118, 1958, after Slack and others, 1957.]

respect of light penetration and substratum, supports a dense vegetation. A new limiting factor here is exposure to wind- and wave-action, a high degree of which results in unstable sand or gravel bottom deposits, which do not support a real phytal zone. All around southern Loch Lomond, and in similar circumstances elsewhere, such as the shores of the Finger Lakes of upstate New York, suitable exposure to wind-action with a fetch of a few kilometers across the water, results in extensive shallows of exceedingly low productivity. Around such lakes, the direction of the prevailing winds can almost be deduced from the existence of gravel shores without rooted plants. On their more shel-tered shores and around small inlets, such medium-sized lakes of temperate latitudes show the most characteristic development of a series of vegetation zones. In the most shallow water closest to the lake margin is a zone of emergent vegetation, consisting of reeds and rushes of such genera as *Typha, Phragmites, Scirpus,* and *Sparganium.* Most of their photosynthetic surfaces are out of the water, and their contribution to productivity is—like that of *Spartina* in marginal marine waters—largely indirect as detritus. In slightly deeper water in most temperate lakes, we have a zone of plants with floating leaves including the water-lilies of the genera *Nymphaea* and *Nuphar* and certain species of the pondweed genus *Potamogeton.* In some lakes of moderate size, including Loch Lomond, the plants of this zone may be replaced by a turf-like vegetation of *Littorella* and *Isoetes,* probably as the result of wave-action. A third zone, still deeper and further offshore, consists of the typical submerged water plants with finely divided leaves, including many species of the genus *Potamogeton* along with *Myriophyllum* and *Elodea.* Though living as submerged aquatics, these are all "higher" flowering plants, probably evolved from land vegetation forms. In some lakes, they are overlapped by the lower macrophytes which can elsewhere form a distinct fourth zone and include species of *Nitella* and *Chara.* As we move through these zones from the stiff rushes to the finely divided leaves of the submerged plants which are often only two cells in thickness, we see a major shift in the proportions of plant tissues, a shift which is of great significance in secondary productivity. A great deal of the synthetic activities of the emergent vegetation is channelled—as is the case with terrestrial plants—into buildup of supporting tissues containing much cellulose; such tissues are largely absent from the submerged aquatics. Most aquatic herbivores cannot use such supporting tissues directly as food, and the decay and recycling of the emergent vegetation is slower than that for the true aquatic plants. As already noted, throughout all the zones of the marginal vegetation, the attached diatoms and filamentous algae which form the *Aufwuchs* make up a significant part of the primary production. They are immediately available to abundant small benthic animals of the second trophic level, including insect larvae and snails. Benthic animals living among and on the marginal vegetation are largely insects, belonging to the many aquatic orders, but also include flatworms, rotifers, crustaceans, arachnids, bivalves, and snails. Many of these have feeding mechanisms which allow them to function as micro-browsers on the *Aufwuchs,* while others have biting mouth-parts, better suited to ingesting pieces of the larger plants which support them. As was the case with attached marine diatoms (see page 48), the diatoms of the *Aufwuchs* show seasonal peaks of productivity like the phytoplankton and occasionally exhibit a clear succession of species (see also Figure 3·10).

In lakes, characteristically the largest numbers of benthic animals are found in the marginal zone. For example, in Loch Lomond, the phytal zone of the lowland loch supports mean densities of over 6000 animals per square meter, while offshore in greater depths the densities run (under different conditions) from 30 animals per square meter to a maximum of 500. The rich benthos of moderate depths in the sea has no equivalent in most temperate lakes.

In the plankton cycle, the primary producers in lakes usually include diatoms, but other single-celled green algae such as desmids may also be important. Not uncommonly in fresh waters, the availability of silica may be a limiting factor for diatom production (as more rarely occurs in the sea). When sufficient phosphates are available in a lake and yet diatom production is inhibited by lack of silica, then outbursts of blue-green algae commonly result. Such blooms of blue-greens are not much utilized as food by the zoöplankton and other animals which feed on diatoms, and this can have economic consequences (see below). In the case of the marine phytoplankton, the only important reduction comes about by the grazing of copepods and of other zoöplankton organisms. The phytoplankton of lakes, on the other hand, can be reduced by other biological agencies, including outbursts of fungi which parasitize the planktonic algal cells, and similar sudden increases of heterotrophic protozoans which consume the phytoplankton. In both cases, the "disease" organisms can themselves be consumed by the zoöplankton, but the occurrence of such fungal or protozoan "epidemics" inevitably results in a reduction of the fraction of primary productivity which is available for higher animals in the lacustrine food-chains. Once again, this contributes to the variability of total productivity in lakes when compared to the open sea.

In general, the seasonal cycle of phytoplankton production in fresh waters is similar to, but much more variable than, the marine pattern. Just as in temperate seas, the seasonal peaks of phytoplankton production involve relatively few species, and a single diatom species may dominate the spring outburst in the open waters of a large lake. Even in marginal conditions in fresh waters there can be some of the "improbable" dominance which was discussed in Chapter 3. A recent investigation of the polluted marginal waters in Lake Erie near Sandusky revealed that, although some sixty species of phytoplankton were found in water samples, only four species were responsible for 98 per cent of the primary production. As discussed below, there is usually a spring diatom outburst which depends upon the return of nutrients to the surface waters during the spring overturn period when temperature stratification is broken down. The seasonal details of thermocline formation differ somewhat from those in the sea (see page 129). In the majority of medium-sized lakes there are other, more variable, factors affecting the availability of plant nutrients in the lit surface waters, and these may include the incidence of strong winds and wind-induced currents, and chemical factors such as the changing degrees of oxygenation of the bottom deposits. The more variable—but still seasonal—crop of phytoplankton which occurs in lakes is fed upon directly by animals of the lacustrine zoöplankton. At this trophic level there are considerable differences between large lakes and small. In the largest lakes, calanoid copepods such as species of *Diaptomus* can occupy a similar prominent position to *Calanus* in the sea, but microherbivore cladoceran genera such as *Bosmina* and *Daphnia* can also be important constituents of the zoöplankton. In smaller lakes and ponds, cyclopoid copepods like the many species of the genus *Cyclops* itself and certain other cladoceran genera are important: all forms which can live equally well among vegetation as in the open water. In larger lakes, the second trophic level of *Diaptomus* and *Bosmina* is fed upon by the young of many fishes, certain insect larvae, and—occupying a similar niche to that of the species of *Sagitta* in the sea—certain predaceous cladocerans of such genera as *Leptodora* and *Bythotrephes,* which are specialized carnivores with huge eyes and reduced thoracic appendages and carapace. There are also a few adult fishes—like herring and menhaden in the sea—which are able to feed directly on zoöplankton. In large, cold temperate lakes, these include species of coregonid "whitefish," such as occur in the Great Lakes of North America, certain Alpine lakes, and Loch Lomond. The coregonid in Loch Lomond is the powan, and it forms large shoals throughout most of the year and can be taken by seine- or ring-netting, just like marine herring. There is a significant seasonal variation in the diet of powan, however, since benthic animals can also be consumed. The summer diet of adult powan is nearly 90 per cent planktonic by volume, but in the winter months, more feeding on benthos occurs. In larger lakes (just as in the sea), apart from plankton-feeding fishes, the majority of other fish species are nourished indirectly (that is, at a higher trophic level) by the major fraction of primary production which was first incorporated into animal tissues in the zoöplankton. Although the kind of zoöplankton varies with the size of the lake, the amount of plankton production varies with degree of eutrophy.

## Trophic classification of lakes

The most generally accepted biological classifications of lakes are based on the midwinter amounts of, and recycling rates of, inorganic plant nutrients in their waters. Obviously, there can be every possible degree of intermediate condition, but three major types are named in such trophic classifications. Those with waters relatively rich in plant nutrients are termed eutrophic; those usually low in plant nutrients and highly oxygenated are oligotrophic; and those brown-water lakes where high concentrations of humic acid inhibit bacterial decay and thus recycling of nutrients are termed dystrophic. Lakes of this third, humic acid, type may be of any shape or size (although the majority are medium to small lakes which are relatively shallow), but the two principal lake types—eutrophic and oligotrophic—can, in a majority of cases, be distinguished on bathymetric characteristics. Eutrophic lakes are usually those with a high surface : volume ratio, being relatively shallow with gently sloping banks which can support wide belts of marginal vegetation. Oligotrophic lakes mostly have a low surface: volume ratio, being deep, and characteristically having steep rock sides and relatively small amounts of organic material in their bottom deposits. Stylized cross-sectional diagrams of these two major lake types are shown in Figure 6·2, and lake echo-soundings showing these bathymetric characteristics are illustrated in Figure 6·5. As might be expected, there are exceptions to complicate this classification when it is applied to the wide variety of actual lakes in the world, and perhaps the most important of these is that not all lakes of appropriate bathymetric characteristics (for example, surface:volume ratios) will show appropriate conditions when measured in terms of turnover of plant

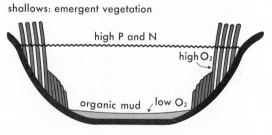

[A] Eutrophic    high surface:volume ratio

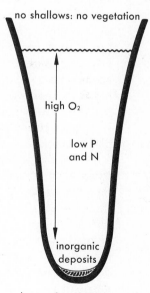

low surface:volume ratio

[B] Oligotrophic

**Figure 6·2. The two principal lake types,** in stylized cross sections. **A:** The typical **Eutrophic** lake with a high surface : volume ratio, waters rich in plant nutrients and partly of low oxygen tension, much marginal vegetation, and high organic productivity. **B:** The typical **Oligotrophic** lake with low surface : volume ratio (deep and usually with steep rock sides), waters low in plant nutrients but highly oxygenated, neither extensive marginal vegetation nor organic bottom deposits, and low productivity. See also Figures 6·3 and 6·5.

nutrient salts. As a result, wide shallow lakes which show low concentrations of plant nutrients are said to show only bathymetric eutrophy; while those few deep lakes which, in spite of their low surface:volume ratio, have relatively high concentrations of nutrient salts are said to exhibit bathymetric oligotrophy.

Historically, this trophic classification of lakes based on the actual or potential level of primary productivity was first developed by August Thienemann nearly fifty years ago. It is of interest that, for the identification and classification of lakes, Thienemann and his associates developed a system of using biological indicator species, rather as we saw the various species of the arrow-worm genus *Sagitta* could be used to identify oceanic waters of different levels of productivity (see pages 77 and 101). In the case of lake waters, the indicator species used were mostly chironomid larvae (the aquatic larval stages of dancing-midges or gnats), but also included certain other aquatic insects. In Europe, the majority of Swiss Alpine lakes provided typical examples of oligotrophy, while many lakes in Denmark and Fennoscandia were typically eutrophic. If intermediate conditions and dystrophic lakes are neglected, it is relatively easy to characterize the lakes of any temperate region of the world in terms of this main trophic dichotomy. It is therefore worth considering in a little more detail.

In temperate latitudes, by late winter a eutrophic lake will have (almost diagnostically) high concentrations of phosphates and nitrates in its surface waters, which will, at appropriate spring sunshine levels, support a rich phytoplankton increase. Generally, such lakes have widespread surfaces lying over relatively shallow basins. There are wide belts of marginal vegetation on the gently sloping shoreline and a rich accumulation of rapidly decaying organic material in the midlake bottom deposits. As a result, the total nutrient supply is good, and return of nutrients to circulation relatively rapid. In moderate- and large-sized eutrophic lakes, this results in a characteristically rich phytoplankton and zoöplankton. Eutrophic lakes which are large enough for a thermocline to form in their waters in summer may develop reduced oxygen conditions and even areas of anaerobic decay as a result of the intensive bacterial buildup in the waters cut off from the surface by the thermocline. If we consider the general topography of continental land surfaces, the majority of lakes of this shape lie in "plains," "lowlands," or gently rolling countryside which—in temperate latitudes of sufficient rainfall—either is subjected to intensive agriculture or supports rich deciduous mixed woodlands. Drainage into such lakes is thus usually nutrient-rich.

Apart from the vastly greater biomass per unit volume, the faunas of eutrophic lakes are usually much more varied in terms of numbers of species than those of oligotrophic or dystrophic lakes. Although the most characteristic feature of eutrophy remains the relatively high turn-over rate of phosphates and nitrates, one can draw up for any region of the world lists of organisms which specifically characterize different levels of eutrophy and, like Thienemann's chironomids, can be used as biological indicators of trophic condition. It is inappropriate to detail such lists here, but certain characteristic *exclusions* of freshwater species from eutrophic conditions have a more general physiological interest. For example, from many medium-sized and large temperate lakes with a high level of eutrophy, most trout and several other salmonid species are normally excluded. Such fish species physiologically require conditions of high oxygenation, relatively low temperatures, and a small annual range of temperatures. These conditions are not provided in our characteristic eutrophic lakes where the only cooler water in summertime lies below the thermocline, where bacterial concentrations will have produced conditions of low oxygenation. Similarly, "relict" species are rarely found in eutrophic lakes. In general, many of the species of molluscs, of insect larvae, and of fishes which are found in eutrophic lakes are also found in the slow-flowing "mature" sections of rivers (that is, just above the estuarine zone) in the same latitudes.

In the earliest lacustrine classifications, the eutrophic condition was typified by the lakes set amid farm and woodland of Denmark, and one such, the Esrom Lake, has had its biology exhaustively and beautifully documented by the work of Kaj Berg. Other eutrophic lakes which have been studied are Loch Leven in Fife, Scotland, and Lake Suwa in Japan. In the United States, examples of eutrophy which have been the loci of extensive biological investigations are Lake Mendota in Wisconsin, Lake Oneida in upstate New York, and Linsley Pond in Connecticut—this last being used over many years for the important investigations of the dynamics of lake productivity carried out by G. Evelyn Hutchinson, Edward S. Deevey, Gordon A. Riley, and other workers from Yale University. A brief survey of Lake Oneida can provide a less hypothetical recapitulation of conditions of eutrophy. It is a wide, shallow lake (approximately 19 miles long by 5 miles across) ; it is relatively shallow (with a maximum depth of 16.5 meters, and average depth of 7.5 meters), with a number of islands and very many offshore shallow banks and reefs; and it receives its drainage partly from limestone country, and partly from flatlands lying to the south and east with rich, deep black soils on which potatoes and onions are profitably grown. There is a little pollution with sewage, normally insufficient to cause foul, abiotic conditions but in general merely enhancing the rich nutrient supply. The spring phytoplankton increase, which occurs about three weeks after the breakup of ice cover, is well supplied with plant nutrients and is spectacularly intensive. For several years, my associates and I have been sampling snails at Oneida at the time of the spring increase, and several of the chemical and physical changes brought about by the period of intensive plant growth are particularly impressive. In inshore waters in daylight the rate of photosynthesis is such that the waters show supersaturation with oxygen and in still water bubbles can be seen rising to the surface from the dense phytoplankton soup (oxygen tensions near dawn after a dark period are correspondingly reduced) and the alkalinity of the waters is increased, the pH rising to 8.9 and the conductivity to values corresponding to 110 parts per million of dissolved solids. One's hand held in the surface waters disappears in the soup at a depth of about 17 inches. If part of the surface water's phytoplankton crop is driven onshore by wind action, the buildup of dying and decaying plant cells may have deleterious effects on the benthic animals of that part of the shore. Once again, as is characteristic of a eutrophic lake, although some fish species are excluded from Oneida by these and other conditions, the lake supports very large numbers of well-nourished, rapidly growing specimens of other fish species (including both small-mouthed and large-mouthed black bass, pike-perch, yellow perch, pickerel, eels, suckers, and catfish), and its well-known fishing grounds are highly productive.

Small-scale equivalents of eutrophic lakes are found in the smaller natural ponds of lowland farmlands and deciduous, mixed woodlands. These show almost all the characteristic features of high trophic productivity, except that they may lack the rich zoöplankton of larger eutrophic lakes and usually are too shallow to show thermal stratification and potentially anaerobic conditions in the hypolimnion.

In contrast, oligotrophic lakes have low overall productivity, and show relatively minute concentrations of phosphates and nitrates in their waters, even in late winter. Primary productivity—of both marginal vegetation and phytoplankton—always has low values in relation to lake size. Generally deep with steep rock sides, oligotrophic lakes are often long and narrow, one characteristic group of them occupying glacially overdeepened valleys amid mountains. Characteristically, marginal vegetation is almost entirely lacking, in some lakes in the Scottish highlands being reduced to a sparse covering of species of aquatic mosses like *Fontinalis antipyretica*. The bottom deposits of oligotrophic lakes are made up of silts of inorganic mineral particles derived from rock erosion, rather than decaying organic deposits. Overall, the nutrient supply is poor and the total amount of nutrients available in any oligotrophic lake is always small. In spite of this, plant nutrients may show relatively rapid turnover rates in local areas of an oligotrophic lake. Only the larger oligotrophic lakes have any important plankton crop, the spring increase in phytoplankton is never spectacular, and the

**Figure 6·3. Two Scottish lakes** which correspond to the principal trophic categories. **A:** An example of eutrophic conditions—emergent vegetation in a bay of Loch Leven, Fife, Scotland. **B:** An example of oligotrophy—the northern part of Loch Lomond looking southeast, with Ben Lomond in the background. [**A:** Photo courtesy of Drs. Peter S. Maitland and J. Morton Boyd, © The Nature Conservancy of the United Kingdom. **B:** Photo © Tom Weir, Gartocharn, Scotland.]

**121**

density of zoöplankton is always low. Because of the typical bathymetric characteristics, most temperate oligotrophic lakes develop a thermocline in summer and large masses of cold water are isolated from the lit productive zone. On the other hand, the waters below the thermocline (that is, those of the hypolimnion) are always highly oxygenated and the greater depth of an oligotrophic lake ensures that there are always proportionately large volumes of water which are cool. In fact, in many such lakes in temperate latitudes, this mass of deeper water does not vary by more than a degree from 4°C throughout the year. Therefore such lakes can always support lake trout, cisco, coregonids, and other cold-water species which are sensitive to low oxygen tensions or high temperatures. Trophic conditions are usually such that these cold-water fishes are poorly nourished and slow-growing.

Once again, we can characterize the typical geomorphology of the land surfaces on which oligotrophic lakes occur. Mountainous country, or highlands, with thin, poor soils, supporting little agriculture or deciduous woodlands are where oligotrophic lakes are found (Figures 6·3B and 6·4B). The drainage into them is often of "soft" waters, with little content of dissolved inorganic salts and almost no plant nutrients. Obviously, one result is a much smaller biomass per unit volume, but oligotrophic faunas are also poorer in numbers of species. Once again, although the diagnostic features of oligotrophy is low winter concentrations of phosphates and nitrates, we could prepare lists for any part of the world of organisms characteristic of oligotrophy. In this case, the biological indicator species would often be "relict" forms or cold-water species. A considerable number of the species of invertebrates and fishes of oligotrophic lakes are also characteristic of the headwaters of streams, which are typically cold and well-oxygenated in the mountains of the same latitudes.

In the earliest classifications, oligotrophic lakes were typified by those of the Swiss Alpine region. The majority of the lakes of Scotland, including Loch Ness, Loch Morar, and the "highland" section of Loch Lomond, are characteristically oligotrophic. In North America, the Finger Lakes (Seneca, Oswego, and the rest) of upstate New York, the lakes of the Adirondacks, the lakes of the Yellowstone region, and the lakes of the Canadian Rockies are all examples of such scenically beautiful lakes, which are always of low productivity. As an example of the typical bathymetric form, Seneca Lake is 35 miles long, and mostly under 2 miles across, being a long, narrow trough with a maximum depth of 188 meters and an average depth of 89 meters. The contrast with Lake Oneida (see page 119) is obvious.

The small-scale equivalents of oligotrophic lakes are found in the tiny lakes—termed rock lochans in Scotland—which often occur in scooped-out glacial hollows (corries or cirques) high on mountainsides. These show the features of larger oligotrophic lakes, but even more markedly the feature of paucity of species. The few species which can be found in most mountain lochans seem to represent those which happen to have arrived there by the chances of passive dispersal and been able to survive in the frugal trophic conditions and severe climatic variations of these "tough" aquatic habitats. Even the low productivity possible will vary greatly from year to year in the same lochan.

Most authorities distinguish as the third lake type, termed dystrophic, those typically brown-water lakes with a relatively high content of the acidic organic materials in solution which are known as "humic acid." The important biological effect of this chemical condition is to reduce the rate of, or even prevent entirely, the processes of bacterial breakdown which, in other lakes, result in the return of plant nutrients to the water from dead organic material on the bottom. The bottom deposits of dystrophic lakes consist largely of unrotted organic material which accumulates as peat. As a result of the practically aseptic conditions, humic acid waters are essentially infertile, and the faunal productivity of dystrophic lakes is very low. The amount of phytoplankton in a typical dystrophic lake is usually very small and there are no important seasonal increases. Even in winter, the concentrations of plant nutrient salts such as phosphates and nitrates are extremely small. In a few dystrophic lakes, the presence of colloids of ferric iron create a further reduction of nutrients by "locking up" phosphates at the bottom. Extant dystrophic lakes and sites of former lakes of this type are characterized by deposits of peat, within which the processes of organic decay by bacteria are so retarded that the plants (and occasional animal remains) which form the peat are sufficiently preserved to allow detailed investigation centuries or millennia later. This has been of importance to the archeologists of prehistory. It is to the exclusion of bacteria from dystrophic lake waters and the preservative powers of humic acid that we owe our only chances to see our ancestors of 3000 years ago *in the flesh*. Skeletal remains of early man are not uncommon, but the only *whole* human remains of that age have come from various peat bogs in Danish Jutland. One of the earliest is a beautifully preserved girl of the Early Bronze Age (probably about 3000 years ago) from Skrydstrup in Jutland, the details of whose coiffure, including a cosmetic horsehair pad, have survived. Perhaps the most famous, however, is the Iron Age Man (perhaps 2100 years old) from Tollund in Jutland, whose facial expression is well preserved, and one can discern—after twenty-one centuries—a mien of wry but ineffable content (in spite of the fact that he probably died by ritual strangulation). As regards productivity under dystrophic conditions, it is important to realize that the stored organic energy of a peat deposit results from plant growth in humic acid waters and forms a fossil-fuel resource (utilized by the Scots and the Irish, among other peoples) which, though smaller in scale, more local, and more recently formed, is exactly similar to coal and oil in terms of the origin of its energy content.

Generally speaking, extremely humic and most extremely oligotrophic lakes are poor in calcium salts, while many—though certainly not all—eutrophic lakes have hard water. As noted earlier, the dissolved calcium content of natural fresh waters can vary 200-fold. Usually, other conditions being more or less equal, increasing content of lime will bring about increasing aquatic productivity, though very high levels of dissolved calcium salts may again inhibit primary production, largely by interfering with the carbon dioxide → bicarbonate cycle at the surfaces of green plant cells. It is also important to make lake comparisons only within similar climatic conditions; for example, changes of latitude and of altitude have complex effects on productivity. For pedagogical reasons, I have suggested elsewhere that the biological classification of lakes could be better regarded as falling within a system of three distinct and *continuous* variates. This can be conceived as a three-dimensional system of rectangular coordinates: along one axis would range values from nutrient-sterility through oligotrophy to eutrophy (pragmatically best expressed as late-winter concentrations of nitrates and/or phosphates) ; along the second axis, values for humic content of the water; and along the third, values for calcium content. A lake with maximum organic production would correspond to optimum calcium content, minimum humic content, and eutrophy. As has been already stressed, it is essential to realize, whatever conceptual system is used, that no lake can be permanently classified at any one point in any system; the trophic and other characteristics of each lake are changing continuously. This again reflects the matters discussed above (see pages 110 and 215) regarding the transience—in a geological time-scale—of the environment provided by any body of fresh water. Lastly, lake classifications involve arbitrary grouping of data, and this (as always) involves loss of information. In other words, no lake is the exact productive twin of any other lake. Another difficulty in the objective classification of lakes is that there are a surprisingly large number of continuous bodies of fresh water which are made up of interconnected lakes, which units may differ in their bathymetric and trophic characteristics. Loch Lomond in Scotland is one example. It is very briefly reviewed here, not only because of this and because I have been personally involved in work on it, but also because it provides a convenient recapitulation of many of the factors which are important in determining the level of aquatic productivity in lake waters.

# Loch Lomond

As we have seen, the level of productivity of any body of fresh water is determined by the incidence of solar energy, the physical and chemical conditions of the medium, and the nature of the substratum. All of these are in turn determined by topographical—and more especially bathymetric—features. Loch Lomond is best understood if it is considered as two different lake regions, very distinct in their configuration, which will be termed here the "highland loch" and the "lowland loch" (see Figures 6·1, 6·4, and 6·5). (In discussing certain faunistic characteristics, it is sometimes conceptually useful to divide Loch Lomond into *three* lake basins, but this refinement is unnecessary for our present purposes.) The differences between highland loch and lowland loch reflect not only the solid geology of the rocks on which they lie, but also their erosional history. The highland loch north of Inverbeg is a deep, narrow trough, running through metamorphosed rocks of Dalradian age (mainly mica-schists, but including slates, greywackes, and granites), being a preglacial valley overdeepened by ice action. This 12-mile-long trough has an average width of just over ½ mile and an average depth of over 90 meters, with much water between 150 and 180 meters deep. In contrast, the lowland loch south and east of Luss is wide, relatively shallow, and studded with islands and submerged reefs and banks. It lies largely over sedimentary rocks of Carboniferous and Devonian age (mainly coarse-grained sandstones and conglomerates), and occupies a shallow depression which results partly from "ponding" when it was an area of glacial deposition during the erosion of the highland loch, but partly also from interglacial marine incursions. This lowland loch, some 6 miles long by 4 miles wide, has no water deeper than 23 meters, and considerable areas shallower than 15 meters deep. (The region north of Luss and south of Inverbeg is in many ways intermediate in character, and constitutes the conceptual third lake mentioned above.)

Characteristic echo-sounding records, prepared by my former colleague Harry D. Slack, across the highland and lowland lochs are shown in Figure 6·5, and, though the "deposit" records must be interpreted with caution, one further signficant feature shown is the occurrence in the lowland loch, but not in the highland, of a series of deposits as infillings of depressions in the rock floor. Significantly, the country surrounding the lowland loch has extensive cover of drift deposits, mainly boulder clays along with some marine and fluvial deposits, while the only extensive cover in the highland region is blanket peat.

It will be obvious that as a result of their different shapes, the highland loch receives markedly less light energy per unit volume of water

**Figure 6·4. Lowland and highland sections of Loch Lomond. A:** The wide, relatively shallow lowland loch, studded with islands and submerged reefs and banks, and surrounded by arable farmland, is viewed from above its south shore. **B:** The deep, narrow trough of the highland loch, occupying a preglacial valley overdeepened by ice action, and surrounded by hills used only as rough grazing for sheep, is seen from Ardlui looking south. See also Figure 6·5. [Both photos © Tom Weir, Gartocharn, Scotland.]

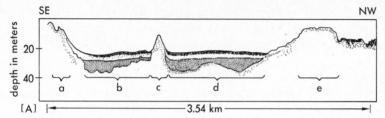

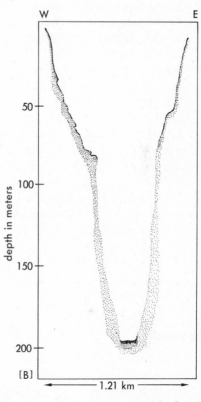

**Figure 6·5. Echo-soundings across lowland and highland Loch Lomond. A:** In this transect across a part of the lowland loch lying northwest of the island chain, the reefs and banks under shallow water (a, c, and e) are apparently not covered by any fine deposits, while in the troughs (b and d) there are two types of deposits as infillings of the irregularities of the rock floor. **B:** In this transect across the highland loch the traces obtained by echo-sounding demonstrate the return of a relatively weak signal from the very steep slopes, while the bottom shows no layered deposits. Compare with Figures 6·1 and 6·4. [From W. D. Russell Hunter in *Brit. Assoc. Handb.* (*Glasgow, 1958*), 5:97–118, 1958, after Slack, 1957.]

for phytoplankton growth than the lowland loch. A further physical difference is that temperature stratification in the deeper highland loch persists through more than half of each year (approximately May to December), while any stratification in the lowland loch is transistory. The chemical nature of the waters flowing into Loch Lomond is again dissimilar in the two regions. The highland has a catchment area of metamorphic rocks yielding little in the way of nutrient salts, and largely covered with peat. The Devonian and Carboniferous sediments which surround the lower loch, with their overlying beds of boulder clay and other drift deposits, are richer in soluble nutrients and indeed in all inorganic salts. At times, the calcium content of waters flowing from the Endrick Water at the southeast corner of Loch Lomond is about fourteen times greater than that of the River Falloch at the northern end of the loch. This disparity is enhanced by markedly different agricultural utilization of the two areas; the highland region being only used as rough grazing for sheep, while the lowland is largely arable farmland (like that around Lake Oneida in upstate New York; see page 119), which receives additional nutrient salts in the form of fertilizers. As a result of all these factors, it is undoubtedly true that the biomass per square meter produced annually in the lowland loch is considerably greater than that for the highland part. A detailed study of the carbon and nitrogen content of bottom deposits throughout Loch Lomond by Harry D. Slack has shown that the highland loch deposits have greater organic content and a higher carbon to nitrogen (**C:N**) ratio. The implications of such ratios will be discussed in Chapter 8 of this book, but the values for Loch Lomond obtained by Slack indicate that the highland loch is both more dystrophic and more oligotrophic than the lowland loch. Such comparison should not obscure the fact that, considered in a general eutrophic/oligotrophic scale, even lowland Loch Lomond is poor in nutrient salts, and would be assessed toward oligotrophy.

For the last few pages, we have been stressing the bathymetric and trophic variety of lakes, which variety makes lake classification difficult (but pragmatically makes such systems necessary for human comprehension). Another aspect of the variability in lakes is that their seasonal cycles of productivity, while similar to those in the sea, show much greater variations from year to year than are ever found in the environment of the open oceans.

## Lake seasons

Any large lake in temperate latitudes shows a seasonal pattern of primary productivity essentially similar to that in the oceans and basically controlled by the same limiting factors. The seasonal changes in solar radiation received at the lake surface affect the trophic condition directly through the changing compensation level (see page 38) for the green plant cells concerned, and also indirectly by differential warming of the lake waters and the formation of thermoclines (see page 41). The direct effects of the availability of light for photosynthesis are exactly similar to those in temperate seas: the spring phytoplankton increase occurs when a threshold level in solar radiation is reached, and any autumnal phytoplankton bloom is ended by the declining sunshine levels of fall rather than nutrient depletion. The indirect effects of thermal stratification show a number of features which do not occur in the sea and are worth discussing in more detail.

Once formed in a medium-sized or large lake, temperature stratification can involve a very definite and abrupt thermocline which is considerably more stable over periods of months than a thermocline in coastal marine waters of approximately the same depth. In fresh waters, the layers between the surface and the thermocline are referred to as the epilimnion, and those below the thermocline, cut off by the temperature and density gradient, as the hypolimnion. The maximum density of water occurs at 4°C, and therefore there are two types of thermal stratification involving thermoclines which can be formed in lakes in temperate latitudes in summer and in winter, respectively. The seasonal changes in temperature at the different levels are illustrated diagrammatically in Figure 6·6, which shows the complete mixing which can occur in spring and late fall (termed the spring and autumnal overturns), and the thermoclines separating epilimnion from hypolimnion characteristic of both summer and winter periods. Full circulation occurs only at or near the temperature of maximum density, and this occurs only twice a year. It should be noted that wind-action

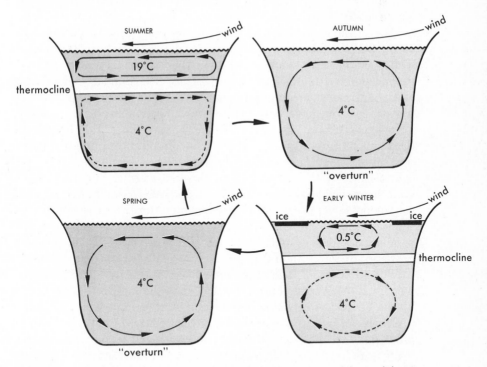

**Figure 6·6. The four seasons in a dimictic lake.** The majority of larger lakes in temperate regions of the world show the changing patterns of water temperature which are stylized here and involve temperature stratification and the formation of a thermocline both in summer and in winter, and two periods of general water mixing (or "overturns") in autumn and spring. Compare with Figure 3·6, and for further discussion see text.

when the thermocline is present in summer or in winter (before ice cover is complete) causes mixing only in the waters of the epilimnion. If this stirring is sufficient to cause water currents in the hypolimnion, these deeper currents circulate in the reverse direction and are completely separated from the directly wind-induced circulation by the density gradient of the thermocline. As in the sea (see pages 39–42), while the thermocline persists inorganic nutrients liberated by bacterial action in the bottom waters of the lake cannot become available to the green plants of the euphotic zone (which corresponds to the upper layers of the epilimnion in most cases). Only the spring and early-winter (autumnal) overturns can recirculate nutrients produced at or near the bottom into the water bathing the living primary producers. Like so many other basic concepts of limnology, this seasonal pattern of thermal stratification with two overturns was elucidated near the end of last century by F. A. Forel.

Obviously, the pattern will be modified at different latitudes. A lake in a somewhat warmer climate than the lake illustrated in Figure 6·6 will never have water falling below the temperature of maximum density, never have a winter thermocline, and, of course, never have ice cover. Such a lake may show one circulation period or overturn in winter and for ten or eleven months of the year remain in the *summer* thermocline condition illustrated in Figure 6·6. Similarly, some lakes at high latitudes (or altitudes) may have only a short summer period free of ice cover, have water temperatures never above 4°C, and have a single overturn at the height of their brief summer. It is best to use the terms introduced by G. Evelyn Hutchinson in any thermal classification of lakes. The classic temperate lake of Figure 6·6 with two overturns he terms dimictic, with the two warmer and more polar cases mentioned above being termed respectively warm monomictic and cold monomictic. Forel's original designations for these were temperate, tropical, and polar, but some of the best-known examples of warm monomictic lakes—Forel's "tropical" category—occur in the West of Scotland, in a mild maritime climate which, however, can hardly be considered tropical. This was pointed out by the great Scottish limnologist E. M. Wedderburn, in 1910, when the massive data collected by the Scottish lake survey on thermal stratification were first being presented. In fact, all smaller and many large lakes in the actual tropics differ from all the above thermal patterns. Such lakes, termed oligomictic, can have relatively warm waters, no thermocline at any time of the year, and rather irregular mixing, which is not determined by seasonal temperature change. Thus in temperate latitudes we find both dimictic and warm monomictic lakes, and the seasonal course of changes of nutrient availability in the lit waters will obviously differ in the two types. Warm monomictic lakes, including those of coastal

Scotland and near the Pacific coast in North America, will have seasonal changes in nutrient availability essentially similar to those already described for temperate seas (see pages 42–48). The seasonal changes in phytoplankton production in such lakes—though paralleling those in adjacent seas—will differ in detail from those in the much more common dimictic lakes of the temperate latitudes of continents. Among the lakes we have already discussed, all the lakes of the northeastern United States are dimictic, including the Finger Lakes and Lake Oneida; the Scandinavian lakes, except those at higher altitudes, are likewise dimictic; while in the British Isles there are both dimictic and warm monomictic lakes.

It is important to realize that a warm monomictic lake may still be one with a large volume of relatively cold water persisting throughout the year below the thermocline. Loch Lomond again provides a significant illustration of this. In the majority of years the highland loch (as defined above) is characteristically warm monomictic. It may be dimictic in the very few years with exceptionally severe winter conditions. The "summer" pattern of temperature stratification involves a markedly abrupt thermocline which may persist from late April to the following December. A single period of mixing can extend over the months January, February, and March. In spite of its classification as a warm monomictic lake, the water temperature at the bottom near Tarbet in depths of 180 meters is low and varied only from 4.7° to 6.4°C over four years of recording. It is the persistence of this large mass of cold water which allows relict species to survive in such lakes. In this part of Loch Lomond we have among the deep-water benthos a minute bivalve, *Pisidium conventus,* which is an uncommon species in the British Isles, being more typical of Swedish Lapland and northern Norway, and occurring as the only mollusc species in certain summer fresh waters in the high Arctic. For physiological reasons, it could not survive in those other parts of the waters of Loch Lomond which can rise to temperatures of 22°C in summer.

In larger lakes which are relatively shallow, or which have their underwater contours interrupted by many islands or submerged banks, temperature stratification is liable to be more transistory. For example, in lowland Loch Lomond (see Figure 6·5A), a thermocline may become established early in summer only to be broken up by any period of strong winds. This is characteristic of many large but shallow lakes in which wind-induced mixing can produce nutrient replenishment of the surface waters irregularly throughout the summer and result in an irregular series of increases of phytoplankton production. Another aspect of such variability in summer productivity is also illustrated by data from Loch Lomond. In the highly oxygenated waters of oligotrophic lakes (including in this case the lowland region of Loch Lomond), bottom sediments may be largely overlaid by colloids of ferric iron which can absorb nutrient salts. In more eutrophic lakes, conditions of low oxygen tension occurring seasonally may bring about a reduction of part of this layer to the ferrous state, resulting in a period of release of nutrient salts. In Loch Lomond, dissolved-oxygen concentrations are always high and such release never occurs. On the other hand, on a number of occasions, Harry D. Slack has demonstrated the phosphate content of the water to be higher in the lowland loch immediately after periods of strong winds. It is thought that under these conditions wind-induced currents in the relatively shallow waters can be strong enough to lift sediments from the bottom and mechanically bring about some release of absorbed nutrients. In the summer, this could result in a short phytoplankton increase. If we reconsider the effects of the winter overturn in the light of the conditions apparently necessary for the release of nutrients from the ferric colloids, it seems not improbable that the extent of the spring crop of phytoplankton may well depend upon the frequency of gale-force winds in the preceding winter. In general, such effects may largely account for the seasonal pattern of plankton production in fresh waters being less stereotyped than that in the sea.

The major trophic effects of thermoclines in lakes are those on nutrient salt distribution, and they occur because the sharp density gradient prevents mixing, rather than as a direct result of water temperatures. Given this importance of the density gradient, it is highly significant that there are a number of lakes (termed meromictic by Hutchinson) where increased concentrations of dissolved mineral salts in the hypolimnion have enhanced the density difference at the thermocline (or, in some cases, replaced the thermal density gradient) by creating a mechanically stabilized zone of dead water in the hypolimnion. Unlike the case of a true thermocline, the stability of this new type of density gradient (effectively separating the waters of the epilimnion from those of the hypolimnion and perhaps best called a chemocline) could apparently increase with time. There are several ways in which a meromictic condition could arise in a lake. Perhaps one most readily conceived is a case where the meromictic condition has arisen as a result of saline springs delivering dense water into the depths of the lake. Hutchinson has distinguished as biogenic meromixis the case where salts liberated by bacterial action at or near the bottom bring about a chemical reinforcement of a thermocline which thus becomes a permanent chemocline whose stability can increase with time. In general, the meromictic condition, once established, implies that productivity will be comparatively low, since dissolved nutrient salts produced in the bottom waters can *never* be recirculated to the photosynthetic organisms of the surface waters. A number of meromictic lakes have been studied in recent years, including Big Soda Lake, Nevada, and the small but deep Green Lake near Fayetteville in up-state New York. There is circumstantial evidence that some degree of meromixis occurs in several deep tropical lakes, which would otherwise be oligomictic, and one of the earliest demonstrations of the existence of a near-permanent chemocline was in Lake Edward in East Africa by E. B. Worthington. Meromictic lakes show lower levels of productivity than would otherwise occur with their bathymetric characteristics, and at their latitudes.

One final aspect of stratification in lake waters is worth mentioning, although its effects on productivity are slight. Even a moderate wind blowing across a large lake with temperature stratification will produce some net movement of the waters of the epilimnion toward the down-wind shore of the lake. The layers of rapid density change—the thermocline—will be depressed on that side of the lake and correspondingly elevated on the upwind side. If the wind then ceases to blow, the forces which opposed gravity in bringing about the "slope" of the thermocline are withdrawn, and the thermocline may begin to oscillate about an axis initially at right angles to the wind direction, and continue harmonic movements rather like those of a clock-pendulum until the oscillations are gradually damped out and the thermocline has come back to a horizontal position. Deflections of over a meter can occur, and the resultant oscillations are known as seiches, again first studied by F. A. Forel. Strictly speaking, the most usual oscillations of the thermocline should be designated as *internal* seiches, since movements of many meters in a vertical direction by the thermocline toward the end of a lake may be reflected by vertical movements of the water surface of only a centimeter or so. On rare occasions there occur seiches of another sort where relatively large vertical movements of the surface waters occur in harmonic oscillations. In large lakes, these may be caused by local or distant earth tremors. An early record of such a superficial seiche is for Loch Lomond on the morning of November 1 1755, at the time of the great earthquake at Lisbon. Contemporary records suggest that the recurrent period of the oscillations was about 10 minutes and the maximum rise and fall of the water level at any point of the shore about 2.5 feet.

Seiches are essentially standing waves whose oscillations have a periodicity which depends upon the dimensions of the lake. The hydrodynamics are complex and have attracted several brilliant applied mathematicians. In the early years of this century the foundation of our knowledge of internal seiches was laid by the extensive work of two members of the Scottish lake survey: E. M. Wedderburn and G. Chrystal, the former a distinguished Edinburgh lawyer who was also a amateur physicist. Their work included the first extensive field obser-

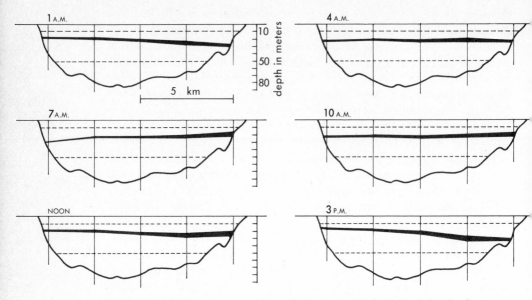

**Figure 6·7. Seiche movements in Loch Earn, Scotland.** Each of the six diagrams represents a longitudinal section of the lake with considerable vertical exaggeration (Loch Earn is nearly 11 km long), and shows depths of 10 and of 50 meters as broken lines, with the zone between the isotherms for 9°C and 11°C (that is, within the thermocline) as a blackened area. These isotherms were derived from actual depth-temperature measurements made by a team of observers at successive hours on 9th August, 1911, the temperature at the lake bottom being consistently 6.2°C and the surface temperature varying from 15.5°C (1 a.m.) to 16.1°C (3 p.m.). Such oscillations of the thermocline in a stratified lake are termed *internal* seiches, and are essentially standing waves whose periodicity depends upon the dimensions of the lake. The hydrodynamics are complex, but theoretical calculations are possible and give a periodicity of about 15 hours for Loch Earn. The actual temperature measurements plotted in this figure show a seiche periodicity which is a close fit to the predicted value. Compare especially the depth-temperature readings at 7 a.m. and at 3 p.m., which are almost exactly out of phase (that is, are separated by almost exactly half of the period of oscillation). [Based on figures and tables of E. M. Wedderburn in *Trans. Roy. Soc. Edinburgh*, 48:629–695, 1912.]

vations of the movements of thermoclines and a series of model experiments, which together led to the development of predictive equations for the range and periods of the oscillations based on the shape and size of each lake basin. More recently, similar studies by Clifford H. Mortimer, initially in the English Lake District and now in the Great Lakes of North America, have led to further sophistication of the predictive theory. Again, it is important to emphasize that the periodicity of seiches in any lake shows constant or constantly varying characteristics which are dependent solely on the bathymetric form of the lake. Figure 6·7 presents some of Wedderburn's original data from

Loch Earn in Scotland where studies were continued between 1904 and 1911. Loch Earn is about 6 miles long, and internal seiches have a periodicity of about 15 hours and a vertical range of up to 8 meters, Wedderburn's theoretical calculations correctly predicting the 15-hour periodicity. Loch Ness, which was studied in detail by Wedderburn and, nearly fifty years later, by Mortimer, is 24 miles long and has a seiche periodicity of 57.6–60 hours, another close fit to predicted values. By contrast, Lake Baikal in Siberia, which has the greatest volume of any purely freshwater lake, is 395 miles long and internal seiches have a periodicity of 38 days.

## Human use of lakes

The trophic classification of lakes is of some significance in relation to their value to man. Eutrophic waters will obviously make the best fishing grounds, while oligotrophic lakes are closer to the ideal as reservoirs of drinking water. Some aspects of this generalization require further examination.

As regards productivity of fish, it is clear that the most eutrophic conditions will be suitable for only a limited number of fish species. To take a somewhat extreme example, the maximum crop of trout could probably be harvested from a moderately oligotrophic lake rather than one near to eutrophy. The greatest successes of tropical freshwater fish-farming have been achieved with the African genus *Tilapia,* several species of which are able to feed directly on plant plankton and on the filamentous algae of the *Aufwuchs,* while two species have strong grinding teeth and can feed directly on larger plants. Maximum standing crops of up to 2 tons per acre can be achieved in fertilized ponds with heavy supplementary foddering of plant material (that is, in conditions which correspond to extreme eutrophy). This optimal example of the production of fish protein will be related to other examples of fish-farming in Chapters 13 and 15.

The best possible supply of fresh water for a city would come from a relatively large oligotrophic lake whose waters had a low concentration of dissolved salts (that is, were "soft"). A few cities are thus fortunate. The city of Glasgow in Scotland derives most of its water supply from Loch Katrine, oligotrophic with soft waters, whose catchment area has an annual rainfall in excess of 65 inches. The oligotrophic Finger Lakes of upstate New York are used for water supply, Skaneateles Lake supplying the city of Syracuse, but here the content of mineral salts, including calcium, is somewhat higher. However, many cities have to draw their water supply from eutrophic sources, and this commonly requires more extensive biological management and filtration. The case of the city of London is biologically interesting.

Much of London's water supply is stored in large artificial reservoirs which have become eutrophic lakes. Good management implies maintaining a fairly full organic cycle with food-chains ending in fishes and other large organisms which will not pass into and block the filters. In a well-managed reservoir of the metropolitan water board, the spring concentrations of phosphates and nitrates characteristic of moderate eutrophy are quickly utilized by a diatom crop, which in turn is quickly disposed of by the zoöplankton and other second-trophic-level benthic invertebrates, and these in turn are consumed by fishes. Unfortunately, in fresh waters of this sort where diatoms are the dominant organisms of the phytoplankton, an important nutrient which can be limiting is silica. If, in one of these reservoirs, the available silica is used up before the other nutrients such as phosphates and nitrates are completely utilized, then the phytoplankton production may shift from diatoms to blue-green algae. These blue-greens are not consumed by zoöplankton, or by any other animal organism, and pass disintegrating through the filters. The segment of the London population served by that particular reservoir will then call the water board to complain about "a fishy taste" in the water. The corrective action then taken by the biologists of the board is to arrange for quantities of silica to be broadcast through the waters of that reservoir, resulting in a return of the primary production to a diatom crop which takes its appropriate place in the food-chain. Thus, to prevent complaints about a fishy taste in the drinking water, paradoxically, the biologists managing these artificial lakes have to encourage the proper growth of fish.

A very brief consideration of human misuse of fresh waters—particularly with regard to water pollution—will be found in the next chapter.

# Streams, rivers, and water pollution

THE AQUATIC PRODUCTIVITY of most of the environments provided by running fresh waters can be compared to that of moderately oligotrophic lakes in the same latitudes. The environments of a typical river system can be serially arranged as: springs (sources) → brooks → creeks → river → estuary (or other outfall). Of these, estuaries are regularly regions of high productivity (extreme eutrophy), and the source springs can be eutrophic under certain conditions. Otherwise, the productivity is lower than might be intuitively expected, given the "greater efficiency" of trophic energy transfer which is possible in a unidirectional flow system.

Although only a tiny fraction of the water in the oceans, the annual flow through the river systems of the world back to the sea is equal to 9000 cubic miles. This represents less than 38 per cent of the annual rainfall and other precipitation over land surfaces (the rest being evaporated) or about 9 per cent of the world's annual overall precipitation. In spite of this vast runoff flow, in global terms, streams make only a small contribution to aquatic productivity and to human food supplies. However, certain extremely important ecological studies on the energetics of food-chains have been carried out in streams.

In running waters, both the distribution and the productivity of the flora and fauna are largely determined (and in a strict sense limited) by the changing velocities of the current. Any classification of riverine habitats and trophic chains must hinge on rates of water flow.

## The abiotic environment

The distribution of organisms in streams and the levels of their productivity are largely determined by physicochemical factors, including the oxygen content and temperature range of the waters and the nature of the bottom deposits. In turn, all of these factors are related to the velocity of the current. Although such matters are almost impossible to quantify, it seems clear that, when compared to organisms living on land, in lakes, or in coastal seas, the organisms of freshwater streams, because of the continual flow, can modify their environment to only a small extent. Unusual in his distinction as both a comparative physiologist and an oceanographer, Alfred C. Redfield once emphasized, in discussing what he called "the physiology of the environment," the ways in which regular changes in most aquatic and other environments are brought about by the metabolic activities of the organisms living in them. This side of the reciprocal action between the living community and its abiotic environment is necessarily less extensive in streams. Current velocity is the dominant—and unmodifiable—factor in their ecology.

The speed of water flow in a stream is primarily determined by the steepness with which the stream bed slopes down, although this can be affected by the roughness of the stream bed and its cross-sectional size. More usually, however, bed roughness and size are themselves determined by current velocity. In the simplest circumstances, "slope" and current speed decrease in a regular fashion from source to outfall. It will be easiest to consider the changing physical factors if, as in Figure 7·1A, we draw a *Thalweg* curve with height above outfall plotted against distance from source with the usual vertical exaggeration of topographic models. A threefold division is crude but useful: into the steeply sloping headstream (brook or beck or burn), the middle course (young river or creek), and the mature river of low gradient and slow flow. Since higher velocities mean increased rates of erosion, the stream will cut back into its bed most rapidly near its headwaters. This is shown diagrammatically in Figure 7·1B, and it can be seen that, with the passage of time, the characteristics at one geographic point in the stream could change from those of the headstream to those of the middle course. In fact, in the time-scale of recent geology, all running waters are continually evolving: middle course into mature river, and headstream into middle course. It is perhaps worth mentioning here that, compared with ponds and lakes, the major river valleys are features of some geological permanence (see pages 110 and 215). *Thalwegs* are often more complicated in mountainous regions which have been recently glaciated. The curve of a stream in such country is illustrated in Figure 7·1C in which a small stream has reached some maturity with low gradient and slow flow but then drops over the "edge" of a U-shaped glaciated valley and is "rejuvenated," reacquiring the characteristics of steep gradient and rapid and eroding flow of a headstream. Such streams with an abrupt step in the *Thalweg* curve are often found around lakes which occupy glacially overdeepened valleys —such as Loch Ness and highland Loch Lomond in Scotland, and Cayuga Lake and Seneca Lake in upstate New York.

If we return to consideration of the simplest *Thalweg* (Figure 7·1A) with decreasing gradient from headstream to mature river, we find: decrease in current velocity; changing bottom deposits, reflecting decreasing erosional and transport capabilities of the flow, from large boulders or bare rock in the fast-flowing headstream, through cobblestones and gravel, to sands and then fine silts in the mature river; in-

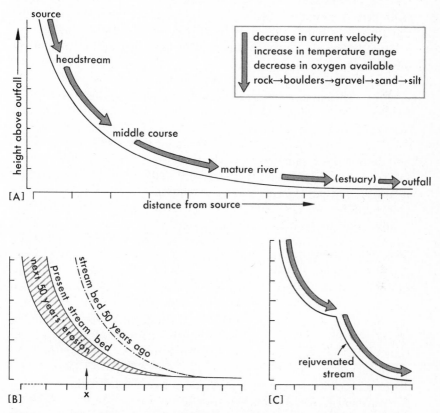

**Figure 7·1. The abiotic environment of streams** as demonstrated in *Thalweg* plots which show, with considerable vertical exaggeration, the steepness of the stream bed. **A:** A simple *Thalweg*, showing the changes in velocity, temperature, oxygen, and bottom deposits to be expected in moving from the headstream to the mature river. **B:** Erosional effects on the stream profile of the passage of time. Note that at one geographic point, x, the stream characteristics can change from those of a headstream to those of the middle course. **C:** Effects of glacial erosion: the "rejuvenated" profile of a small stream falling into a glacially overdeepened valley.

creasing average temperature, and increasing diurnal and seasonal range of temperatures; and, very characteristically, a decreasing oxygenation of the waters. These current-determined factors obviously control faunal distribution. Because these abiotic factors change more rapidly in the headstream than they do in the mature river, changes in the animal communities are more pronounced in the first few miles below the source in many rivers than they are for the last several hundred miles of the slowly changing as well as slowly moving mature river.

The animal species living in the headstream must either have hooked appendages or suckers to hold on or be sufficiently strong swimmers to maintain their position at high velocities of water flow. On the other hand, they can be species which require highly oxygenated waters of low and relatively constant temperature. In contrast, the animal species living in mature rivers do not require attachment organs, a special shape, or powerful swimming muscles, but must be tolerant of turbid and silting conditions (perhaps be able to burrow in soft substrata), and must be resistant to conditions of low oxygen tension and of high and variable temperatures. In most river systems, this difference is particularly well illustrated by the fish species. Trout and certain other salmonids are characteristic of headstreams: powerful swimmers, they require highly oxygenated and cold waters, and die if transferred to typical mature conditions. Minnows and several cottid species are characteristic of the gravel reaches of the middle course, while in the mature lowland river, we find carp and bream and roach. These last forms are not strong swimmers, but all are tolerant of low-oxygen, high-temperature, and silty conditions. The few freshwater flatfish, including some species of the genus *Pleuronectes,* are found in the last purely freshwater reaches above the estuary. There are also groups of invertebrate species—particularly of insect larvae—characteristic of each region of the river. Freshwater limpets, including *Ancylus* in Europe and *Ferrissia* in North America, which are pulmonate snails with conical, streamlined shells and the foot modified to a powerful sucker, are characteristic animals of highland headstreams. In closely related species of insect larvae, living in different regions of a river one can see, moving downstream in the species series, both the decreasing importance of attachment organs and the increasing surface area of the gills or other respiratory organs in proportion to the body size.

Many stream animals show rather specific behavior patterns which allow them to maintain their position in the appropriate region of the stream. Many of these involve rheotaxis or a reflex reaction to the direction of water flow so that they automatically swim against the current or crawl upstream. In many cases, one period of the life-cycle

involves a considerable upstream migration. In spite of the structural
adaptations and behavioral mechanisms, a considerable proportion of
the populations of animals in headstreams die each year, not because
of any endogenous senescence, but by being swept downstream into
a physically or chemically unsuitable environment. In typical highland
stream populations of *Ancylus,* I have shown that there can be an
environmental limitation of size (and therefore of age), which in
any stream is dependent upon the rate of water flow and on the growth
of algae attached to the limpets' shells. In other snails there can also be
an environmental limitation of age dependent upon respiratory needs
in summer. Such features affecting survivorship in animal populations
are only one small part of the continuous processes of "export" downstream of biomass from the communities living in the headstream and
middle courses of river systems.

## Food-chains and productivity

In the majority of streams and river systems, the primary production
which supports the animal communities is allochthonous. Except in
some very large mature rivers, there is no phytoplankton, and the
attached diatoms and filamentous algae and few aquatic mosses and
other plants which live in the upper reaches of rivers contribute only a
small fraction of the basic food supply to the fauna of the stream.
Detritus, derived originally from terrestrial vegetation, and to a
lesser extent from communities in standing fresh waters, is of major
trophic importance, and autochthonous primary production proportionately small. Thus almost all riverine animals of the second trophic
level are detritus-feeders. As already stressed, the few producers and
all the animals of the lower trophic levels cause little or no "conditioning" of their environment because of the water flow. As a result, smaller
streams, and particularly springs, have living communities which
appear to be in a steady state with a relatively constant standing crop
in spite of rapid growth of individual organisms, and lack the
obvious successional stages such as occur cyclically or seasonally in those
standing marine and fresh waters which can be altered by the metabolic
activities of the organisms. Neither the decomposer-induced lack of
oxygen in the summer hypolimnion of eutrophic lakes (see page 119),
nor the locally high pH and supersaturation with oxygen created by
the photosynthetic activities of the phytoplankton in daylight in Lake
Oneida (see page 120), could occur in a spring or swiftly flowing
stream.

The intermediate trophic levels in stream faunas are almost always
involved in relatively complex food-webs (see Figure 7·2). As mentioned at the end of Chapter 2 and discussed more fully below (see

pages 213–215), there are both empirical and theoretical grounds for supposing that an increased complexity of links in a food-web can create increased stability of such a stream community. To some extent, the chances of starvation and even extinction for a species at a higher trophic level living in a community with a fluctuating and allochthonous basic food supply, such as that in a stream, are decreased when that species is not restricted to a single prey species in the trophic level immediately below it, but has a choice of prey not only at that level but to a varying extent through several lower trophic levels. In the

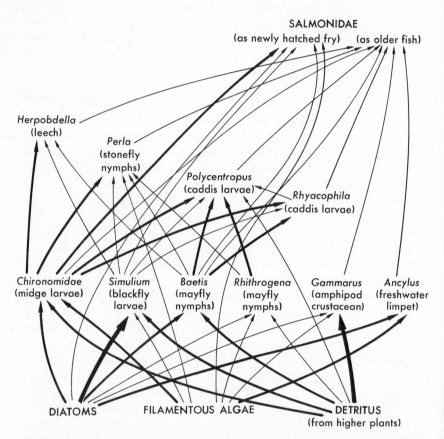

**Figure 7·2. The relatively complex food-web of trout** and similar salmonid fishes in a stream community. Note that an important primary food resource is in the form of detritus derived from the productivity of land vegetation (that is, allochthonous to the stream itself). Increased complexity of links in such a food-web can probably create increased stability for such a stream community. Compare with Figures 2·8 and 4·14. [Based on data tabulated for streams in the Dee river system, Wales, by R. M. Badcock in *J. Anim. Ecol.*, 18:193–208, 1949.]

animal communities of most streams, as in the examples of Figures $2 \cdot 8$ and $7 \cdot 2$, the bulk of the units at intermediate trophic levels are young stages—larvae or nymphs—of insect species. Other invertebrate groups are represented, including molluscs, flatworms, leeches, and crustaceans, but these are usually of secondary importance in the biomass of the standing crop.

The top trophic levels in streams are occupied by fish species, and these have been the subject of several important studies on the energetics of feeding, of growth, and of reproduction. Early and extremely important work on the energy balance of several freshwater fish species was carried out by V. S. Ivlev and his colleagues in Russia, and a now almost classical field study of the energetics of a trout population was carried out by K. R. Allen in the Horokiwi stream in New Zealand. Although some of Allen's approximations regarding percentage assimilation and maintenance rations have had to be further refined, his data from this trout population on fecundity, differential growth rates and survivorship remain significant. For example, in Figure $7 \cdot 3$ are presented some of his data on the growth and survivorship of young trout in the Horokiwi. One year's recruitment to the trout population of successfully hatched fry—amounting to a half-million individuals— was followed for two and a half years. The survivorship figures show a characteristic pattern similar to that which has been computed for most of the natural populations of invertebrates and fishes which have received sufficient study. There is an extremely high mortality early in life, but those few individual trout which survive past the fifteenth month after hatching have a relatively high expectation of further life. If we incorporate into this pattern the average weights of the fish surviving to each stage and the cumulative total of the fish dying in each interval, we can obtain biomass figures for the productivity of this trout population. With reference to the human exploitation of fish stocks, which we will discuss in more detail later (see Chapter 10), it is worth noting that the maximum biomass of fish crop would have been obtained by cropping this group of recruits to the population when they were about one year old, with an average weight of 170 grams. This results from the fact that, at the end of one year of growth and death, 1843 kg of fish had been produced, of which 595 kg, or 3500 individuals, was still alive. During the next year only a further 368 kg of fish was produced, giving a total cumulative production of 2211 kg, of which only 340 kg, or 1000 fish, remained alive. This decrease in the trout productivity available for cropping after the first year's growth is not a result of the changing incidence of mortality. In fact, the result would obtain even if the input of trout food per unit weight of trout remained constant. This is because a young, fast-

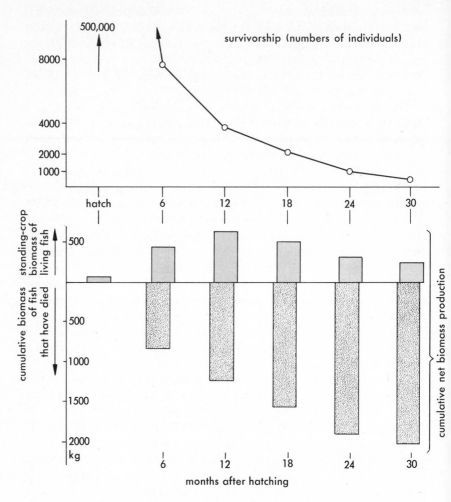

**Figure 7·3. Mortality and biomass production in a population of stream trout.** The upper part of the figure shows the actual survivorship (at intervals of six months) for a cohort of a half-million trout hatched within one month. The standing-crop biomass figures are derived by multiplying the numbers of fish surviving by the average weight of a fish in each age-class, and the biomass of fish which have died involves the numbers dying between each census and the average weight midway between each age-class. The cumulative biomass of fish which have died added together with the standing-crop biomass gives a measure of cumulative net biomass production at each six-month sampling. For further discussion, see text. [Based on data tabulated for a population of trout in the Horokiwi Stream, New Zealand, by K. R. Allen in *N. Z. Mar. Dept. Fish. Bull.*, 10:1–238, 1951.]

growing fish has not only a higher conversion efficiency than an aging one, but the proportion of the non-respired assimilation (N-R.A.), or intake available for growth, to the maintenance assimilation, which is respired, is much higher in young fish. Given a proportionate input of food, a young fish can show a more efficient and more rapid growth increase than an older one. The above may seem to involve some over-emphasis, based on admittedly crude data, on a fairly simple distinction between the growth efficiencies of young and older fish. However, if the point can be understood in this relatively simple form, then some of the more complex applications of it in the practical management of the cropping of natural populations, and in theoretical considerations of population homeostasis, will be more readily comprehended. Un-fortunately, many biologists not immediately involved in bioenergetics or population dynamics may need to be reminded of this simple dis-tinction—known to every canny farmer—in growth economics between young and old animals. If we now return to possible human cropping of the trout population in Horokiwi, obtaining the maximum yield would imply in this case: (a) altering human feeding habits so that these relatively tiny trout constituted an acceptable source of high-grade protein, and (b) maintaining uncropped a stock of breeding trout to spawn annually the number of eggs required for the optimum recruit-ment as fry of the stock to be cropped as immature trout at one year old. At present, neither is likely in the management of the trout stock in the Horokiwi. However, future fish-farming may well require such procedures (see Chapter 15).

More recently, rather more sophisticated attempts have been made to prepare energy balance-sheets for natural populations of a few animal species. Kenneth H. Mann is responsible for two such studies on fishes of the River Thames in England. His work on natural popu-lations of the roach (*Rutilus*) and the bleak (*Alburnus*) showed that in both the ratio of respiration to growth was about 12.8 or, to put it another way, the N-R.A. amounted to only 7.8 per cent of the total energy assimilation. Another significant aspect of Mann's work involved the productivity of the benthic organisms in the river which served as fish food and, in particular, the relation of their annual productivity to their mean standing crop. The data are still not completely published, but it seems that, in the region of the Thames studied, animals taking two years to complete their life-cycle have an approximate ratio for productivity to mean standing crop of 2:1, annuals have a 5:1 ratio, and those benthic species going through several generations each year may have ratios up to 10:1. Here again is a feature of aquatic pro-ductivity which cannot be overemphasized. The length of life-cycle in the unit species at lower trophic levels is of prime importance in assess-ing potential productivity. Some studies of the marginal benthos of eutrophic ponds have suggested that, with species of short life-cycles, the ratio of productivity to standing crop can approach 25:1 (this is an assessment of *potential* productivity without limitation of input). It seems likely that in streams and rivers where the input of organic detritus as food for the benthic organisms is likely to be limiting, the intensity of fish predation on the benthos will itself determine the ratio of productivity to standing crop. This could range from less than 3:1 with light fish-grazing to nearly 10:1 with optimal predation by the fish population. Further substantive data on this topic from natural benthic communities are urgently required. At present, we have little field data on the effects of life-cycle length and intensity of predation on this all-important ratio of annual productivity to standing crop. In many aquatic invertebrates, the length of life-cycle itself can vary. My own studies have revealed that, in a number of species of freshwater snails, there are considerable infraspecific interpopulation variations involving the seasonal course of the reproductive cycle—and the number of generations per year—as well as growth rates and fecundity. Most of these interpopulation variations can be environmentally evoked, but some differences seem genetically determined. As regards different rates of predation, there exist very few reliable field data. Recently, intensive laboratory studies on predator/prey relationships by Lawrence B. Slobodkin and others have allowed the development of more sophisticated concepts of efficiencies (see Chapter 9) and predictive hypotheses regarding what Slobodkin has elegantly termed "prudent predators and efficient prey." Field data on natural populations are required not merely to test these hypotheses but also to re-examine their implications in the light of the naturally occurring variations in the ratio of productivity to standing crop. For both marine and freshwater stocks, fisheries scientists have accumulated a certain amount of data of this sort (see Chapter 10), but much more is required if the future exploitation of aquatic productivity by man is to have a rational basis.

To return from the energetics of species-populations to consideration of whole communities in running fresh waters, two of the most complete analyses of energy flow in natural ecosystems have been made on the source springs of freshwater streams. One advantage in such studies derives from the aspect already noted that there is little biological conditioning and consequent succession. An early study on natural energy flow by John M. Teal also illustrates the advantages of a small scale and a limited number of species. Teal completed an annual-energy-flow survey on Root Spring near Concord in Massachusetts involving studies of the growth and respiration rates of all the species in this small freshwater spring (about 2 meters in diameter and 15 cm deep). Only forty animal species were present, and only twelve of these contributed significantly in terms of energy flow. His results can be expressed in kilocalories per square meter per year (kcal/m²/yr). The autochthonous algae in Teal's spring had a gross productivity of 710 kcal/m²/yr, of which 55 kcal/m²/yr was lost in respiration, 655 kcal/m²/yr being available to the animals of the second trophic level. A larger contribution was made by the detritus, entering the miniature ecosystem from outside, which amounted to 2350 kcal/m²/yr. Of the combined basic food supplies, 705 kcal/m²/yr formed deposits not utilized as food, which presumably were later flushed out of the spring, but some 2300 kcal/m²/yr was available for the second-trophic-level animals. Their respiratory heat production amounted to 1746 kcal/m²/yr, and their net productivity amounted to 576 kcal/m²/yr, of which 208 kcal/m²/yr provided food for the carnivorous animals in the spring of the third trophic level. Heat loss from the third trophic level by respiration amounted to 89 kcal/m²/yr, and the net productivity of that level amounted to 123 kcal/m²/yr. The slight discrepancies in balancing these figures result from the standing crop of the second trophic level (herbivores) and of the third trophic·level (carnivores) being smaller at the end of the year's study, in each case by 4 kcal/m²/yr. Presentation of these figures gives little idea of the vast amount of work involved in this study. For example, for one of the twelve important species—the midge larvae, *Calopsectra*—energy balance-sheets involved the heat losses not only of the standing crop for each month but also of the larvae which lived for a time after one sampling but died before the next one, as well as the calorific content of the larval exoskeletons which were molted. The gross productivity also involved assessment of the calorific content of emerging adult insects, which represented an export from the ecosystem. Several aspects of the data gained by Teal from Root Spring are highly significant. The gross ecological efficiency of the second trophic level can be calculated. Since the input flow ($\lambda_2$) is 2300 kcal/m²/yr, and the output energy flow to the next trophic level ($\lambda_3$) is 208 kcal/m²/yr, the gross ecological efficiency of the second trophic level ($\Lambda_2$) is 9 per cent (or $\lambda_3/\lambda_2$ expressed as a percentage). This figure for gross ecological efficiency derived from a natural mixed community, albeit a small one, is remarkably close to the generally predicted figure which was set up as a result of laboratory experimentation by Slobodkin and others.

It is obvious that most natural ecosystems are much more complex than that studied by Teal, and the completion of energy budgets for more than a few of them seems unlikely. However, Howard T. Odum with a team of associates carried out a relatively complete study of the trophic structure and productivity of Silver Springs, Florida, a considerably larger source spring, in which the great bulk of the basic food supply resulted from local photosynthesis. The steady state with a relatively constant standing crop, already discussed (see page 141), means that at most times of the year classical biomass pyramids can be constructed. One such, with the biomass expressed in grams of dry weight per square meter, from Odum's data for Silver Springs, would have 809 grams of plant tissue, 37 grams of herbivores, 11 grams of carnivores, and 1.5 grams of the fourth trophic level (so-called "top carnivores"). Energy-flow figures include a gross plant production of 20,810 kcal/m²/yr, giving a net production after respiration of 8833 kcal/m²/yr. Of this primary productivity, 3368 kcal/m²/yr passed to the second trophic level, 383 kcal/m²/yr to the third trophic level, and 21 kcal/m²/yr to the fourth trophic level, where about 6 kcal/m²/yr was fixed as organic biomass. From these figures the gross ecological efficiencies of the second trophic level—$(\lambda_3/\lambda_2) \times 100$—at 11.4 per cent, and of the third trophic level—$(\lambda_4/\lambda_3) \times 100$—at 5.5 per cent, were computed. Once again these values lie within the range of the predicted hypothesis, and this is also true of the few field determinations of gross ecological efficiency which have been made on other natural communities (but see discussion in Chapter 9).

To recapitulate, freshwater springs have provided a testing ground for the hypothesis that the ratio of the energy content of any trophic level consumed by the next higher trophic level expressed as a percentage of the energy content of the food intake of that lower trophic level would lie around 8–10 per cent for most natural ecosystems. Values of this order were used in our initial consideration of trophic levels and energy transfer (see Chapter 2), and the bases of a predictive theory regarding them will be examined more closely in Chapter 9.

## Organic pollution

Unfortunately, it is appropriate to end this chapter on the productivity of running fresh waters with a brief consideration of water pollution in rivers. This unnecessary misuse of natural waters represents only one of the ways in which the activities of man have modified the ecology of fresh, estuarine, and marine coastal waters.

By far the greater part of such human activities—dredging, damming, water abstraction, modified drainage, and the rest—tends to reduce the productivity of the waters concerned. While much of this must be accepted as a by-product of economic progress, there remains one type of human activity which can never be fully justified: the pollution of natural waters. Throughout Europe and North America, educated public opinion has become increasingly unwilling to regard rivers and estuaries as merely providing cheap means of disposal for unwanted substances. With an "all deliberate speed" increasing somewhat over the last few years, systems of legislation have slowly been forged. In spite of this, there is serious and increasing pollution of waters in the majority of river systems draining into the North Atlantic.

In most cases, two major types of pollution are involved: sewage wastes and effluents from various industrial processes. Unfortunately, the sequence of biological processes which can allow the waters of a river to recover from the effects of pollution with small amounts of raw sewage is in many cases reduced or prevented by concurrence of the second type of waste. The synergic (more than simply additive) effects of sewage wastes and certain toxic industrial effluents occurring together cannot be overemphasized because they are clearly responsible for the worst cases of foul pollution in rivers today.

Obviously, the concentration of the polluting waste determines the effect: small quantities of raw sewage or some other organic wastes may have merely a fertilizing effect on a stream, bringing about a tendency to eutrophy. Similarly, in coastal waters, parts of Long Island Sound and the North Sea probably have increased organic productivity as a result of urban sewage discharge (see pages 102 and 235). All greater concentrations will have adverse effects on the aquatic organisms, but various degrees of these can occur. The pollution may be such as to allow survival of most invertebrate animals normal to the habitat, except the more sensitive fish. Moderate organic pollution of this sort acts almost entirely indirectly through the enhanced processes of bacterial decay bringing about a reduction in the available oxygen in the stream waters. Still greater concentrations may only allow a limited fauna—worms, certain insect larvae, and some leeches—all tolerant of low oxygen conditions. It should be remembered that, particularly in the smaller headstreams, a large proportion of the invertebrates living in running water require high and constant conditions of oxygenation (see page 140). With even greater concentrations of organic wastes, the water will be dark, foul-smelling, thick with suspended matter, and almost totally lacking in dissolved oxygen. No organisms will survive other than a few bacteria and fungi.

It is when sewage pollution reaches this last stage that it becomes of immediate concern to public health. It is noteworthy that the first British legislation against river pollution dates from about the middle of the nineteenth century, at a time when cholera outbreaks were occurring in London.

In many cases where a small town discharges quantities of untreated, or imperfectly treated, sewage into an otherwise clean river, the different conditions mentioned above can (in reverse order) be found downstream of the sewage outfall. There will be a zone of foul, lifeless pollution, a zone of mild pollution with modified fauna and flora, and a recovery zone, with the fauna returned to normal except for the fish. This natural cleansing of the stream usually requires a few miles of distance, considerable aeration, and involves complex food-chains of organisms (for example, waste → bacteria → protozoans → tubificid worms → midge larvae → fish). The relatively large number of trophic levels involved should be noted. Of course, there is now no reason why any small town should discharge imperfectly treated sewage; there are several efficient biological treatments, including percolating filters and the activated sludge process, which will produce a final effluent pure enough to drink. In both North America and Europe, the majority of the larger cities treat most of their sewage effectively, and on both sides of the Atlantic, medium-sized towns and large villages are more usually the offenders as regards sewage pollution. It is not improbable that, if sewage wastes were the only pollutants discharged into our rivers, the worst period of water pollution could have passed already. In other words, in spite of increasing population and increasing urbanization, sewage from a proportionately greater part of the population is being treated each year. As regards the need for conservation of freshwater resources in the future, it is not often realized that a coastal city like New York could exist on a fraction of its present freshwater consumption, if a separate piping system were arranged to use seawater for all sanitary purposes. This is now practicable, using corrosion-resistant plastic piping, and the real cost of fresh water may increase to the point where such a measure becomes necessary.

When we turn from sewage to pollution with industrial wastes, the situation at present is more grim. In more highly industrialized areas, such as the northeastern United States and much of the British Isles and Germany, a fantastic variety of industrial effluents is produced, and a considerable proportion of them discharged without adequate treatment into the rivers of these areas. For example, small quantities of exceedingly toxic substances are discharged. These include salts of copper, lead, and zinc from metal-plating and from synthetic-fiber and rubber processing; free chlorine from laundries and paper mills; sulfides and cyanides from dyeworks; phenols and ammonia from gas and chemical industries; and further strong acids and alkalis from many of these. Less directly toxic but harmful in the large quantities which are discharged are the hot, deoxygenated waters from various industrial coolers; washing slurries from coal-pits; and waste organic matter, not unlike sewage, from paper works, breweries, creameries, and other food-processing plants. It is important to realize that the small amounts of industrial wastes listed in the first group may have the most important biological effects: for example, very small traces of chlorine or phenols or copper are rapidly lethal to the organisms which were mentioned earlier as important in the natural purification of water from sewage or other organic waste. Thus, when occurring together, sewage wastes and certain industrial effluents are synergic in the production of foul pollution.

The effects of such combined pollution are easy to recognize. Both in the eastern United States and in western Europe, there are many small rivers with, on their slow-flowing stretches, a dirty scum on the surface which, wherever there is a small fall or riffle, becomes churned up into thick masses of evil-smelling soapy foam. Further upstream, such a river has received untreated sewage or relatively large amounts of organic matter discharged with the washing waters from the processing of pulp in paper mills. Possibly both laundries and paper works have discharged some chlorine and ammonia, and the latter, some diluted caustic soda. Other industries may or may not have contributed some lead or copper salts or some cyanides. However, even a little chlorine— or traces of any of the others—is sufficient to kill off the bacteria and other organisms which could break down the organic material. Instead, the organic wastes combine with the soda or other dilute alkali to form a sort of soap. The presence of a little detergent will only add to the texture of the foamy scum and make it additionally difficult for normal processes of bacterial decomposition to take place anywhere along the length of the river and its estuary. As already mentioned (see page 105), the hydrological conditions in estuaries cause polluting matter which has arrived there to be very persistent. The noxious materials may float downstream with the ebbtide, but much returns upstream again with the flow.

Unless legislation against water pollution is made effective in the near future, the characteristic results of combined pollution may become even more widespread. There are several relatively new threats to the health of rivers. Agricultural use of insecticides and weed-killers can create runoff waters indistinguishable in their biological effects from the more toxic industrial wastes. Among insecticides, the chlorinated hydrocarbons such as DDT, dieldrin, and lindane present a greater threat of environmental pollution than do the more deadly organophosphate "nerve-poisons" such as parathion and malathion. The principal reason for this is that the organophosphates are degradable, and thus neither accumulate in environments nor are transmitted along food-chains to accumulate in animal tissues. The chlorinated hydrocarbons, on the other hand, have considerable chemical and biological stability which can result in the toxic accumulation of concentrations in the fatty tissues of vertebrates at distances of hundreds or thousands of miles from the source. Thus, in the late 1960's, near-extinction of natural populations of the peregrine falcon in Europe and North America and the condemnation of coho salmon from Lake Michigan as unfit for human consumption are but two results of about twenty years of extensive use of DDT as an insecticide.

The expansion of nuclear power will certainly create increasing problems in the disposal of radioactive wastes, and some types of atomic plants will also produce warmed and deoxygenated waters—with the same energetic inefficiency as other industries—from their cooling circulation systems. Such pollution is more likely to be important in estuaries and coastal marine waters. As regards the disposal of radioactive wastes in any aquatic environment, it is clear that one cannot entirely rely on uniform dilution by the volume of the lake, river, or ocean. The capacity of living organisms to concentrate substances by many orders of magnitude must be taken into account. Aquatic plants and invertebrates concentrate calcium, silicon, manganese, and many other elements from the medium in which they live. The problem is complicated by interactions of minerals, particularly by biological uptake of an element in relation to the concentration of a related element. An obvious example is the increased uptake of strontium which may occur in a medium with low calcium concentration. This is illustrated on land by the increased deposition of strontium (including radioactive strontium) which has occurred in the bones of sheep and deer pastured on calcium-poor land. The secretion of shells by those molluscs living in aquatic environments with low calcium concentrations may similarly lead to a disproportionate concentration of strontium. In general terms, we already have sufficient ecological and physiological knowledge to control the more usual forms of water pollution by the effective administration of appropriate legislation. As regards radioactive pollution, the problems are not yet widespread, but much immediate research on rates of turnover, both in the metabolic cycles of individual organisms and in the biogeochemical cycles of whole communities, is required if appropriate controls are to be available in time.

# A closer look at the biogeochemistry of some elements

MODERN PHYSICS has pushed the number of elements to well over a hundred, but the number naturally occurring on the Earth's surface remains below ninety. It is not improbable that all of these occur in seawater, though many of them must be present only in fantastically low concentrations. About fifty-five can be detected by the more normal methods of chemical analysis.

All living organisms are made up of carbohydrates, fats, and proteins. These can be subjected to elemental analysis and it appears that some twenty elements are invariably present as constituents of the three classes of organic molecules in the more complex plants and animals. Another twenty elements are known to occur in organic molecules in organisms, but are not universally distributed and are presumably nonessential. Finally, at least seven more elements are found in living organisms and, since it is thought that they are not combined in organic molecules, these are often regarded as contaminants of the organisms in which they occur. In all, over sixty elements have been found in one or more species of living organisms.

When we consider only the forty elements commonly involved in organic materials, the majority of even the invariably occurring, or "essential," elements make up only a tiny fraction of the mass of organisms. On a dry-weight basis, only five elements are present in the organic tissues of the majority of living organisms at levels greater than 1 per cent. These are carbon, oxygen, hydrogen, nitrogen, and phosphorus, in that order. At levels ranging from 1 in 2000 to 1 in 100, we have eight more elements: sulfur, chlorine, potassium, sodium, calcium, magnesium, iron, and copper. Lastly, at levels normally amounting to less than 1 in 2000 parts of the dry organic weight, but still apparently essential, are seven more elements: boron, manganese, zinc, silicon, cobalt, iodine, and fluorine. For a few other elements there is some evidence that certain aquatic primary producers require trace quantities, and these include strontium, molybdenum, bromine, vanadium, titanium, aluminum, and gallium. Perhaps all of these and a few others from the "variable occurrence" list should be transferred to our list of *essential* microconstituents. To recapitulate, ranked in these groups by their fractional weights, we have:

$$C, O, H, N, P,$$

then: $$S, Cl, K, Na, Ca, Mg, Fe, Cu,$$

then: $$B, Mn, Zn, Si, Co, I, F,$$

and perhaps then: $$Sr, Mo, Br, V, Ti, Al, Ga.$$

Given the ready availability of carbon dioxide and of water, it is obvious why the usual limiting nutrient salts of aquatic productivity are the assimilable forms of the two remaining primary constituent elements: nitrates and phosphates. Suitable compounds or ions of the eight secondary elemental constituents (forming the second line above) are available in most aquatic environments and are rarely limiting, although—even in seawater—energy must be expended by some organisms to concentrate calcium and potassium from the environment, and considerable work done in gaining even small amounts of iron and of copper salts. In most fresh waters, *all* of this secondary group require a considerable concentration by primary producers from the usual low levels of the environment. If we turn to the microconstituents (the third and fourth lines above), most of them occur inorganically in very low concentrations, and availability of suitable salts of many of them can create limiting conditions for productivity. In the cases of a few of these elements, the biological significance of this is known to depend on their role as constituents of important enzymes, or otherwise in near-universal metabolic processes. Boron is required in the successful growth of both diatoms and higher plants, and seems to be implicated in the formation of cellulose cell walls. Manganese and silica are necessary for diatom growth, and availability of the latter can be a limiting factor in fresh waters (see page 136). Zinc is a constituent of certain essential enzymes, including carbonic anhydrase, and glutamate, alcohol, and other dehydrogenases. The molecule of vitamin $B_{12}$, or cyanocobalamin, contains cobalt. Molybdenum, cobalt, and vanadium are all known components of certain enzymes involved in nitrogen metabolism in plants and have been similarly implicated in bacterial processes.

## Cycle pattern and carbon

The biogeochemical cycling of most of these elements follows a similar pattern. Most usual cycles involve an element in alternate incorporation in inorganic salts in the environmental medium and in organic molecules as part of the biomass of the ecosystem. Normally, the inorganic form is first taken out of the abiotic environment by an autotrophic green plant, and returns to it after passage through the units of a short or long food-chain as a result of the activities of decomposing bacteria. In an admittedly crude generalization, the rates of cycling—for the secondary constituent elements, at least—are inversely related to the concentrations (as annual average values) of those elements in the environment. This is not strictly true of the rates for carbon, nitrogen, and phosphorus in the open waters of the oceans. As we shall try to quantify below, the annual biological turnover of carbon dioxide in the world's oceans amounts to only about 1 per cent of the total carbon present as bicarbonate, carbonate, and molecular carbon dioxide. On the other hand, in the surface waters of most areas of the seas, the available nitrates and phosphates do not amount to the levels which are turned over in each season. Thus in temperate waters in summer, and in tropical seas throughout the year, the factors limiting primary productivity are clearly the concentrations of these nutrients. In different areas of the seas it would appear that each year soluble nitrogen compounds are turned over from one to ten times annually, while the available phosphates are turned over from one to four times. It is obvious from this, that the gross total amount of carbon fixed in any one year does not accumulate, but that the standing crop of carbon in the biomass at any one time is determined by the availability of the other nutrient salts. One aspect of the rather paradoxical rates of turnover of these three elements is that the relative proportions of the elements in diatoms, and indeed in other phytoplankton organisms, growing in the open ocean is relatively constant. By weight, we have a proportion for carbon to nitrogen to phosphorus of $41:7:1$. Somewhat surprisingly, the elementary composition of mixed zoöplankton feeding on them is closely similar. As H. W. Harvey first pointed out, at Plymouth, and as Alfred C. Redfield and his colleagues clearly demonstrated for the Gulf of Maine, the ratio of nitrate to phosphate is not only similar in phytoplankton and in zoöplankton, but it is relatively constant in samples of seawater taken from any of the world's oceans. As Redfield pointed out, the phytoplankton thus takes up nutrients in the ratio in which they are divided in the water and when plankton animals or plants die and decompose, these materials are restored to the water in the same ratio. As might be expected, the ratios are modified locally in inshore waters: the ratio of available nitrogen to available phosphorus can range from $10:1$ to $6:1$. Further, as Bostwick H. Ketchum first demonstrated some thirty years ago, phytoplankton cells can be "deficient" in either element, and the ratio of nitrogen to phosphorus is not fixed but can vary with the relative concentrations in the medium. To sum up, turnover rates for two of the primary constituent elements, nitrogen and phosphorus, are relatively high, and must vary from place to place, though within the restriction of a proportionality between the two elements in the plankton biomass which has only limited flexibility. Questions of fixed or facultative elemental ratios are of some significance with regard to the nutrition of higher trophic levels, and these will be discussed after brief consideration of the biogeochemical cycles for a few important elements.

The world's organic carbon cycle was briefly considered in Chapter 2 (see page 13 and Figure $2 \cdot 1$). Another simplified version of the carbon dioxide cycle is presented in Figure $8 \cdot 1$. As already discussed, carbon dioxide is liberated into the medium as a result not only of the respiratory exchanges of heterotrophs, both animals and bacteria, but also as a result of the respiratory activities of plants themselves. A small proportion is returned by the nonbiological oxidation of dissolved organic materials resulting from autolysis or partial bacterial breakdown. The corresponding uptake of carbon dioxide from the environment is almost entirely due to the photosynthetic activities of green plants.

Marine photosynthesis, probably corresponding to about 75–80 per cent of the world's productivity, can be estimated to involve between $6.5 \times 10^{10}$ and $2.6 \times 10^{11}$ tons of carbon dioxide annually, equivalent to a carbon fixation in seawater of between $17.5 \times 10^9$ and $7 \times 10^{10}$ tons of carbon per year. (These and other global figures will be discussed more fully in Chapter 12.) Such figures are about three orders of magnitude smaller than the total content of carbon dioxide in the world's oceans, which can be estimated to amount to $1.3 \times 10^{14}$ tons, or about 50 times as much as is present in the atmosphere at any one time. Thus it is obvious why the availability of carbon dioxide is never a limiting factor for primary productivity in the sea.

Although phytoplankton organisms in active photosynthesis have a ratio of carbon dioxide uptake to oxygen liberation which is close to unity, it is erroneous to assume that this implies a direct relationship as is suggested in older textbooks. An early result of radiotracer experiments on photosynthesis was the demonstration that the free oxygen evolved came from the water molecules taken up and not from those of carbon dioxide. It is worth emphasizing this from the point of view of the physical chemistry involved in the most fundamental processes of bioenergetics. The proof that all the oxygen evolved comes from water and none of it from carbon dioxide implies that the carbon

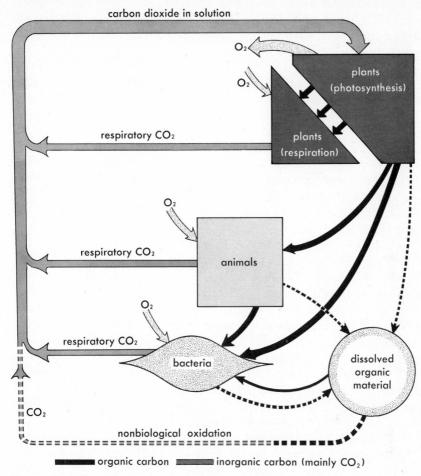

**Figure 8·1. The organic cycle of carbon dioxide.** Uptake of carbon dioxide from the environment is almost entirely due to the photosynthetic activities of green plants, while carbon dioxide is liberated as a result of the respiratory exchanges of bacteria, animals, and plants and, to a limited extent, by nonbiological oxidations. Compare with Figures 2·4 and 8·3.

dioxide is taken integrally into the green plant to be reduced by hydrogen derived entirely from the water. Without attempting to survey the sequential series of processes by which light energy is captured and then transformed into chemical energy, we can state that the overall process of photosynthesis implies the utilization of energy to split the $H_2O$ molecule into hydrogen and oxygen atoms, the former then being used to reduce the carbon dioxide to glucose (water being the electron-donor). Looked at in this way, the total process of photosynthesis is essentially the reverse of the energy-releasing, or respiratory, processes common to plants and animals. If respiration is surveyed in this overall fashion, it always involves the release from substrates of hydrogen which then combines with oxygen at the end of the respiratory sequence; considerable amounts of energy are released, and the final electron-acceptor is molecular oxygen—the final donor being cytochrome oxidase—and the end chemical result is the formation of water.

Other kinds of biological photosynthesis occur. Although they contribute only an infinitesimally minute fraction to total productivity, as compared to that from green plant photosynthesis, their chemistry is revealing and significant in relation to the above generalizations on green plant photosynthesis and on respiration. The so-called *purple* bacteria, which occur on mudflats in estuaries, salt marshes, and elsewhere, do not split water molecules and liberate oxygen during their photosynthesis of simple sugars; instead, they split molecules of hydrogen sulfide ($H_2S$) and release elemental sulfur.

The regeneration part of the carbon cycle (upper left of Figure $8 \cdot 1$) involves the passage of carbon dioxide in solution in the medium; and, as already stressed, oceanic waters represent a reservoir of carbon dioxide corresponding to about a century's uptake by existing marine green plants. In fact, seawater contains carbon dioxide as undissociated molecules of $CO_2$, as carbonic acid, and as bicarbonate and carbonate ions. At any given pH, they are all in equilibrium with each other and with the hydrogen ions present. The concentration of carbon dioxide molecules is normally about 100 times that of carbonic acid, and at normal pH levels for the upper water layers of the open oceans (8.1 or 8.2) there will be about 10 times as many carbonate ions as undissociated gas molecules and 100 times as many bicarbonate ions. The system is a buffered one in seawater, and borate ions are also involved. A locally intensive withdrawal of carbon dioxide from seawater—for example, during a phytoplankton increase—involves a local pH increase with bicarbonate ions changing to carbonate and a dissociation of boric acid. In most cases, the bulk of the carbon intake of the plants will have been provided by the change of bicarbonate ions into carbonate ions locally. In normal oceanic situations, reequilibration of the carbon dioxide system occurs rapidly. Of course, the local effects of intensive photosynthesis can be more marked in lake waters, and involve indirect effects on other ions in solution, for example, in the deposition of calcium carbonate on and around photosynthetic surfaces in "hard" fresh waters. In most other respects, the carbon cycle in lakes is essentially similar to that in the sea.

The rate of absorption of carbon dioxide by seawater is surprisingly low, and minor changes in either the atmosphere or the oceans would take many years to equilibrate. This is thought by some meteorologists

to have some significance in the major climatic cycles of the whole
Earth's hydrosphere, each of which takes between 40,000 and 60,000
years. It is advanced as a hypothesis that increased amounts of carbon
dioxide in the atmosphere bring about a so-called "greenhouse" effect,
increasing the amount of infrared radiation which is absorbed and
warming the atmosphere. This causes recession of glaciers and icecaps,
increasing the volume of water in the oceans, which then reabsorb the
excess carbon dioxide, and a cycle of cooling begins. Both processes
involving changes of sea level—glacier recession and reglaciation—are
even slower than carbon dioxide equilibration of the oceans and require
some thousands of years for completion. Since glacier ice can contain
very little carbon dioxide, a cycle of climatic oscillation (with a period
of about 50,000 years) will tend to be repeated again and again as
long as the total amount of carbon dioxide in the atmosphere plus the
oceans does not markedly change. However, during the last one
hundred years of consumption of fossil fuels (coal and oil) man has
added about $3.6 \times 10^{11}$ tons of carbon dioxide to the atmosphere—an
increase of about 13 per cent. According to calculations based on the
"greenhouse" theory of increased atmospheric carbon dioxide, this
should have caused a rise in the surface temperatures of the entire
world by about one Fahrenheit degree. There exist many detailed
records of the century from 1860 which indicate that exactly this rise
has occurred, although atmospheric carbon dioxide is probably not
the only causal factor, and there may have been a fall in the last
decade. An extrapolated calculation based on present rates of increase
in fuel consumption would suggest that proportionate increased
release of carbon dioxide into the atmosphere could raise average
temperatures by 3.6°F by the year 2000 if the hypothesis is correct.
At present, we simply do not have good evidence on the rate at which
compensating factors, such as rise of sea level, could modify this. Once
again, our species is proceeding with a major alteration of environmental conditions by "atmospheric pollution" without any clear assessment of the long-term results. With this confession of our inability to test
the "greenhouse" theory other than by allowing changes to happen for
another thirty years, let us turn from carbon to the biogeochemistry of
other elements.

## The nitrogen cycle

The biogeochemical cycle of nitrogenous substances was briefly examined in Chapter 2, and Figure 2·4 remains a reasonably complete
though stylized representation of the exchanges occurring in aquatic
environments. As is the case with other essential elements, inorganic
salts of nitrogen, particularly nitrates, are taken up by green plants

where nitrogenous organic materials—principally amino acids, the components of proteins—are first synthesized. These are then passed through successive trophic levels, with organic nitrogenous compounds being liberated by excretion and by death at all levels. Bacterial action is usually necessary to bring about the initial remineralization as ammonium ions, and a sequence of bacterial forms is involved in successive changes to nitrites and then to nitrates. Ammonium-nitrogen can be used by many types of phytoplankton cells as an alternative to, or along with, nitrates. Nitrites can be absorbed by a few species but probably involve less efficient utilization. In spite of the fact that all three inorganic nitrogen compounds can be utilized by autotrophs, the nitrogen cycle is much more dependent on initial and sequential bacterial breakdown than are the carbon, phosphorus, sulfur, or other cycles, where assimilable inorganic compounds are directly liberated by autolysis on the death of organisms (or by respiration in the case of carbon). Thus, under any conditions, recycling of combined nitrogen is likely to be slower as a result of the need for bacterial remineralization. In the sea, proportionately less nitrogen than phosphorus is likely to be remineralized within the photosynthetic zone. A minor exception to this is involved in the ammonium-nitrogen compounds excreted as

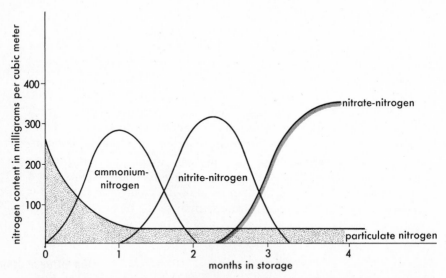

**Figure 8·2. Sequential bacterial decomposition** of nitrogenous materials. Particulate organic material (from diatoms) was stored in the dark in near natural concentrations, and bacterial production of ammonium-nitrogen was followed by its conversion to nitrites and thence finally to nitrates. The sequence is relatively slow and in the open sea takes place outside the photosynthetic zone. [After T. von Brand, H. W. Rakestraw, and C. E. Renn in *Biol. Bull.*, 72:165–175, 1937.]

such by some marine animals as a consequence of metabolic breakdown of proteins.

In a number of sea areas where nutrient cycles have been studied,
it is clear that availability of nitrogen compounds is the factor limiting
productivity in summer rather than availability of phosphates or any
other nutrients. In these cases complete exhaustion of ammonium-
nitrogen, nitrates, and nitrites occurs in the surface layers during summer, and there is a slight surplus of phosphates over available nitrogen
for the requirements of the phytoplankton in these areas. In view of
this, it seems significant that certain phytoplankton organisms, cultured in the laboratory, readily utilize all three inorganic compounds
as alternative sources of nitrogen. In conditions where they have become nitrogen-deficient, such plant cells will absorb either ammonium
or nitrate in the dark and immediately convert it into organic compounds including chlorophyll. Nitrite can be utilized, but not in the
dark.

In the open oceans, the great bulk of remineralization takes place
immediately below the compensation level and usually involves sequential bacterial oxidations ending in nitrates which are then recycled
to the euphotic zone in winter or by upwelling. A series of laboratory
experiments on this bacterial sequence were carried out by Theodor
von Brand and his associates, and Figure 8·2 summarizes some results
of their work. It follows the sequence of changes which occur during
bacterial decomposition in the dark of particulate organic nitrogenous
materials derived from diatoms and stored, at near natural concentrations, in seawater. Ammonia is first produced and then converted to
nitrite and thence to nitrate, the whole sequence taking over three
months. In more complex experiments, where the processes were interrupted by periods in the light and with reinoculation with a few
living diatoms, the regeneration always took place in the same sequence. It is important to realize that nitrate-forming bacteria are
present in considerable numbers from the beginning of all such experiments, but their activities do not become apparent until after the peak
in bacterial conversion to nitrite is passed. To recapitulate, the need for
initial bacterial action in the recycling of organic nitrogen, and the
pattern of this relatively slow sequence of bacterial oxidations taking
place outside the photosynthetic zone, are together of major importance
in limiting the productivity of the oceans. Almost the opposite is true
of many lakes, where phosphate may be locked up, as discussed in
Chapter 6, and the waters in consequence may have a considerable
surplus of salts containing nitrogen. In these cases, the availability of
nitrogen salts is obviously not limiting.

In general, the biogeochemical cycle of nitrogen is self-regulating,
and the total amounts of combined nitrogen in the whole ecosystem

relatively unchanging. In most seas, gain of combined nitrogen appears to exceed the losses (see Figure 2·4). Much of the short-term regulation of the nitrogen cycle depends on the vertical separation of the major levels of remineralization from those of plant utilization, but also upon the existence of "feedback" bacterial activities. These include nitrate-reducing bacteria which can produce nitrite under conditions of relatively rich food supply. Other bacteria are able to fix atmospheric nitrogen and add it to the cycle, while others—the denitrifying forms—can set free gaseous nitrogen as a result of the reduction of nitrates and nitrites, again in the presence of a rich food supply as a source of energy. It is not likely that the activities of nitrogen-fixing or nitrogen-liberating bacteria are ever important in the open waters of the oceans, although the nitrogen cycle in semienclosed waters and estuaries may well be modified by their activities. Such processes represent links between the relatively rapid biological cycling of combined nitrogen and the immense and relatively unchanging reserves of gaseous nitrogen in the atmosphere. Thus they could be of significance in the long-term regulation of the nitrogen cycle.

## The phosphorus cycle

As already discussed, the biological cycle of phosphorus is somewhat simpler and more direct than that of combined nitrogen (Figure 8·3). Again, compared with nitrogen, phosphorus is a rare element, and the ratio of combined nitrogen to phosphorus ranges from 6:1 to 10:1 in the sea and averages about 23:1 in natural fresh waters. Once again we have organic compounds of the element first synthesized in plants and passed through successive trophic levels. Once again bacterial activity is largely responsible for the regeneration of inorganic compounds to be taken up by plants. In this case almost all the phosphorus utilized by the phytoplankton is taken up as orthophosphate ions. However, some autotrophic cells may be able to take up and utilize molecules of dissolved organic phosphate.

Under certain conditions, mechanical breakdown of plant or animal tissues may make inorganic phosphate available for new plant growth without the need for bacterial action. This occurs when the processes liberate not only organic phosphate compounds from the tissues but also phosphatase enzymes which can continue to work extracellularly. Orthophosphate will often rapidly dissolve out from moribund plant tissues and from some animals immediately after death. It has previously been noted that, under natural conditions in the sea, considerable quantities of diatoms and other phytoplankon organisms are destroyed in grazing by copepods but not utilized. In

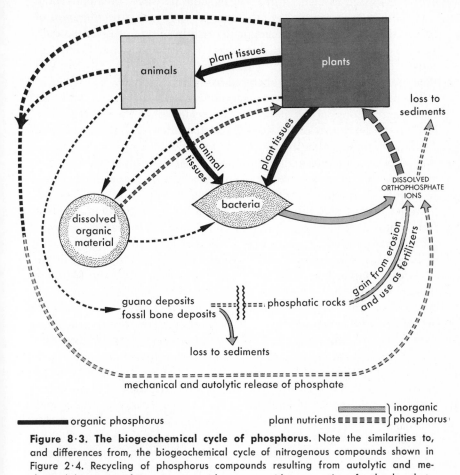

**Figure 8·3. The biogeochemical cycle of phosphorus.** Note the similarities to, and differences from, the biogeochemical cycle of nitrogenous compounds shown in Figure 2·4. Recycling of phosphorus compounds resulting from autolytic and mechanical destruction of tissues can provide a very rapid regeneration of orthophosphate ions as plant nutrients in certain circumstances.

addition, the faecal pellets of zoöplankton organisms often contain much undigested phytoplankton tissues. Once again, both orthophosphate and dissolved organic phosphorus compounds rapidly leach out from the destroyed plant cells and defecated plant material. Recently, D. H. Cushing has claimed that, under certain conditions in the North Sea, the destruction of diatoms by grazing copepods provides a necessary immediate regeneration of phosphorus compounds which can maintain the rate of plant turnover. Obviously, this implies a declining standing crop, but otherwise resembles a human artifact—algal culture in a chemostat. It is also significant that the plant detritus which we earlier discussed as being important in some inshore food-chains (and also those in fresh waters) is often coated with a rich proliferation of bacterial cells, themselves exceptionally rich in phosphorus compounds. If such detritus particles are not consumed by an animal before the supply of organic carbon runs out, then the bacterial cells die and their phosphorus is rapidly liberated as orthophosphate.

For these and other reasons, recycling of phosphorus is relatively rapid, and a considerable part of it can occur above the compensation level in the proximity of the actively photosynthesizing phytoplankton. As already noted, phosphorus can become permanently locked up in lake deposits, and a small proportion of the phosphorus in deeper waters in the sea is lost to the biological cycle by incorporation into sediments. A small amount of phosphorus is added annually to the marine cycle as a result of freshwater drainage. Some of this comes from natural erosion of phosphate-containing rocks but more from drainage from land receiving phosphatic fertilizers in agriculture.

The availability of phosphorus is most clearly a limiting factor in the majority of larger lakes and in certain enclosed seas like the Mediterranean, but not in the majority of sea areas. On the global scale, however, when the long-term future of land and aquatic vegetation including crops is considered, perhaps phosphorus is the element most likely to be deficient and to limit primary productivity. Its biogeochemistry is unusual in that phosphate ions appear to go through whole biological recycling and biogeochemical cycles in geological time without being further oxidized or ever being reduced. Within living organisms, phosphate is uniquely important in energy transfers and this simply emphasizes its ecological significance as an ion (and element) in geochemical short supply. Once again, as G. Evelyn Hutchinson has pointed out, this is a case where the activities of man are accelerating an apparently irreversible loss. A considerable part of the phosphate rocks quarried and used as agricultural fertilizer is washed away and eventually goes to increase the amounts lost to new sediments. Human activities have also reduced the extent of another—though more minor—part of the cycle: the transfer of phosphorus and other materials by seabirds to guano deposits on arid lands is not continuing at the rates sustained in historic or recent geological times (see Chapter 5).

## Silicon and other cycles

As already noted, the cases enclosing diatom cells, termed the tests or frustules, are siliceous. In different kinds of aquatic environments, various diatom species have to concentrate silica from the environmental medium to extents which vary from $10^4$ to $10^6$ times. In a broad generalization, the availability of silica can only rarely be the limiting factor in the sea, but can more commonly be a limiting factor of diatom production—though not of all primary productivity—in certain fresh waters (see page 115).

In the open waters of the seas, silicon occurs as silica, probably in true solution as orthosilicate ions rather than in any colloidal form. Seasonal changes in its concentration in seawater are marked. Over-winter values 200–400 mg per cubic meter in the English Channel can fall after the SDI as low as 10 mg per cubic meter in the water layers above the compensation level. Subsequently, through the sum-mer, concentrations of silica in the surface waters vary widely; al-though they parallel the fluctuations in concentration of the other nutrient salts, the fluctuations in silica concentration are of much greater amplitude than those for assimilable nitrogen salts. This prob-ably implies that, to an even greater extent than is the case with phos-phates, silica is rapidly regenerated in the illuminated layers of the sea soon after the death, or damage by grazing, of the diatoms of a local increase. Apart from this rapid recycling in summer surface waters, high concentrations of silica in the sea during the growing season occur in the waters near the bottom and seem to result from chemical breakdown of dead plant frustules rather than the bacterial action which is simultaneously liberating nitrogen salts and phosphate.

As is true of other plant nutrient salts in the sea, some of the highest concentrations of silica naturally occurring in the oceans are found in the Antarctic deep water. In the majority of cases of upwellings (see page 99), the nutrient-rich cold waters are also characterized by high silica concentrations. High concentrations of silica have also been re-ported for several regions of the Pacific ocean, in areas not charac-terized by high values for nitrogen salts or phosphate.

When we turn to fresh waters, the importance of available silica in limiting primary productivity is much more clearly established, and the effects of this on waterworks management have already been noted (see page 136). In spite of the greater variability in the phytoplankton of smaller bodies of fresh water, diatoms dominate primary production in medium-sized and large lakes. In all such lakes there is marked depletion of silica in the summer months in the surface waters, al-though the details of recycling vary both with the trophic condition and the seasonal temperature stratification of the lake. Although the nature of soluble silica in lake waters is inadequately understood—particularly with regard to the proportions of orthosilicate ions, com-plex ions, and colloidal silica—it is clear that in its annual lacustrine cycle it parallels that of the other nutrients. The depleted surface waters are recharged with silica during temperature overturns, the free dissolved nutrient being regenerated (below the lit zone and thermocline) on and near the bottom. There can be some "locking-up" of silica in bottom muds, and in eutrophic lakes of moderate size the anaerobic and relatively high-temperature conditions near the bottom in summer will cause release of silica to the waters from the muds.

Considered on a global scale for the future, silica need never be a limiting nutrient in *total* aquatic productivity. It is abundant in crustal rocks, and although only a tiny proportion of this can become available through chemical erosion in a suitable soluble form, even this potential fraction is large in relation to the needs of diatom productivity.

A number of the other minor constituents of seawater and of aquatic organisms can—usually under rather special conditions—become limiting nutrients of plant production. One of the best known of these is manganese, and culture experiments with such diatoms as *Thalassiosira* and *Ditylum* have demonstrated the existence of minimum concentration levels of the element for successful growth and reproduction. Some reported concentrations of manganese in particular sea areas, including several parts of the Pacific, lie below the minimum levels established by the culture experiments. The situation is somewhat similar with regard to suitable salts of iron, which occur at very low concentrations in seawater. Some dubieties about the physiology of uptake of iron by single-celled plants give rise to some uncertainty about the element's ecological status as a limiting nutrient. It is probable that most iron in the sea exists as colloidal (and insoluble) ferric hydroxide. There is some circumstantial evidence that diatoms have some mechanism for taking in the extremely insoluble hydroxide through their cell membranes, but direct evidence on this is unsatisfactory. However, H. W. Harvey has concluded that growth of phytoplankton may be limited by the availability of iron in some parts of the open oceans.

There are several essential constituent elements which are always available in sufficient quantity for marine productivity, but whose biogeochemistry has some significant features. Among these is calcium, present throughout the oceans in solution to an extent limited only by the solubility of calcium carbonate. Diatom increases and other changes of production rates in both plants and animals produce changes in calcium concentrations in the sea similar to those in the nutrient salts but always of lesser amplitude. In other words, in the sea, no primary production is inhibited by lack of calcium. Land drainage is continually bringing in calcium to the ocean waters, and inshore waters may show local precipitation as a result. In other cases, supersaturation with calcium occurs and cases of this have been extensively reported from tropical waters. On the other hand, at the lower pH values of the deepest waters of the oceans, undersaturation occurs, and calcium carbonate can be dissolved out from the bottom deposits. In a few situations, calcareous organisms living in the surface waters can cause local reduction of calcium concentrations and affect the specific alkalinity. With some very small exceptions, all the calcareous rocks of the Earth's surface seem to have resulted from deposition as a result of biological activity in aquatic environments, the majority marine. If we consider the biogeochemistry of calcium on a world scale, the turnover through sediments is slow, but overall, sufficient calcium is available for even greatly increased aquatic productivity. The case of dissolved calcium salts in fresh waters is markedly different from that in the sea, largely because differential distribution of calcareous rocks being eroded on land surfaces results in some fresh waters being highly calcareous, or hard, and others being extremely low in calcium (and indeed in all mineral-salt content), or soft. Actual concentrations of calcium in natural fresh waters can range over two orders of magnitude, from less than 0.5 gram per cubic meter to more than 100 grams per cubic meter. As discussed in Chapter 6, the productivity of lakes is affected by the calcium content of their waters, and the characteristic animal species of hard fresh waters may be quite distinct from—though congeneric with—those of softer waters. In general, a moderately high calcium content is associated with eutrophy in the most productive lakes, and a greater species diversity at all trophic levels is characteristic of hard fresh waters.

Many species of freshwater animals, however, can survive and breed in waters with a wide variety of levels of calcium content, and these include forms which must take in largish quantities of calcium for the secretion of skeletons or of shells. In the last few years, my associates and I have been investigating various aspects of growth and metabolism in natural populations of freshwater snails. In one snail species, the extremely euryoecic *Lymnaea peregra,* the thickness (and mass) of the calcareous shell varies according to the amount of calcium available in the waters. In other words, since metabolism of calcium by such freshwater snails and its mobilization for shell-making involve an active direct uptake, then *Lymnaea* probably spends about the same amount of energy in forming its shells no matter the hardness of the water in which it is living. In some soft fresh waters, its shell is obviously so poorly calcified as to be less valuable in protection. We have recently investigated the strikingly different case of a common freshwater limpet, *Ferrissia rivularis,* in a series of natural populations in freshwater creeks in upstate New York, the mineral contents of which are very different. Significant differences between populations of this limpet species occur in their shells. These differences in calcium uptake during growth are not related to differences in environmental concentrations of calcium, and so the concentration ratios (of incorporated calcium to calcium in the environmental waters) can range in this one species from 1609:1 to 10,615:1, implying that the latter limpets have expended approximately 6.6 times more metabolic energy on transport of calcium than those in the former population of the same species. There is circumstantial evidence that these differences may involve genetically determined physiological races, and I believe this to be related to aspects of the peculiar evolution of many freshwater animals (see Chapter 11). We have recently found that the noncalcareous part of the shell, which is proteinaceous, similarly varies from population to population and is not inversely correlated with the calcium content of the shell. In other words, the chances of genetic dispersal among the isolated creek populations of this species have resulted in some rather inappropriate shells in specific environments.

The demonstration that there are considerable interpopulation infra-specific variations in calcium metabolism in animals like freshwater snails involves two significant aspects. In the course of their active uptake of calcium, these organisms also take in strontium without discrimination. Somewhat more strontium is taken from waters of low calcium content. One of the pollutants of the nuclear age is radioactive strontium, which is peculiarly dangerous to man and other vertebrates because, exchanging with calcium in bone tissue, it can cause damage to the very susceptible blood-cell-forming tissues in the bone marrow and elsewhere. Molluscs such as our limpets are possible indicators of environmental radiocontamination with strontium-90, their usefulness as indicators depending on their direct uptake of the radionuclide rather than receiving it after sequential transport through several trophic levels in a food-chain. Thus it is important that some such limpet species have populations which differ signficantly from each other in the extent to which they *do* concentrate calcium (and, therefore, strontium-90) from the environment. Another significant aspect of infraspecific physiological variation of this sort (with regard to theories of evolutionary rates) will be discussed in Chapter 11.

There is an ample supply in seawater of boron, zinc, copper, and several other essential trace elements. The supply in the majority of fresh waters is probably also adequate, though there may be some exceptional cases in soft-water lakes. On the other hand, certain other trace elements can affect productivity in the sea under certain circumstances and these include molybdenum and probably also gallium. Gordon A. Riley has demonstrated that the latter element had little or no effect on the growth of the diatom *Nitzschia* when ample phosphates and nitrates were available, but that it stimulated growth and multiplication when the diatom was in nutrient-deficient cultures. There may well be several other cases where the importance of a trace element is greatly enhanced in conditions of low concentrations of any of the major nutrients. Still other trace elements—such as copper and vanadium—may be of greater importance to certain invertebrate animals at intermediate trophic levels in the sea than they are to the primary producers.

## Bacterial geochemistry

There could be no recycling of nutrients and other constituent elements were it not for the activities of bacteria as decomposers and remineralizers. As Louis Pasteur emphasized (see the preface of this book and Chapter 2), the mere death of living organisms would be incomplete without decomposition. Since Pasteur's time, bacteria have mostly had a "bad press," and to most laymen, the word implies the hundred or so forms which are human pathogens. The many thousands of forms in the sea, in other natural waters, and in the soils, which together make up an average standing-crop biomass at least $10^{10}$ times that of the disease bacteria, are mostly decomposers and all "helpful bacteria" to man and indeed to all higher organisms. On the basis of our earlier discussions of nutrient recycling, we can consider a hypothetical situation—purely fictional science and impossible in nature. If all decomposer-bacteria ceased their activities for only three months, then nearly all green plant production on this planet would cease almost immediately, and no higher animal (including man) could survive the temporary interruption of bacteria recycling.

In this chapter on biogeochemical cycles, it is worth trying to summarize trophic and distributional aspects of the marine bacterial flora. The bacteria of fresh waters differ in many regards, but the broad picture of aquatic decomposition has some universal features.

The great bulk of marine bacteria are heterotrophic. Autotrophic bacteria are found in limited and specialized environments—a few chemosynthetic forms on the sea bottom and a few photosynthetic forms inshore, largely on tidal mudflats. Perhaps the most important are the purple bacteria referred to above (see page 158), but the contribution of all autotrophic bacteria to the primary food supply is negligible. Heterotrophic forms—discussed collectively and loosely as decomposers in the earlier parts of this book—show a rather characteristic pattern of vertical distribution in the open waters of the oceans (see Figure 8·4). In the most intensely illuminated surface waters, there are relatively few bacteria. There are many more lower in the euphotic zone, and very high bacterial counts are found immediately below the levels of maximum diatom photosynthesis and growth. There is still a very high concentration of bacterial cells immediately below the compensation level of the phytoplankton, and then the numbers fall off into the depths of the ocean, being relatively scarce at intermediate depths of between 300 and 2000 meters. However, the greatest num-

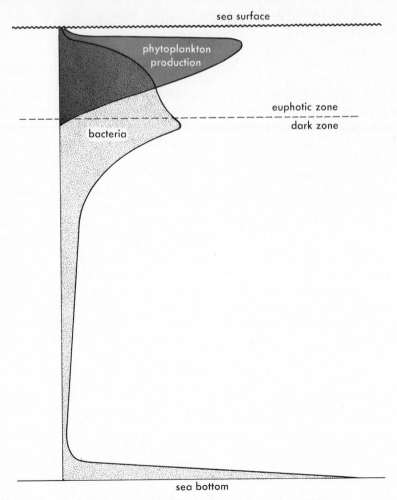

**Figure 8·4. Distribution of decomposer-bacteria in the open sea.** Very high bacterial counts are found immediately below the levels of maximum diatom growth, the numbers fall off in the intensely illuminated surface waters and also in inter-mediate depths, and the greatest counts are found at the surface of the bottom deposits.

bers of bacteria in oceanic waters are found a few centimeters above, and within, the bottom deposits.

For many, perhaps most, of the nutrients remineralized by the oxidative processes of bacteria, this pattern of vertical distribution of bacterial cells would correspond very closely to the *rates of recycling* at various depths. One reason for this is that there are only relatively small fluctuations in marine bacterial population numbers with the seasons. As one of the founders of marine bacteriology, Claude E. ZoBell, first elucidated, neither the numbers nor the kinds of bacteria at any level in the sea show any marked seasonal cycles. This implies that the enormous seasonal variations in phytoplankton production are "smoothed out" by the interposition of the animal trophic levels which provide a steadier flow of faeces, excreta, and dead tissues as the substrates for bacterial decomposition. Another "smoothing" factor must be the relatively long periods of time involved in the sinking of plant and animal detritus from the euphotic zone to the larger concentrations of bacteria on the ocean bottom, whether accomplished passively or by transfer through successive trophic levels from detritus-feeders. As has been demonstrated experimentally, several diverse and important groups of marine bacteria metabolize more efficiently and multiply much more rapidly if solid surfaces for attachment are provided. This may help explain both the enormous importance of the bottom-dwelling forms in the economy of the sea, and the enhanced bacterial flora living on the larger detritus particles.

Extensive functional catalogs of marine bacteria have been prepared by ZoBell and others. Even to summarize these would be inappropriate here, but it is worth noting the major categories as they can be distinguished by the type of bacterial metabolism (or by the ecological equivalent, the type of chemical changes which they bring about in the sea). The first group of general decomposers is by far the most abundant, and includes unspecialized forms, and others which have as their preferred food carbohydrates or fats or specific groups of proteins or specific amino acids. Allied forms tackle the decomposition of what one can regard as the more refractory biological materials. Among these, marine bacterial "species" have been recognized and isolated which can break down the cellulose and lignin of plants, the chitin of arthropods and other invertebrates, and even the "fossil" petroleum hydrocarbons. A second major group of marine bacteria have already been discussed and are concerned in the oxidative processes of the mainstream of the nitrogen cycle (see page 160 and Figure 2·4). Considered in sequence from the initial decomposition, these include: aminifying bacteria, producing ammonium compounds from amino acids and other nitrogen-containing organic residues; an allied group similarly engaged in the decomposition of urea from animals; the nitrite-forming bacteria, utilizing ammonium salts; the nitrate-forming bacteria, utilizing nitrites; and some allied forms (not in the nitrogen cycle) which are sulfate-forming, utilizing sulfides. In general, throughout the oceans, the bacterial forms in these two large groupings of general decomposition and of oxidative processes far outnumber the remaining diverse bacterial forms which carry out reduction processes or what are essentially chemosyntheses. Only in rather limited circumstances, in special conditions of anaerobiosis or modified salt content in inshore waters, do these more specialized bacterial forms flourish. As already noted, nitrogen-fixing bacteria, such as *Azotobacter* species, which are found in inshore waters, are relatively unimportant in the nutrient cycles of the open oceans and require for their activities a relatively rich supply of food. This is also the case with the so-called denitrifying bacteria, including those which reduce nitrate to nitrite, or nitrate to nitrogen gas. Similarly rare are the bacteria which build up ammonium or phosphate salts within their cells, a significant release of these substances occurring after death. Another minor group of bacteria carrying out reduction processes are those which, under anaerobic conditions, convert sulfates to sulfides and sulfides to elemental sulfur. There is some controversy about the importance in normal marine conditions of bacteria which can cause the precipitation of calcium carbonate. Similarly, the concretions or nodules of iron and of manganese oxides which occur on some ocean bottoms could result from the activities of bacteria.

To recapitulate, these last bacterial processes are exceptional, the great bulk of bacterial activity being concerned with the conversion of *organic* substrates into simpler compounds or inorganic ions. It has been claimed, on circumstantially convincing grounds, that there exists no complex organic molecule ever synthesized by plant or animal which cannot be broken down by one or more forms of marine bacteria. In other words, nowhere in the sea do we have continuing accumulation of any specific organic material immune from bacterial action or continuing conditions like those in dystrophic lakes. Thus, death in the sea in Pasteur's sense is *never* incomplete.

## More constituent ratios

As noted earlier in this chapter, the relative amounts available of nitrogen salts and of phosphates will determine which of these nutrients will potentially be involved in the limitation of primary productivity. Relatively simple ratios such as carbon : nitrogen : phosphorus can also be usefully applied to a food resource in assessing the potential for secondary productivity and for production at much higher trophic levels. The reasons for this again reflect the heterotrophic nature of all animal nutrition. In other words, all animals—no matter whether feeding on other animals or on plants—have nutritional requirements for maintenance, for growth, and for reproduction which cannot be expressed as a specific intake rate per day in biomass units (whether dry weight or carbon), or in calories as energy units. Popular—and even misguided political—discussion of human diets in terms of calorific values alone is absurd. As every reader is aware, both man and the common farm animals require a "balanced diet": carbohydrates (sugars and starches) are not enough. The maintenance requirements of a higher animal can be met for a short time by a diet of only carbohydrates, but growing young animals, and reproducing adults, also require some intake of proteins and fats. Of course, this is also true of the longer-term nutritional requirements of adult animals for maintenance (even when neither incremental growth nor reproductive activities are occurring). These somewhat trite truths regarding the nutrition of cows and man are applicable to all aquatic animals at all trophic levels.

Intake of proteins is a nutritional requirement of all animals, but this does *not* imply that higher animals are unable to synthesize their own structural and other proteins. Indeed, it has been estimated that over 90 per cent of that part of the energy required by higher organisms for biosynthesis is involved in the synthesis of proteins alone. What *is* implied by the dietary requirement for protein is the needed assimilation, almost always after digestive breakdown of food proteins, of the unit "building-blocks," amino acids, with which animals *must* be provided for their protein synthesis. In other words, this aspect of the dependence of animals on green plants is that inorganic nitrogen compounds are first incorporated into organic nitrogenous compounds only in autotrophic organisms, the great bulk of amino acids being first synthesized in green plants.

Similar dependence occurs with other elemental constituents. It was hardly necessary to consider sulfur in the above discussion of the limitations on primary productivity resulting from elemental requirements because seawater contains much sulfate and thus, theoretically at least, sulfur requirements need never limit green plant growth in the sea. However, all herbivores and all animals at higher trophic levels have a dietary need for presynthesized organic compounds containing divalent sulfur. Such sulfur-containing building-blocks as cystine, glutathione, methionine, and thiamine must be present in the diet of animals and almost always originate in green plant syntheses. It is highly significant —though the topic cannot be pursued here—that a number of green plants are known to be *unable* to form certain organic sulfur compounds, must take them in after their synthesis by other plants, and are thus not completely autotrophic. In recent years the painstaking work of developing axenic cultures by Luigi Provasoli and others has revealed that a considerable number of algal species require either a single organic substance presynthesized, or several such, being thus partially heterotrophic. As yet we know relatively little regarding such interdependence between photosynthetic species in the open sea and, though there is much circumstantial evidence which suggests that

normally marine diatom production cannot be limited by any requirement for organic substances, the question remains unsettled. As regards
the nutrition of animals, this requirement for an intake of organic compounds containing divalent sulfur as part of their proteinaceous food
could be expressed as a need for a nitrogen:sulfur ratio in the diet of
less than a certain level (for most animals this would be less than
19:1).

## C : N ratio

An even simpler, but more fundamental, ratio—that of carbon to
nitrogen—is of considerable value in assessing the dietary requirements
of animals since it is an effective measure of the percentage of proteins
in the food. In respect of protein fraction, the nutritional requirements
of all animals investigated (excluding only ruminant mammals, see
below) are closely similar to those of man. The minimum protein intake for human health is 12 per cent of the calorific value of ingested
food, or 16.5 per cent by dry weight. Since the **C:N** (carbon:nitro-
gen) ratio for average proteins is 3.2:1, then the required **C:N** ratio
for animal food intake is about 17:1. In cases where the diet shows a
higher **C:N** ratio, there is protein deficiency. Humans with a dietary
**C:N** ratio of greater than about 21:1—and there are many of them in
Asia and Africa—show the symptoms of deficiency diseases no matter
whether their total calorific intake is adequate or not. Much human
protein deficiency arises from the fact that many staple food crops
giving high yields in terms of calorific values are relatively low in protein content. High **C:N** ratios are shown by most of the high-yield
crops of advanced agriculture, including sugar beet, potato, cassava,
sweet potato, rice, corn (maize), and wheat. For example, an average
**C:N** value for sugar beet is 48:1, for potatoes is 30:1, for high-yielding hybrid corn is 29.8:1, for rice is 31:1, and for high-yielding wheat
is 26.2:1. Incidentally, it should be obvious from this that the wheat
and corn surpluses of the plains of North America could not, of themselves and directly, solve any of the problems of protein malnutrition
in Asians or Africans. That these surpluses are of real value in adding
to the total food available for undernourished populations should not
obscure the fact that in many areas their distribution will add to the
nearly critical imbalance of a high **C:N** ratio in the diet. This aspect
of world nutrition alone justifies a vastly increased effort to understand
the processes of aquatic productivity and to exploit them for the benefit
of human protein requirements.

Despite these high **C:N** values for "bulk staples," balanced human
diets are achieved in most parts of Europe, Russia, Australasia, and
North America by a proportionate intake of fish or meat. Good beef

has a **C:N** of 4.3 : 1, so the appropriate proportion of beef to potatoes to bring that mixed diet below a **C:N** value of 17 : 1 can readily be calculated. Obviously, the high-protein diet of the South American gauchos (noted on page 23) involves a **C:N** intake value of approximately 5 : 1 and, by choice, the diet of a few individuals in the United States and western Europe approaches this value. In these cases, the additional protein (in excess of the requirement of 16.5 per cent by dry weight, or of the **C:N** ratio of 17 : 1) is merely of calorific value to an adult human if, in fact, it is completely assimilated.

It is worth noting that development of higher-yield grain crops has pushed up the **C:N** ratio, that is, has decreased the percentage protein content. Over the last half century, yield per unit area has been increased more than twofold for corn (maize) and nearly fourfold for wheat. But the **C:N** ratio of a low-yield corn would be about 18.9 : 1, and of a low-yield wheat about 15.6 : 1, which as staples are easier to "balance" in nutrition than the high-yield values quoted earlier. This can be illustrated from the recent history of pig-raising in the United States. Earlier this century swine could be raised almost exclusively on locally grown, and relatively low-yielding, corn. At the present time, corn from high-yielding hybrid varieties has to be supplemented with protein concentrates (even fish-meal from Peru; see page 100) to be fit for pig-feeding. The despised and low-yielding grain crop of the Scottish Highlands, oats, has a relatively high protein content and a **C:N** ratio of about 15.4 : 1. With milk and a little fish, oatmeal nourished an intellectual and martial people for centuries, despite the sneer at oats of that superior Englishman Dr. Samuel Johnson, "generally given to horses but in Scotland supports the people." Unlike Dr. Johnson, the present-day babyfood manufacturers of North America and of Europe are well aware of the balanced nutritional value of oatmeal (compare the analyses on their packets and jars).

Broadly, shift of crops to higher-yield varieties usually means decreased **C:N** ratios (lowered protein content). Any major change of staple-food crops from grains to those with greater yields in calories per acre—such as sugar cane, potatoes, cassava, or sugar beet—means greater "food" production but once again implies increased **C:N** ratios and thus greater nutritional imbalance. Protein-deficient diets are obvious in infants. The tragically swollen "sugar-babies" of Jamaica, and kwashiorkor-distended, "red-bodied" infants in West Africa, have both had their hunger abated with adequate amounts of calories from sugar cane and from cassava, but they lack dietary protein. Regular administration of relatively small quantities of high-grade protein—dried milk or, once again, fish-meal—is the best medical treatment for these unfortunate children, and a few weeks of this will bring about a spectacular disappearance of the obvious symptoms (and also of the less apparent risks of developmental damage to the brain and nervous system associated with infantile protein deficiency). Particularly in the tropics, increased yields of cheaper calories may aggravate rather than solve the problems of malnutrition.

Balancing protein for human and farm-animal diets *can* come directly from plants. Soybeans are almost half protein with a $C:N$ ratio of 6:1, and provide the principal supplement to cassava and rice in Brazil, and (as a major food import, along with fish-meal and other fish products) to sweet-potato and rice in Japan. Leguminous plants of all kinds yielding peas, beans, and other pulses (for example, navy-beans have a $C:N$ ratio of 9.7:1), make up the major resources of high-protein plant production on land, though the rapidly growing green shoots of all plants, and a few ripe nuts (walnuts, pecans, brazil nuts) have similarly low $C:N$ ratios. Rapidly dividing algal cells—like diatoms during an increase—correspond to fast-growing shoots and have relatively low $C:N$ ratios (relatively high protein content) so that, in most circumstances, the herbivores of the zoöplankton do not face the dietary "balancing" problems which confront vegetarian pigs and humans on land.

The case of ruminants, including cattle, is peculiar in this regard and worth brief consideration. Alone among herbivores, they can take in food such as grasses of *high* $C:N$ ratio, and actually absorb through their gut-walls a balanced intake of *low* $C:N$ value. To do this they rely on a mixed intestinal "flora" of microörganisms—mainly bacteria and protozoans—which not only breaks down plant cellulose (which cannot be achieved by the ruminant's own enzymes) but also synthesizes amino acids assimilable by the ruminant. Early "hunting" man gained his necessary protein from the primary productivity of high $C:N$ ratio of grasslands and forests as a result of the work of microörganisms in the gut-rumina of deer, antelopes, buffaloes, and other ruminant "big game." "Agricultural" man has for centuries relied on the activities of two groups of microörganisms which can modify $C:N$ ratios and thus provide his needed high-protein foods as milk and meat from cattle, goats, sheep, and camels. These two groups are: first, the organisms in the gut-rumina, and secondly, the nitrogen-fixing bacteria of the root nodules of leguminous plants, including the clovers and alfalfas of grazing as well as the legume crops: soybeans, groundnuts, peas, beans, and other pulses. Given the tendency of natural land vegetation to devote much of its gross production (for mechanical reasons in an aerial environment) to cellulose and lignin of low nitrogen content, and given that, over much of the world's soils, availability of combined nitrogen is a limiting factor for primary production (as it is with many natural waters), then it could be claimed that, without these two groups of microörganisms, the standing-crop biomass of terrestrial life could never have reached its present levels. It is also interesting to reflect on the limitations upon man if our species operated only at the second trophic level. It is possible to be a "pure" vegetarian, living on locally produced food, only in the tropics or warm-temperate regions, where low-C:N legumes can ripen, or such rapidly dividing green shoots as asparagus (the C:N ratio of the tips alone is about 6:1) could be available, throughout the year. Vegetarianism in cold-temperate climates or at high latitudes must rely on such foods as nuts and pulses imported from warmer countries to provide supplementation with appropriate low C:N ratio.

As will be discussed in Chapter 13, these aspects of terrestrial nutrition are not much modified by man's ability to synthesize nitrogenous fertilizers. Additional "balancing" protein production of low-C:N crops does not result from added nitrates or ammonium fertilizers; rather, the result is the increased C:N ratios of bigger yields of carbohydrates. Paradoxically, phosphatic and sulfurous fertilizers are required to produce additional leguminous nitrogen-fixation, and hence lowered C:N ratios in the crops. Further, all so-called artificial fertilizers are expensive in terms of fuel-energy—but this is especially true of the synthesis, by "fixation" of atmospheric nitrogen, of nitrogenous artificials.

This discussion of C:N in human nutrition may appear to have digressed away from aspects of aquatic productivity—though not from the problems of global nutrition which form part of the *raison d'être* of this book. Many matters raised in the above paragraphs have general relevance even in the oceans where there are neither legumes nor ruminants. In particular, the limits of global productivity (of the living crop of biomass, the planet Earth can support) are finite, and depend not only upon the annual efficiency of photosynthetic conversion of solar energy (see Chapters 9 and 12) but also on the C:N ratio of primary production per year, which in turn depends on the C:N weight ratio (in this case of noncarbonate carbon to combined nitrogen) of the materials reprocessed annually by the decomposers of all environments. If we return to questions of aquatic productivity, it is worth emphasizing that, except for ruminants, all animals of all trophic levels, so far investigated, have adult nutritional requirements for protein amounting to about 16.5 per cent by dry weight of their diet, that is, a dietary intake corresponding to a C:N ratio *below* 17:1. Recent confirmation of this for the filter-feeding crustacean *Artemia* (with a growth pattern and a feeding mechanism closely comparable to those of many zoöplankton organisms similarly feeding at the second trophic level) comes from studies of Luigi Provasoli and his associates in establishing axenic culture methods. Optimal growth and development in cultures were obtained with albumin:starch ratios of between 1:5

and 1:3, which correspond to **C:N** ratios between 17:1 and 11:1.

As already noted, aquatic animals at higher trophic levels than the second will rarely have problems of protein deficiency (high-**C:N** diets), and this is also true of the second-trophic-level zoöplankton while they are cropping actively dividing diatom cells. During the spring increase, most of the phytoplankton cells, including diatoms, will have contents of **C:N** ratio about 6.5:1. Forms like *Calanus* should not face dietary deficiency problems even during the relatively unproductive summer in temperate seas. However, through much of the year in polar seas and in winter in temperate waters, any *plant* intake by copepods or euphausiids may require balancing. Ratios of **C:N** of 10:1, and perhaps even more significantly of **C:P** of 60:1, are exceeded in senescent, dying, and dead plant tissues. Reported carnivorous activities of calanoids and krill are significant under such circumstances. Sheina M. Marshall and A. P. Orr have reported on the gut-contents of *Calanus* throughout the year. Although populations of *Calanus* apparently consume some smaller crustaceans at all times of the year, the least number of individual copepods feeding in this way (7–9 per cent of the samples) was found immediately after the SDI in April and May, and the greatest number of individuals ever detected as carnivores (48 per cent of the samples) occurred just before the SDI in February. When we turn from phytoplankton-based communities, second-trophic-level animals in detritus-based food-chains are more likely to face at times a high **C:N** ratio in their available food. This can probably be most acute in certain running-freshwater environments (see page 141), where the primary food supply is allochthonous plant debris, almost entirely from land vegetation and of high cellulose content. Unfortunately, there has been little investigation of the nutritional requirements of the midge and blackfly larvae, oligochaete worms, and crustaceans like *Asellus* and gammarids, which are detritus-feeders in such circumstances. As already discussed, some aspects of detritus food-chains are better known in estuaries. The rise in protein content of the detritus derived from *Spartina* as it undergoes conversion by microörganisms (page 106) corresponds to a drop of **C:N** ratio from 45:1 to 11:1. Thus a balanced diet is provided by microbial action for the detritus-feeding benthos of the estuary— mainly species of bivalves and crustaceans. Other enrichment of the basic food supply in some estuaries may result from the activities of nitrogen-fixing bacteria and blue-green algae.

Throughout fresh waters, the macrophytic primary production is not subject to much direct grazing, but is valuable to invertebrate food-chains either as detritus (with some microbial conversion, except in dystrophic waters) or as a substrate for the important crop of attached diatoms and other *Aufwuchs*. Macrophytic production in the sea—of the brown and larger red seaweeds between and just below tidemarks—is again little grazed upon directly by marine animals. Large brown algae such as the "kelps" have **C:N** ratios in the 40:1 to 80:1 range, and much is indigestible by the usual repertoires of invertebrate enzymes. In this respect, the Scottish experiments in local addition of agricultural fertlizers to sea inlets (see pages 234 and 284) showed that although there was significantly increased production of plankton and hence of fish, a very great proportion of the added fertilizers, including nitrogenous compounds, was used by attached seaweeds which did not contribute to fish food. The parallels with the "disappointing" results of agricultural use of nitrogenous salts in producing high yield but low-protein crops, is striking, and raises questions for future theoretical and applied studies in productivity. With the large seaweeds once again, death and some microbial action must precede any incorporation into secondary marine production. Possible exceptions to this are the dugong and the manatee—the so-called sea-cows—which are said to graze on coastal seaweeds. These are aberrant marine mammals, possibly distantly related to the land ungulates with rumina, and they have complex stomachs and very long intestines. I know of no detailed studies on their intestinal "flora" or on any predigestive conversions.

Little is known about the changing dietary requirements of aquatic invertebrates during their earliest development or during periods of reproductive activity. It is certain, from the work of Marshall, Orr, and others on calanoid copepods, that rates of egg-production in forms like *Calanus* are closely linked to the availability of food. As discussed in Chapter 4, this is also true for the successful development and survivorship of young naupliar stages. It seems possible that the food intake in such cases must lie below certain maximum levels of **C:N** ratio for successful fecundity or juvenile growth. Recently my colleagues and I have been examining **C:N** ratios in eggs and reproductive adults of several freshwater and marine littoral snails and, in the course of our studies on turnover in natural populations and infraspecific variations, a few tentative generalizations regarding the ratios have emerged. In most snail species studied, if adult or preadult individuals are building up individual biomass before overwintering, their **C:N** ratios tend to increase (reflecting some storage of fats and glycogen), but buildup of biomass by adult snails before a reproductive period is typified by decreasing **C:N** ratios (reflecting protein storage which will be involved in reproductive output). In some cases there are possible links with the seasonal availability of foods: mainly detritus of higher **C:N** ratio in fall and mainly new primary production of lower **C:N** ratio in spring. There is unlikely to be direct proportionality in this, however. During the actual reproductive period, the drain of nitrogen is disproportionate and **C:N** ratios of adults tend to rise (a slightly more complex example of this in *Melampus* is discussed below). As was true of *Calanus,* in several snail species egg production is directly linked to food intake, and from our figures for one snail species, it can be calculated that 87 per cent of the N-R.A. (non-respired assimilation) is directed to egg output. Eggs of different snail species have somewhat different **C:N** ratios on laying, and this is also true of other aquatic invertebrates.

Our preliminary studies on a variety of molluscan eggs have suggested certain generalizations which may also prove appropriate for other aquatic invertebrates. Relatively "large" eggs, which usually involve a degree of direct development and corresponding suppression of larval stages, fall into two main **C:N** categories corresponding to three biological classes. Large eggs with relatively high **C:N** ratio can give rise to young which carry food stores (such as yolk-sacs) and do not feed for some time after hatching. Secondly, eggs similar in their large size and high **C:N** ratio can have a markedly different pattern of development with fully formed and active ciliated larvae retained *within* the egg-membrane. A third class of large eggs have relatively low **C:N** ratios, correspond to truly direct processes of development, and give rise to "miniature adults" immediately capable of most adult behavior, including appropriate patterns of feeding. Most relatively small eggs are of low or intermediate **C:N** ratio, and very many typical marine species lay such eggs in enormous numbers. These eggs usually give rise to long-lived larval stages whose further development involves trophic—if not other anatomical—metamorphoses. There remains a class of eggs of moderate size (when size is related to adult individual biomass, or compared with eggs of closely related forms), which have a relatively high **C:N** ratio. These all involve, rather than suppression of larval stages in the strict sense, retention within the egg membrane of active full-formed ciliated larval stages such as trochophores or early veliger larvae. Some common littorinid snails, including *Lacuna,* fall in this class, and it could be characterized as a level of partial adaptation to the appropriate dispersal and environmental conditions of life between tidemarks.

These differences can be taken as reflecting the differing importance of "building-blocks" for development and provision for energy requirements. I have suggested elsewhere that the evolution of larger eggs in nonmarine environments has been influenced not only by the need to suppress free larval stages, but also by pressures to reduce the temporal extent of immature growth. The "start in life" of being born large is important in environments with marked seasonal changes, and this determines the most efficient patterns of **C:N** output in fecundity.

The specific case of a salt-marsh snail, *Melampus,* is revealing in terms of **C:N** turnover in reproduction. This snail, an ellobiid, retains a free-swimming planktonic veliger, and is of considerable evolutionary interest, being almost certainly related to the stem-group of both land snails and freshwater pulmonates. In a natural population of *Melampus* in a salt-marsh on Cape Cod, the annual reproductive period always occurs between early June and mid-July, with normally three cycles of egg-laying. The onset of the overall reproductive period is determined by changing day-length in the spring controlling the onset of gonad maturation, but each individual cycle of egg-laying has a definite semilunar periodicity. Egg-laying is strictly confined to four days in phase with the spring tides. The overall fecundity per "standard" snail per year averages 33,150 eggs or a reproductive output of 7.3 mg of dry organic material annually. The detectable organic depletion of the gonads during the entire reproductive period only amounts to about one seventh of this, so that much concurrent assimilation is directed immediately to reproductive output. Carbon and nitrogen values were determined for excised gonads, and the **C:N** ratio of gonad tissue rose from a value of 6.3:1 during the first egg-laying cycle to one of 15:1 at the end of the third cycle. This implies that gonadial protein turnover was not keeping up with egg output and, more generally, that availability of organic nitrogenous material was limiting fecundity, and that the organic carbon turnover in egg production could have been longer sustained. If we can conceive of the gonad in *Melampus* as a microcosm analogous to an ecosystem then, just as plant productivity in many aquatic environments which we have discussed is limited by the rate of recycling of suitable inorganic nitrogen-salts, so egg-production in the gonad is limited by the rate at which suitable organic nitrogenous materials can be made available from the other tissues and ultimately by the rate at which they are assimilated from the snail's food. Whether a similar limitation exists in the fecundity of other aquatic invertebrates is not yet clear.

A similar situation to that of egg production is involved in the mucus production for feeding and defense by many invertebrates. Different mucous secretions have different **C:N** ratios, reflecting the occurrence of mucopolysaccharides and mucoproteins. There is no real energetic problem with those suspension-feeders using a mucous net for food capture, such as sea-squirts, certain worms, and the slipper-limpet *Crepidula*, where the mucus which is secreted is ingested along with the food and need represent no organic debit to the animal's economy. The situation is different for the many marine gastropods which secrete abundant mucus for defense purposes, and for those large carnivorous moon-snails like *Polinices* which secrete vast quantities of mucus in the course of prey capture, little if any of which is re-ingested. Energy losses, and their **C:N** ratios, are not yet completely investigated.

Since we have discussed the **C:N** ratios necessary in the nutrient intake of both producers and consumers, it is appropriate to end this chapter with some mention of the need for appropriate $C:N$ balance in the organic materials acted upon by decomposers. As was mentioned above (page 128), high $C:N$ ratios in the bottom muds of freshwater lakes can be a reliable measure of oligotrophy. A balanced "food supply" of low $C:N$ ratio to the decomposing bacteria is a necessary part of the efficient lacustrine recycling which we term eutrophy. Since the seventies of last century, sewage chemists have realized that $C:N$ ratios (as well as assessed oxygen demand) provide simple measures which can allow the most efficient control (by flow rates) of biological treatments such as the activated sludge process. In the controlled decomposition of sewage, as in the decomposer segments of all cycles of aquatic productivity discussed herein, the *rate* of remineralization by bacteria depends on the $C:N$ ratio of the substrate supplied to them.

As noted above, and further discussed in Chapter 13, if application of nitrogenous fertilizers is increased in agriculture, the usual result is increased carbohydrate production, rather than increased protein production which would lower the $C:N$ ratio of the crop. Both the primary producers and the decomposers show compensatory responses which make it possible to conceive of normal organic cycles as tending to maintain a "dynamic equilibrium" in values of $C:N$. There need be nothing mystical about this—no need to invoke an external monitoring "of a balance of nature," or with the more metabiological ecologists, "a homeostasis of the ecosystem." Pragmatically, the concept of $C:N$ ratios being in a dynamic steady state in ecosystems could be as useful as Liebig's concept of limiting factors. Apart from its pragmatic value, this hypothesis reflects a fundamental feature of all living organisms. The biomass of producers, consumers, and decomposers alike varies but little in its constituent ratios as long as only young, actively dividing cells or tissues are considered. (This rules out most of the biomass of a tree, on the one hand, or of a "soft-coral" on the other.) The limited variation possible in the $C:N$ ratio, and for that matter in the $N:P$ and $N:S$ ratios, reflects the necessary protein levels for active cell growth and, beyond that, the unique proportions of organic phosphates necessary for the transfer of chemical energy as well as the unique properties of divalent sulfur in amino acids. Our hypothesis can be extended to claim that the dynamic steady state of elemental constituents characteristic of active cell metabolism determines the dynamic steady state of these elemental ratios in ecosystems. Apart from the value of this hypothesis in developing a predictive theory for some aspects of aquatic productivity, the practical consequences of a demonstrable steady state in $C:N$ and other ratios in natural communities, in relation to man's future nutrition, are immense.

# A closer look at energy transfer

*energetics*

ALL LEVELS OF organic productivity can be considered in terms of the continuous energy flow through them. Energy generated by solar nuclear fusion first reaches biological systems when, as the sun's radiation, it is absorbed by green plants. This radiant energy in part is converted to the potential (or chemical) energy of the organic substances produced by green plants. Recycling and conservation of energy are characteristic of living organization. Such processes occur in plants —but are even more readily recognized in heterotrophic organisms such as animals and bacteria—and they are largely responsible for slowing the inevitable conversion of this potential energy to kinetic energy and thence by dissipation as heat to the environment and to entropy. The existence of ecosystems with a number of heterotrophic levels depends on transfer of the potential energy from plant to animal and from animal to animal with a moderate level of efficiency.

If we avoid defining this "transfer efficiency" more closely for the present, circumstantial evidence justifies the use of words like "a moderate level of efficiency." Clearly, in the animal organism, the fractionation of the potential energy ingested (noted in Chapters 2, 7, and 13) implies that a transfer efficiency corresponding to even 35 per cent of that of Carnot's ideal heat-engine is impossible. The continued existence of some of the ecosystems discussed in Chapters 3–7 would suggest intuitively that transfer efficiencies as low as 2.5 per cent through the animal components of the systems would be unlikely to occur, being insufficient for community survival. Quantitative demonstration that the "moderate level of efficiency" actually lies around 10 per cent, in most cases, requires a more rigorous treatment of data derived both from field studies of natural ecosystems and from "experi-

mental laboratory ecosystems" (such as those of Lawrence B. Slobodkin). Before we pass to consideration of these, it is worth stressing
again (see Chapter 2, page 16) the principal difference in the
energetics of living organisms as compared to analogous man-made
machines. Living organisms are maintained by the continuous flow of
energy through them, and the loss of some part of the energy involved
to heat and to entropy would seem to be an essential feature of life.

Whole living organisms—and, even more clearly, individual living
cells—form open systems in that they continually exchange parts of
their biomass with their surroundings. In other words, their energy
exchanges are such that they cannot exist in a strict thermodynamic
equilibrium. The maintenance of such systems is essentially as in a
dynamic steady state. It is significant that when such a steady state is
achieved, then the rate of entropy production by the system is minimal
for the level of energy flow taking place. Inefficiency, in this case
meaning a higher rate of production of entropy, results from every
move away from the steady state. Thus we now return to Isaiah's
theme, now rather more with his own emphasis. Both flesh and grass
are transistory, but in any conceivable time-scale, any units of their
biomass (or of their content of potential energy) are even more transitory.

## Energy flow and green plants

Flow diagrams of various sorts are commonly used in the presentation
of ecological energetics. With increasing sophistication in community
ecology, these visual models have evolved: from the block diagrams
prepared by Petersen in the second decade of this century, through the
widespread use of "plumbing" flow charts (of which Figure 9·1 is
merely a variant), to elegant electronic analogs wherein feedback
systems can be particularly well depicted. However, it is important to
realize that all are models which mirror, with varying degrees of
distortion, the energy relationships of natural communities. As already
stressed, biological systems could not continue their physical existence
as organized matter if energy flow through them ceased entirely. If
the energy flow through an organism does not continue to some extent,
then it is no longer living, and its components can pass almost immediately by both autolysis and decay to dissolution. Further, despite
the universal presence of energy-conserving cycles within living cells,
organisms, and communities, the *net* flow, whether in heterotrophic
organism or in complex community, is unidirectional and all inevitably
is lost to heat in the end. Another aspect of the distortion in energy-flow
models arises from the fact that the energy exchanges depicted in a
diagram, like Figure 9·1, of a natural community with both autotrophic

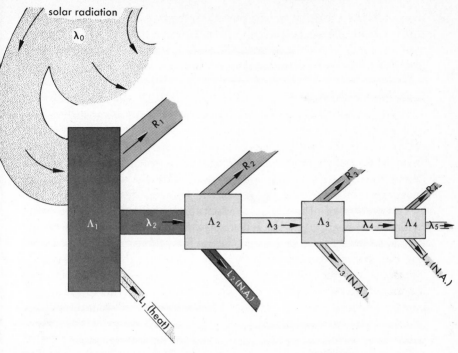

**Figure 9·1. The energy flow through an ecosystem.** The energy content of the primary producer plants ($\Lambda_1$) and of the various trophic levels of animals ($\Lambda_2$, $\Lambda_3$, $\Lambda_4$) is represented by the rectangles, and the amounts of energy passing between them per unit time by the paths marked $\lambda_2$, $\lambda_3$, $\lambda_4$, and $\lambda_5$. Energy losses by respiration are marked $R_1$, $R_2$, $R_3$, and $R_4$ and by egestion of faeces from animals by $L_2$, $L_3$, and $L_4$. For further discussion of the three different forms of energy involved, see text.

and heterotrophic organisms actually involve three different forms of energy. These include the radiant energy input to the first trophic level and the kinetic energy deployed to the environment by every trophic level, as well as the units of potential (or chemical) energy which are transferred between trophic levels. In contemplating these diagrams, one must remember that the nutrition of heterotrophic organisms does not involve energy "flow" in a strict sense, but rather the transfer of potential energy as contained *in pieces of the biomass* of a lower trophic level. Thus, in efficiencies of energy transfer through trophic levels, for example, the energetics of green plants are not strictly comparable to those of heterotrophic organisms. The only autotrophic organisms whose conversion efficiency or growth efficiency could appropriately be assessed in the same terms as for heterotrophs would be the relatively rare chemosynthetic autotrophs which are not light-dependent.

The community energy flow represented diagrammatically in Figure

9·1 is labeled according to the method introduced by Hutchinson and Lindeman in representing trophic-dynamic relationships in energy terms (see also page 25). The gross ecological efficiency of any trophic level, for a steady-state population at that level, is the ratio of the yield in energy to the next higher trophic level divided by the energy input from the level below, for example, $\lambda_3/\lambda_2$ or $\lambda_4/\lambda_3$ (see pages 25 and 191). These efficiency ratios and others are usually expressed as percentages. As noted, the energy relationships of all trophic levels except the first are similar, that of the green plants being qualitatively different. It is worth briefly considering the efficiency of green plants (which can be expressed as $\lambda_2/\lambda_0$) before passing to a zoöcentric view of more usual energy relationships.

The average efficiency of green plants under field conditions in fixing as potential energy in synthesized organic materials the light-energy they absorb was estimated by E. I. Rabinowitch as about 2 per cent, and this is accepted by most authorities. Values for the "photosynthetic efficiency" of green plant cells in culture can be very much higher— those for *Chlorella* under certain conditions and at certain wavelengths being reported as over 20 per cent. On the other hand, estimates of the efficiency of the ocean as a whole—that is, the ratio of the energy content of photosynthetically fixed carbon to the radiant energy at the ocean surface—such as those of Gordon A. Riley, lie about 0.2 per cent. Still other figures quoted for the efficiency of the first trophic level involve different definitions of efficiency, none of which is strictly comparable to the gross ecological efficiency which we can employ for higher trophic levels assessed in the steady-state condition.

As regards green plants, it is perhaps best to avoid direct comparison with energy transfers between trophic levels and, accepting that the overall efficiency of photosynthesis in the field probably lies about 2 per cent, recognize that the thermodynamic efficiency of energy conversion in green plant cells in the laboratory during periods of exponential growth may be much higher. There have been a number of recent studies concerned with assessing the quantum yield, or the efficiency in terms of carbon fixed per quantum of light energy. Work on the diatom *Navicula minima* by T. Tanada was concerned with the quantum yields at different wavelengths. Tanada's data as recalculated by John H. Ryther suggest that the averaged efficiency for the entire visible spectrum is about 17.5 per cent (for intensities *below* saturation values, see page 52). As noted elsewhere, the somewhat elaborate molecular system for capturing light energy and incorporating it in the potential energy of the synthesized organic materials is not yet fully understood in terms of electron energetics. For example, there is still some uncertainty about energy exchanges in some of the intermediate

*gross efficiency*

*efficiency*

reactions, and particularly between those cyclic reactions which can continue in the dark and those of the so-called "light phase" which involve the passage of electrons from light-excited chlorophyll to a phosphate electron-carrier. Here once again energy-conserving cycles are involved, and thus even assessments of quantum yield can only be concerned with the ends of a long series of energy transfers. Happily, for almost all questions of community ecology, the detailed energetics of the sequential molecular changes involved in photosynthesis need not concern us because, from the point of view of increase in primary producer biomass and thus of availability for transfer to other trophic levels, a molecule of glucose has always the same content of chemical energy. In other words, the series of reactions which result in the synthesis of this simple sugar always involve an energy fixation equivalent to 3811 calories in heat units per gram.

In any community of living organisms, all other energy transfers are between trophic levels of organisms and thus concern nutritional transfer of actual biomass.

## Various efficiencies

Comparison of energy budgets for individual animals and for populations, and of the efficiency in trophic transfer of energy, has been hindered by different biologists employing many incompatible definitions for the various efficiencies of energy transfer involved. Here we will only be concerned with two older and widely accepted definitions for growth efficiency in individual animals, one "lifespan-cost" measure of individual growth, and two modern measures of ecological efficiency (in forms first rigorously defined by Slobodkin).

Measures of growth efficiency involve ratios derived from the energy budgets of individual animals (see Figure $9 \cdot 2$). The earliest work on such efficiencies long antedates recent interest of "pure" theoretical and experimental ecologists, and was largely carried out by agricultural scientists, much being summarized in Brody's classic book. Other early work on energy budgets was carried out on fish, notably by V. S. Ivlev and his associates in Russia, but also by other fisheries scientists throughout the world (see also Chapter 10).

As presented in a stylized fashion for the individual animal in Figure $9 \cdot 2$, some of the energy content of the ingested food passes as the energy content of the faeces to egestion, while the rest, the total assimilation, is itself partitioned into two main fractions. A considerable part of the potential energy of the total assimilation is degraded to kinetic energy for the maintenance activities of the animal—even including the energy expenditure of food collection and intake—and only the

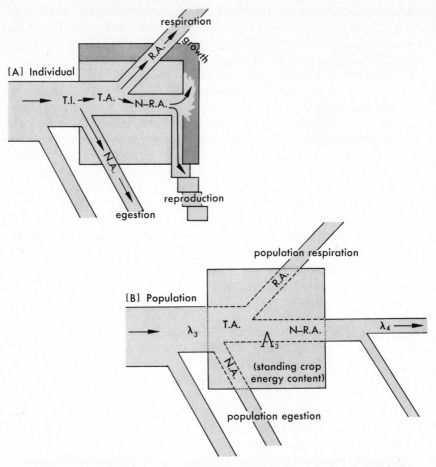

**Figure 9·2. Energy flow in the individual animal and in the animal population.**
**A:** In the energy budget of an individual animal, the non-respired assimilation
**(N–R.A.)**—remaining from the total ingested after losses in defecation and respiration—is partitioned between growth of the individual and reproduction. **B:** In a "steady-
state" animal population, the non-respired assimilation **(N–R.A.)** of the population
represents the fraction of the energy "input" (here $\lambda_3$ from the trophic level below)
available as "output" to the next higher trophic level. For further discussion of the
ratios derived from these energy budgets, see text.

rest, the non-respired assimilation, remains available for growth and
reproduction of the animal organism. As regards individual growth
efficiencies of animal organisms, no one has yet assessed the losses
to entropy associated with the energy expenditure of food assimilation.
As Slobodkin has succinctly put it, it is very difficult to get an organism
to undigest a meal and thereby measure the energy exchanges of the

reverse process. The individual gross growth efficiency can be defined as:

$$\frac{\text{calorific content of non-respired assimilation} \times 100}{\text{calorific content of food intake}}$$

while the net growth efficiency can be defined as:

$$\frac{\text{calorific content of biomass of growth} \times 100}{\text{calorific content of total assimilation}}$$

Reports of individual gross growth efficiencies vary from 3.5 to 40 per cent, and for individual net growth efficiencies from 5 to 65 per cent. For range-reared beef cattle we have gross growth efficiencies of about 4 per cent and net efficiencies of 11 per cent; for broiler chickens, intensively reared calves, and young pigs the gross growth efficiencies can be over 30 per cent and the net efficiencies as high as 60 per cent. Apart from the differences in growth efficiencies between the broiler industry and traditional methods of rearing agricultural livestock, there are biologically more fundamental differences associated with age and with the rates (and kinds) of food supply. Fish show the same differences with changes in age and nutrition as do chickens, swine, and cattle. In general, a young fast-growing fish usually has a markedly higher individual growth efficiency (both gross and net) than an older mature one, and the difference is even greater with a large senescent fish. In several fish species, the individual gross growth efficiency changes with the availability of food. Crudely, when food is plentiful, an individual fish will spend more energy on the processes of digestion and assimilation than at times of food scarcity. In order to even out the changes in growth efficiency with age, Slobodkin has used a growth efficiency which is roughly a lifespan-cost-of-replacement measure, which can be defined as:

$$\frac{\text{calorific content of individual biomass at age } x \times 100}{\text{calorific content of food intake to age } x}$$

This is essentially the energy value of the individual animal expressed as a percentage of the energy cost of making the animal.

An important aspect of these efficiencies of individual animals is the ratio between respired assimliation and the non-respired assimilation which is available for growth and reproduction. This has as a major component the effect of age differences, but it also varies with degree of homeostasis. "Population" energy budgets prepared for fish species by Ivlev, by Allen (see Chapter 7), and more recently by K. H. Mann in England and S. D. Gerking and others in the United States, suggest that the energy respired is usually between 11 and 15 times the non-respired assimilation in these poikilothermic vertebrates. Respiration: growth ratios for several invertebrates are only about a third of these values. Studies by Eugene P. Odum and his colleagues have given us much higher ratios for homoiothermic vertebrates (birds and small mammals), and these represent a range of 40–90 times the growth energy being involved in respiration.

Obviously, the bias in all these figures is that they are derived from studies on adult animals, and the respiration:growth ratios, even for homoiotherms, are known to be much lower for young, actively growing individuals. It is highly significant that the growth patterns of many invertebrates, including molluscs, and of the majority of fish groups differ markedly from those in most arthropods and vertebrates which have been more extensively studied. As I have discussed elsewhere, many molluscs show a continuity in the growth processes throughout life which is largely independent of the processes leading to sexual maturity. Thus the growth rates of such molluscs often show clearcut effects of environmental differences and environmental changes. Critical sizes, for respiratory and other physiological shifts, may be determined by environmental conditions and have little or no relation to maturation. The infraspecific variations in patterns of life-cycle and in fecundity in pulmonate snails represent a special case of this, and are partly responsible for the success of these forms in the transitory environments of fresh waters. A further characteristic of many invertebrates and of fish is that there can be considerable variations in the fractions of non-respired assimilation going to individual growth and to reproduction, respectively. In the primitive, pulmonate, salt-marsh snail *Melampus,* my associates and I have found that during the breeding season 87 per cent of the non-respired assimilation is directed to reproduction. This corresponds to 46 per cent of the total annual N-R.A. for *Melampus,* or 32 per cent N-R.A. if spring prebreeding growth rates were sustained throughout the year. Within one species of freshwater pulmonate snail, we have found populations where 40 per cent of the N-R.A. in the breeding season is directed to reproduction, and other populations where 66 per cent is so directed. It should be mentioned here that prospects of fish-farming are particularly attractive (see Chapter 15) precisely because the individual gross growth efficiencies are potentially higher than those for warm-blooded farm animals.

Over the last twenty-five years there has been a steadily increasing interest in experimental and theoretical ecology, and much of this has been directed toward ecological energetics at the population level.

Laboratory ecosystems—or systems of predators and prey in culture —were designed by Lawrence B. Slobodkin and others, and their analysis led him to what are the most rigorously defined measures of efficiency in terms of transfer through trophic levels. Earlier ratios of "ecological efficiency" by R. L. Lindeman and others involve ambiguities or even conceptual errors. It is important to emphasize that the measures of population efficiency defined by Slobodkin are set up for steady-state populations only. In other words, we are concerned with a situation dependent on the rate of predation from the population so "balancing" the food intake by the population that the population remains in a steady state as regards biomass and energy content. A measure of the efficiency with which a food supply is exploited is defined by Slobodkin in his food-chain efficiency as:

$$\frac{\text{calorific content of yield of population to its predator} \times 100}{\text{calorific content of food supplied to the population}}$$

This food-chain efficiency is based on measures of energy content per unit time of both food supplied and yield to predator. There is an optimum value of food-chain efficiency at a certain level of predation, and hence of food supply to the steady-state population. Lower values of this efficiency correspond to underpredation and overpredation, respectively. A precisely similar matter of trophic efficiency—though formulated in a different fashion—has long been the concern of fisheries workers involved in establishing rational management of fish stocks under exploitation by man, and their extensive work will be briefly summarized in Chapter 10. In the special case of optimum level of food-chain efficiency, the food supply becomes identical with the food intake of the population, and so Slobodkin defines as gross ecological efficiency the ratio:

$$\frac{\text{calorific content of yield of population to its predator} \times 100}{\text{calorific content of the food intake of the population}}$$

In terms of the Hutchinson-Lindeman method of trophic representation, this gross ecological efficiency would be:

$$\frac{\lambda_4 \times 100}{\lambda_3} \quad \text{for trophic level } \Lambda_3.$$

Gross ecological efficiency will always be greater than or equal to any food-chain efficiency for the same steady-state population. It should also be noted that—by this definition—a gross ecological efficiency could not be calculated for the first trophic level (the primary producers) and that the *top* trophic level in any community of organisms would have a gross ecological efficiency of zero.

Perhaps the most successful laboratory ecosystems have been those involving populations of *Daphnia*, for which the maximum food-chain efficiency has been found to be about 8.5 per cent and the maximum ecological efficiency about 12.5 per cent. When Slobodkin summarized this work in 1960 and 1961 (see further reading at the end of this book), there were a number of field estimates of gross ecological efficiency available and these, with certain exceptions, fell in a range essentially identical with those obtained from the laboratory ecosystems. The majority of the field estimates then lay in the range from 5.5 to 13.5 per cent. Some authors have claimed that the gross ecological efficiency is higher in the higher trophic levels, but the evidence supporting this is probably inadequate.

Over the last decade, such further direct estimates of food-chain efficiencies as have been made in field and laboratory ecosystems have been in the range of from about 6 to about 15 per cent. (In Chapter 13, and elsewhere in this book a "low average" value of 8 per cent is used in general discussions.) After his work on *Daphnia* and *Hydra* populations, Slobodkin had suggested that gross ecological efficiencies in natural ecosystems were likely to be constant and to lie close to a value of 10 per cent. Derived from laboratory cultures (though corresponding to most field data then available), the precise value of 10 per cent was presumably a "straw man" set up against future data to be gained from increasing knowledge of natural ecosystems. As such, it has been remarkably resilient, except for some computations based on marine communities, and it will continue to stand as a modal value for most circumstances. There have been suggestions, however, that it is too low in relation to figures computed for the productivity of certain communities. For example, Howard L. Sanders found that for certain benthic communities the observed quantities of carnivores are much greater than those that would be predicted for the food-webs using an efficiency of 10 per cent. Similarly, J. H. Steele of the fisheries laboratory at Aberdeen in Scotland has back-calculated from yields of fish in the North Sea and his computations would require an efficiency *somewhere* in the food-chain of about 20 per cent. Such data seem to establish that such high values of gross ecological efficiency can occur, but, as mentioned on page 183, there are sound physiological reasons for assuming that transfer values in excess of about 35 per cent could not possibly be sustained in natural circumstances (that is, excluding human artifacts occurring in the factories of intensive agriculture). Actually, a parallel to the economics of intensively reared chickens may occur in the feeding "efficiency" of some larger copepods of the marine zoöplankton for a *temporary* period at certain growth stages. R. J. Conover has shown that, under certain conditions in larger calanoid copepods, as a result of direct accumulation of storage fats assimilated with little or no metabolic alteration from the fats stored in diatoms of suitable age and nutrition, short-term pseudoefficiencies (which would correspond to net growth efficiencies as defined above) in excess of 50 per cent can be assessed. Transfer efficiencies of this sort do not really correspond to growth of copepod tissues, cannot continue through the molt-stages of a copepod's life-cycle, and thus are inappropriate in cost-of-replacement measures. For steady-state population efficiencies, therefore, 25 per cent would seem to be the extreme upper limit possible for gross ecological efficiency in natural communities, and there is no reason to doubt the ecological generalization that food-chain and ecological efficiencies can only have a narrow range of values. However, although Slobodkin's "straw man" may stand up to this extent, there is an important practical aspect involved in the possibility that ecological efficiencies may reach values of the order of 20 per cent. Assessed across several trophic levels, the difference between 10 and 20 per cent efficiency becomes highly significant in terms of the productivity of the higher trophic levels.

Thus, in attempts to assess the potential fish harvest which man can crop from the oceans (see, for example, Chapters 12 and 13), a small shift in the transfer efficiencies employed can have a major effect upon the computation of potential crop. It hardly requires a canny Scots appreciation of the effects of compound interest rates—here applied negatively—to comprehend that, after four transfers, the yield at the fifth trophic level if the transfer efficiency were 20 per cent would be 16 times the yield if transfer efficiency were 10 per cent, or 39 times the yield from 8 per cent. This greatly exaggerates the difficulty, since little of the marine harvest is taken from the fifth trophic level. The conservative view taken in the computations of Chapter 13 is that about half the potential crop for man (by conventional fishery methods) is derived from fish of the third trophic level (zoöplankton-feeding) and half from the fourth trophic level. Based on this mixed cropping, the potential yield computed for 8 per cent gross ecological efficiency would be increased by about 1.6 times if the efficiency were actually 10 per cent, by 3.7 times if 15 per cent, and by 6.9 times if 20 per cent. As already noted, an efficiency level between 10 and 15 per cent is more probable than one of 20 per cent. Thus a two- to fourfold upward correction may need to be applied to assessments of the potential marine harvest if the trophic conditions deduced by Steele and Sanders are at all extensive in the oceans.

If one accepts the dubieties and the imprecision in such estimates which result from other causes, including the arbitrary assignment of particular trophic levels to populations of animal species whose mere survival through the changing trophic circumstances of the seasons is evidence for shifts in proportional use of links to more than one lower trophic level in the food-webs, the difficulty of estimating a precise average value for the transfer rates (measured as the gross ecological efficiencies of each population) can be seen in perspective. That estimates of harvestable productivity in the sea differ by as much as a factor of ten is of less significance to man's future than the facts that estimates *can be made,* that the energy budgets of marine (and all other) ecosystems are finite, and that such harvestable food resources are not "inexhaustible."

Happily, such imprecision in estimates of the total marine harvest does not affect the immediate pragmatic matter of rational planning to obtain the maximum yield from conventional fisheries. There have been available theoretical models of exploited fish populations since 1931—earlier fisheries management having been almost entirely empirical—and since at least 1946, more sophisticated equations for the annual yield from an exploited fish population at any steady state which have permitted sufficient prediction of the dynamic processes for successful regulation. The basic features of the simpler models, and some recommendations for fisheries management arising from the more complex ones, are discussed in Chapter 10.

# "Over-fishing" and "Under-fishing"

ONE INSTANCE in which the relations of prey to predator have long been studied concerns the natural fish stocks exploited by man. The nineteenth century saw the development both of the steam trawler and of the otter-trawl (see Chaper 14), the first deployment of which together in the North Sea soon brought about the first clear demonstration of stock depletion. Earlier, the attitude toward the "inexhaustible" marine resources was that of Walter Scott, "There is as good fish in the sea as ever came out of it." By the beginning of the twentieth century both Frank Buckland in Britain and C. G. J. Petersen in Denmark believed that they had good evidence of reduced fishing yields *exploited* resulting from over-fishing of particular stocks.

The best early exposition of the dynamics of an exploited fish population was given in 1931 by E. S. Russell of the Lowestoft laboratory. Subsequently, there has been some controversy on the relative importance of fishery-dependent and other year-to-year changes in fish stocks, together with more disagreement on appropriate measures to prevent over-fishing. However, there is now no dubiety about the occurrence of over-fished species and, although much more sophisticated models of exploited populations have since been constructed, Russell's equation remains a convenient and easily understood statement of the factors involved. Further, control experiments have been provided in European waters by two World Wars, and these have not only confirmed that fishery-dependent changes do occur in population dynamics but that the process of stock depletion is truly reversible.

In both wars, the seas around the British Isles were closed to most commercial fishing by the extensive minefields which were laid from 1914 to 1919 and from 1939 to 1945. Catches of such fish as plaice from the North Sea and hake from off the Irish coast were unusually high in 1919 and again in 1945. Even more significantly, the catch assessed per unit of fishing effort was about tripled for many fish stocks after each "close season." This is clearly shown in Figure 10·1, which presents for the years 1905–1950 the catches of haddock by Scottish trawlers in the North Sea expressed as weight of fish per unit of fishing effort. The point not shown by the figure is that in the catches of such years as 1911–1915 and 1923–1939, the average size of fish captured became smaller. The greater returns of the years after each war show that during the other years fishing effort was being wasted in merely reducing the stocks to uneconomic levels. Apart from the accidents of war, there have been a few fish stocks for which periods of regulation have been possible, including the Pacific halibut stocks controlled by Canada and the United States in the years between 1930 and 1960.

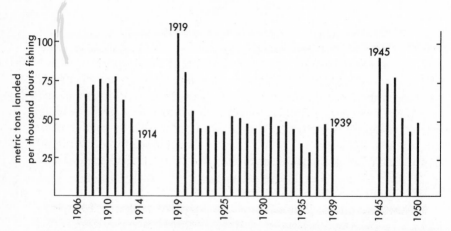

**Figure 10·1. Catches of haddock by Scottish trawlers in the North Sea, showing the effects of two wars.** In each case extensive minefields caused closure of the fishing areas for some years, and record catches were made in 1919 and 1945 when commercial fishing could be resumed. The effects of over-fishing from 1911 to 1913 and from 1922 to 1939 proved to be reversible. [Modified from figures in M. Graham, *Sea Fisheries*, Edward Arnold, London, 1956.]

Here a sustained reduction in fishing intensity was accomplished by treaties, and this has permitted a buildup after over-fishing. The restored halibut stock was tripled, and over several years the permitted catch amounted to about 60 per cent more than the yield of the fishery in its uncontrolled, over-fished years. A brief examination of the simple equation first set out by E. S. Russell will show why such regulation can work.

## Russell's model

This simple theoretical model of an exploited fish population is based on a self-evident axiom. It is that the biomass of a population remains stabilized if, over a given period of time, the biomass increments are equaled by the biomass decrements. There are four primary factors contributing to this balance in a closed fish population (without emigration or immigration), which, in the simplest case, is in a steady state. Of these four, two are incremental: recruitment of individual fish to the exploitable stock, and growth of individual fish in the exploitable stock; and two are decrimental: the "natural" mortality of individuals in the exploitable stock, and the catch or yield of exploited individuals. In its simplest symbolic form, Russell's equation can be written thus:

$$S_2 = S_1 + (A + G) - (M + C)$$

where $S_1$ and $S_2$ represent the total biomass of the exploitable stock of fish at the beginning and end, respectively, of the time interval—usually one year—for which the four primary incremental and decremental factors are defined. The exploitable stock can be defined as the fish big enough to be caught by the trawls or other nets used in this particular fishery. Thus $A$ represents the additional biomass gained by the younger "recruits" which have grown up into the exploitable stock during the time interval, and $G$ represents the biomass added by the growth of individuals in both $S_1$ and $A$ of the exploitable stock. $C$ represents the biomass of fish caught by the fishery during the period, and $M$ is the biomass of fish lost to the exploitable stock by natural causes during the same time—that is, the deaths due to disease, to predation other than human fishing, and so on.

It is important to note that the four primary factors involve considerable interdependence; for example, $A$ is not independent of $C$ or $M$ since the rate of recruitment to the exploitable stock depends on earlier growth, which can be density-dependent and thus affected by the rates of removal of older fish. Other interactions are considerably more complex. Partly because of such interdependence among the primary factors, the working models now used in assessments of fisheries are also much more complex. Essentially, the failings of Russell's equation consist in the primary factors being represented by their effects. Thus, while it can be a revealing formulation of past events, in its simplest form it is of less value in predicting the future prospects of a fishery. In spite of that, it does describe the basic dynamic properties of exploited stocks very clearly, and we do not need to consider the more sophisticated working models in order to understand something of the effects of exploitation on yields and something of the theoretical bases for the management of fishery resources. For example, the biological background of both under-fishing and over-fishing can readily be demonstrated by a closer examination of some of the properties of Russell's model.

Obviously, depending on whether $(A + G)$ is less than, equal to, or more than $(C + M)$, then $S_2$—the exploitable stock at the end of the period—will be less than, equal to, or greater than $S_1$—the original stock. The simplest theoretical case is that of an equilibrium condition in the stock where $S_2 = S_1$ and this must have resulted from:

$$(M + C) = (A + G)$$

In practice, even with a sustained level of exploitation, a true state of equilibrium is rarely attained because of variations in natural factors affecting particularly the terms $G$ and $A$. Any variations from year to year in the quantity of food available will affect $G$, as will certain other environmental factors including temperature for inshore stocks. As discussed earlier (see page 102), for several fish species there is great variation from year to year in the numbers of young fish surviving from their larval stages, and this variation at a later age will affect term $A$. In spite of such variations in natural factors, the stock size may remain nearly constant for many years of fishing, fluctuating to a relatively small extent about an average level. It is important to realize that there are a whole series of levels of stock size at which equilibrium may be established. In other words, if $C$ is sustained at an "equilibrium catch" level, a state of equilibrium can exist between the fishery and the exploited stock, but there are a whole series of levels of exploitation for which equilibrium conditions can be established. In the broadest terms, equilibrium may be established at any level of stock size between the maximum (that is, a previously unfished or virgin stock) and the minimum population size for its survival. It might be expected intuitively that the maximum yield of a fishery would lie somewhere between these two extremes, and fisheries experience provides factual confirmation of this. The theoretical basis for the effect of fishing intensity on yield may be illustrated by examining the features of population structure which affect the term $G$ (the biomass added during each time interval to the exploitable stock). As reiterated throughout Chapter 9 and elsewhere in this book, the biomass of food available to, or even ingested by, a heterotrophic organism like a fish does not all go into growth. Of the fraction assimilated, a considerable part is required for maintenance, locomotion, and so on, and can be measured as respiration, while the remainder, the non-respired assimilation

(N-R.A.), is divided between reproductive output and individual growth. Now the proportions of respired assimilation (R.A.) to N-R.A. will vary considerably with the age and size of even completely healthy fish. In general, younger fish can put more of their food intake to N-R.A., and hence to growth, while older fish have to put more of their food intake into maintenance. Thus the proportions of younger and older fish in the exploitable stock will affect $G$, if there is a limited food resource (and this is the case with most fish stocks), and if younger and older fish compete for food (and this is usually the case within the size range covered by the term, exploitable stock). Thus an exploitable stock with proportionately more older fish will have a lower value for $G$ than a stock similar in all other respects except for its age structure involving more younger fish (being a broader-based pyramid of age classes). This difference of term $G$ with age structure of the exploitable population partly explains why under-fishing can occur, that is, why at lower levels of fishing intensity the yield can be increased with increasing fishing effort while the stock remains within an equilibrium situation. Consideration of the case with a virgin stock may clarify this. This will be an equilibrium case with $S_2$ equaling $S_1$ (at whatever the maximum value for $S$ is, depending on the availability of food for the stock), and since there has been no fishing the term $C$ can be omitted. Therefore, in the virgin stock, $M$ must equal $(A + G)$, and if natural mortality is small, this implies that recruitment and growth must also be small. This theoretical conclusion is borne out in practice, and when a virgin stock is first exploited, the first catches are often found to include a large proportion of older large fish in poor condition. Particularly for bottom-dwelling fish such as haddock and plaice, such catches have been reported for the first years of new fisheries all over the world. Similar catches are also characteristic of the first angling returns from a previously unfished lake.

To return to the more general point, in any properly exploited fishery the fish stock remains in equilibrium (with $S_2 = S_1$) from year to year, but this equilibrium may be established at different levels of $C$. In the first years of exploitation of a previously virgin fishery, the combined term $(C + M)$ is small, and thus $(A + G)$ is also small and the annual yield of the fishery will be well below the maximum possible. This is the case of an equilibrium situation with under-fishing. Many —perhaps most—present fisheries are in the opposite condition of being grossly over-fished. In these, the yield per unit of effort is much less than it could be. Before we discuss this most usual case of an equilibrium situation with over-fishing, it is worth briefly considering the less usual condition where the size of the exploitable stock is changing.

For example, if $A$ and $M$ remain constant and there is a considerable decrease in fishing intensity (that is, a smaller value for $C$), there can be a temporary increase in $G$ and $S_2$ will be greater than $S_1$. This is the case when, after a period of gross over-fishing, further exploitation of a fish stock is abandoned. Conversely, if $C$ increases and the growth rate $G$ remains the same, $S_2$ will be less than $S_1$. This is the peculiar case of over-fishing carried to the uneconomic intensity which can lead to extinction of the population—at least as an exploitable stock.

More usually, over-fishing involves an equilibrium situation but a relatively low yield per unit of fishing effort. All fishery management is intended to establish an equilibrium situation with the maximum yield per unit fishing effort, and this means conducting the fishery with the fishing effort sustained at the optimal intensity. One relatively crude method of assessing the fishing mortality is as the percentage actually

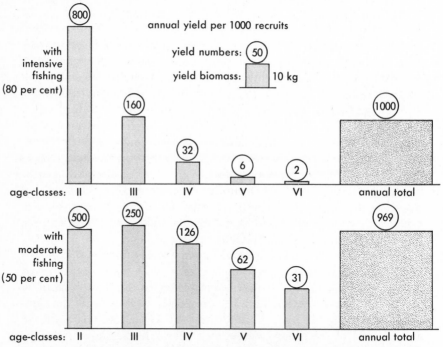

**Figure 10·2. Variation in yield at two rates of fishing intensity.** Both are assumed to be "equilibrium" situations (each 1000 recruits to the fishery in age-class II are balanced by 1000 fish caught annually), and the numbers cropped from each age-class are multiplied by the appropriate average weights to give each yield biomass. It can be seen that the lighter intensity of fishing effort (50 per cent level) gives the greater yield in terms of biomass units per year. More intensive fishing (at the 80 per cent level) represents further over-fishing, and yields less annual biomass for increased effort. [Prepared from tabulated examples in E. S. Russell, *The Overfishing Problem*, Cambridge University Press, 1942.]

captured each year of all age classes in the exploitable stock. A very heavy fishing rate involving 80 per cent of the stock per year is contrasted in Figure 10·2 with one in which there is a 50 per cent rate of fishing. In terms of weight of yield it can be seen that the 50 per cent level—the lighter intensity of fishing effort—gives the greater yield in biomass per year. The further over-fishing of the 80 per cent rate yields less annual biomass for increased effort. Crudely, over-fishing means that more and more fish are taken from the exploitable stock before they have grown to a size that makes their capture worthwhile. As noted above, for a series of fishing intensities, we can have a series of sustained equilibrium catches, and in Figure 10·3 is presented the general relationship between the sustained yield and the intensity of fishing effort over the range of equilibrium situations. Starting from the zero level of the virgin stock, increases in fishing effort produce sustainable yields (that is, equilibrium catches) which increase at a decreasing rate. Thus the shorter, ascending, left-hand part of the curve in Figure 10·3 represents conditions of under-fishing. At some point in our generalized diagram, a maximum yield is accomplished, and this is the optimal intensity of fishing effort at which all fishery management should be aimed. All further increase in fishing effort actually reduces both the total biomass of the catch and the average

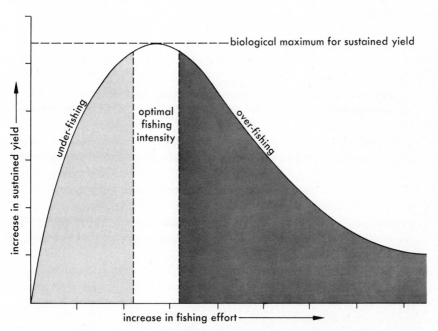

**Figure 10·3. The general relationship between the sustained yield and the intensity of fishing effort over a range of equilibrium situations.**

size of fishes in it. This right-hand part of the curve in Figure 10·3 represents cases of over-fishing. When we also consider the economics of commercial fishing, it is easy to see why, in most instances, over-fishing does not reach the level of destroying the exploitable stock biologically, but often reaches levels where further increase of effort would be completely uneconomic. Unfortunately, in cases of "mild" over-fishing, it is very difficult to persuade competing commercial fishermen—or competing fishing nations—to reduce the fishing intensity in order to reach the maximum possible equilibrium level of $(A + G) = (C + M)$, and thus paradoxically by reduction of effort achieve a higher level of C, the annual yield. Nevertheless, if the maximum yield from marine fisheries using conventional methods of capture is to be attained, it will require national or international regulation restricting fishing effort for any exploitable stock to a narrow range around the optimal intensity (see Figure 10·3).

## Obtaining maximum yield

Even if we disregard for the moment the great legal difficulties which can arise in fisheries management because of the common-property status of the fish stocks, and the peculiar economic side-effects which can arise from some methods of regulation of fishing intensity (for example, vessel size), there remain major biological differences between fish species which necessitate rather different types of regulation in order to achieve optimum yields. Changes in the equilibrium situation of an exploitable stock can be brought about by fisheries regulation affecting two principal kinds of biological variables. These are: first, the age (or size) of recruitment to the exploitable stock; and, secondly, the total effective fishing intensity, to which the fishing mortality rate is proportional.

Control of the age of recruitment can be accomplished by fixing mesh sizes of trawls and other nets or by establishing minimum landing sizes. With certain fish stocks, where there are known young fish areas, regulations banning fishing in part or the whole of such areas can be an effective control of the age of recruitment to the exploitable stock. Regulation of fishing intensity is always more difficult, but can involve the setting of catch quotas or the imposition of partially closed fishing areas or of closed seasons.

It should be intuitively obvious that differences in natural lifespan, and in growth rates between species, must affect the types of fishery regulation which are most likely to be effective in obtaining optimal fishing intensities and maximum yields. However, regulations for particular fisheries are now recommended by biologists on the basis of analytical population models, considerably more sophisticated than that

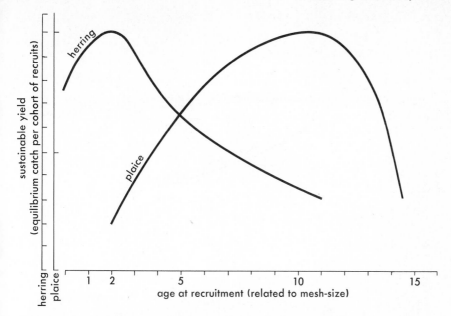

**Figure 10·4. Sustainable yield in a fishery in relation to the age (or size) at recruitment.** The curves are plotted for a long-lived, slow-growing species, the plaice, and for a fast-growing species of relatively short natural lifespan, the herring. The data for both are derived from Scottish fisheries conducted in the North Sea. For further discussion, see text. [Adapted from B. B. Parrish in *Symp. Inst. Biol., 11*:79–93, 1963, partly after Beverton and Holt, 1957.]

of Russell, which incorporate components of direct and indirect interdependence of the primary factors, and allow prediction. Although Figures 10·4 and 10·5 are based on them, it would be inappropriate to attempt to set out these elegant but mathematically complex model systems here. Two excellent books can be recommended to the interested reader: *On the Dynamics of Exploited Fish Populations,* by R. J. H. Beverton and S. J. Holt of the Lowestoft fisheries laboratory, and *Handbook of Computations for Biological Statistics of Fish Populations,* by W. E. Ricker of the Canadian Fisheries Research Board.

Perhaps the best way of visualizing the predicted yields which can be generated by these complex models is to plot, for different fishing intensities and for different ages of recruitment, the sustainable yield in terms of the equilibrium catch per cohort of recruits. This is done in Figures 10·4 and 10·5 for a long-lived slow-growing species, the plaice, and for a fast-growing species of relatively short natural lifespan, the herring. The data are derived from Scottish fisheries conducted in the North Sea, and were originally prepared by Beverton and Holt, and by B. B. Parrish of the Aberdeen fisheries laboratory.

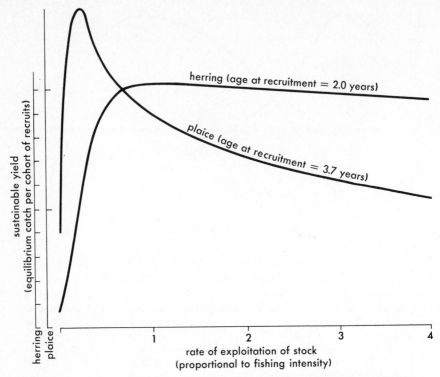

**Figure 10·5. Sustainable yield in a fishery in relation to the intensity of fishing effort.** The curves are plotted, as in Figure 10·4, for plaice and for herring and are based on data from Scottish fisheries. For further discussion, see text. [Adapted from B. B. Parrish in *Symp. Inst. Biol.*, 11:79–93, 1963, partly after Beverton and Holt, 1957.]

From the figures it is obvious that in the case of the plaice the maximum of the equilibrium catch will occur at low fishing intensities and at a relatively high age of recruitment. On the other hand, in the case of the herring, the maximum of the equilibrium catch occurs at a fairly high fishing intensity and is not greatly modified by considerable increases in fishing intensity, while the age of recruitment for maximum equilibrium catch is considerably lower than that for the plaice. If either fishery is to be regulated to obtain the maximum yield, control of mesh-size or other regulation of the age of recruitment is essential, but in the case of the plaice, there is a much greater need for regulation of the total fishing intensity in order to prevent the biological over-fishing to which this species is obviously much more susceptible.

It is thus possible to set up the biological criteria for fisheries regulation necessary to achieve maximum yield. It is much more difficult to assess the relative merits of the economic returns of different fisheries in the same area and of differences in commercial or national interests. Mixed fish stocks exploited by several different fishing methods, and fished in international waters by fishermen from several countries, present peculiar problems of regulation.

## Lessons from whaling

In a minor Irishism, the best cases of over-fishing concern whales. The history of whaling is largely a well-documented series of cases of overexploitation of limited stocks. Whales are mammals, mostly producing only one young every other year, and so, unlike some fish species, recovery from over-fishing in exploited whale populations is a long and slow process and does not always occur. The northern right-whale was reduced almost to extinction in Arctic waters about a century ago. Whaling for rorqual became uneconomic in the Arctic and North Atlantic about the beginning of this century. Antarctic whaling, for several species of whalebone whales, including the blue-whale, the fin-whale (or common rorqual), and the sei-whale, began about that time and the effects of overexploitation were already apparent by about 1935, despite British attempts to control the intensity of whaling around South Georgia by systems of licensing and taxation of "landings." Antarctic whaling has been regulated since 1946 by an international whaling convention through which thirteen participant nations agree to yearly quotas for various species. Largely because quotas have been set too high—as a result of pressure from the three principal whaling nations, Japan, USSR, and Norway—the last two decades have seen a more than fivefold decline in the returns from Antarctic whaling. In the Antarctic summer of 1947–48, 8000 blue-whales were captured; by 1957–58, only 1684; and by 1964–65, only 20. As this gross overexploitation of blue-whales brought about disastrous reduction of returns, the Antarctic whaling industry turned to the smaller whalebone whales and exceeded optimum rates of exploitation for each species in turn. The international commission has long used as a basis for regulation of Antarctic whaling the blue-whale unit which is equivalent to one blue-whale or two fin-whales or six sei-whales. The peak capture of fin-whales, amounting to over 26,000, came in the Antarctic summer of 1961–62, and decline was rapid to just over 7000 in 1964–65 and just over 2000 in 1967–68. For the still smaller sei-whale, the highest returns are those for 1964–65, and overexploitation had already brought about reduced returns by 1968. The economics of greatly reduced returns for effort expended have caused the withdrawal of several nations traditionally involved in Antarctic whaling, including Britain in 1963 and the Netherlands in 1964.

Tragically, Antarctic whaling is a case where the means of regulation could have been effective, had the quotas been set in accordance with the advice given by the biologists concerned. Agreement had been reached, and inspectors representing the international whaling commission have been aboard all the factory ships and at the shore stations over the last two decades. Running tallies have been kept during each season, and continued daily radio contacts between the inspectors have allowed operations to be stopped when the quotas were reached. However, the quotas for the last two decades were set too high, largely as a result of pressure from those nations with a high capital investment in factory ships and other equipment. Admittedly, there is very little else one can do with a fast, high-bowed, specialized whale-catcher (and a trained master gunner and his Foyn harpoon gun) but shoot whales. Evidence that the quotas were being set too high had mounted through the 1950's and, in the seasons of 1962–63 and 1963–64, in spite of the most intensive efforts, the total catch was below the quotas set. For the 1964–65 season the biologists of the commission recommended the quota be drastically reduced to 4000 blue-whale units, but Norway, Russia, and Japan insisted on the limit being set at 8000 units. This quota was not reached, and the catch was actually less than half what it had been four years before. The agreed quota for 1967–68 was 3200 blue-whale units, but even with intensive hunting over a relatively long season this quota could not be reached, and the actual catch was less than one-sixth of returns achieved only seven years before.

Whaling scientists of almost all countries would agree in their computations of the yield which could have been obtained from the Antarctic stocks of whales under proper management. Most estimates suggest that annual catches of around 6000 blue-whales and 20,000 fin-whales could have been continuously cropped from the Antarctic. About fifteen years of overexploitation has resulted in the loss of this potential catch—which could have yielded about 3 million tons of whalemeat and oil for the world. It is difficult to assess the chances of Antarctic stocks of whales ever recovering to a level which could again support such annual catches.

Another uncertainty is the biological status of such species as the blue-whale. We simply do not know what the minimum world population still capable of effective reproduction would be for such a species of widely dispersed large mammals. From circumstantial evidence on other species, it is not likely to lie below 500 individuals. With protective legislation almost entirely respected, stocks of the smaller and more local Californian gray-whale made a remarkable recovery in the early 1960's from population levels reduced to "a few hundred" in 1938. One set of census data would provide an estimate of 18,300 gray-whales in 1967. Estimates of the world blue-whale population prepared from data collected in 1964 lie between 600 and 2000. Elsewhere in the southern oceans, outside the Antarctic areas of regulated whaling, uncontrolled exploitation of blue-whales has continued, and 70 were known to have been killed in 1966–67. Mankind may have already hunted to extinction the largest animal species which has ever existed on the planet Earth.

## Future regulation

The biological factors involved in establishing the optimal intensity of fishery effort to obtain maximum yield are not the only factors involved in establishing management of fishery resources by regulation. Economic aspects of increased fishing intensities in terms of vessels, men, and money will be of considerable importance. If the curve in Figure 10·3 is considered it can be seen that just below the maximum there is a nearly flat sector of the curve where a significant reduction in fishing intensity will result in only a negligible reduction of catch. In crude terms, perhaps about 75 per cent of the effort required to take the maximum catch will give a return of about 95 per cent of that maximum catch. The costs per ton of catch will be markedly reduced. On the other hand, in a fishery where the fish are particularly valuable, intensity of fishing will become stabilized economically at a level where the value of the catch is only a little above the total costs of the fishing. In this case the "economic equilibrium" level of fishing may be much greater than that corresponding to the maximum yield. Thus over-fishing in the biological sense will occur unless the regulations imposed restrict the fishery to a level well below that suggested by "economic" returns. Where over-fishing is already occurring and returns per unit fishing effort are dropping, there is a tendency for individual fishing skippers, and for companies owning fleets of fishing vessels, to keep on fishing at ever greater intensities as long as they can cover the immediate running costs of their fishing effort. As with whaling, this is dictated by the background of capital investment which has no alternative use. This tendency to keep fishing is clearly rational in an economic sense but totally irrational and self-defeating from a biological standpoint. This dichotomy is a major factor in making the introduction of fishery legislation difficult, and the future development of controls for such resources uncertain.

In marked contrast to the situation in Antarctic whaling, regulation has proved highly successful biologically in the fishery for the Pacific halibut carried out by vessels from Canada and the United States. This fish is a long-lived, slow-growing species comparable to the plaice whose population dynamics under exploitation were discussed above (see page 203). Regulation of the halibut fishery has continued for more than thirty years; the stock had risen in the early 1960's to more than three times its population level during earlier over-fishing, and the annual yield in the 1960's was 60 per cent greater than in the 1930's. Biologically, therefore, the management of this fish stock has been highly successful. However, the regulation itself has created a fishing industry operating at very low level of efficiency. The quota system and enforced layover agreements involve a fleet of about four times the number of vessels (with their specialized gear) which are required to bring in the maximum catch. Thus, these vessels can only be operated one day in eight, on average. The biologically successful management of this halibut fishery would be unlikely to be acceptable economically in the majority of international fisheries elsewhere in the world.

It is unnecessary to discuss the difficulties which are likely to arise in attempting the restriction of an international fishery where as many as six different national interests are involved. However, it is worth considering the similar complications which arise when exploitation of a mixed stock of two or more fish species is concerned. In the North Sea, trawlers fishing for herring often catch numbers of small haddock. Thus the maximum yield of haddock could only be achieved by prohibiting trawling for herring. Although the herring are also exploited by other fishing methods (see Chapter 14), prohibition of trawling could markedly reduce the catch of herring. In this case, there is no single biological policy since there are two fishery resources with conflicting interests. Here economic considerations are involved, and since the damage done to haddock catches by herring trawlers is less than the extra value of the herring catch taken by the trawlers, prohibition of herring trawling in the North Sea is not justified. Obviously, even in this very simple case of mixed fishery resources, there is difficulty in balancing the interests of different groups of fishermen. In the case of the Pacific halibut fishery, an agreed reduction of fishing effort by say 33 per cent would mean that fishermen from both Canada and the United States would reduce their efforts by 33 per cent and their proportionate shares in the halibut catch would be unaltered. In our North Sea example, however, there can be no such proportionality. The decision not to protect the haddock fishery by regulations restricting trawling results in losses being sustained by the haddock fishermen (who are almost entirely Scots), while the gains are those of the herring trawlers (largely from other countries). In more general terms, the aim of management of fisheries to ensure the greatest total net yield from all the stocks in a region, taken together, may involve considerable inequities in the economic effects of biologically appropriate regulations. A supernational regulatory authority could perhaps arrange for appropriate compensation to be paid for a period after the imposition, or change, of regulations. The susceptibility of certain fishes—chiefly long-lived, slow-growing species—to over-fishing, and hence reduction of yields, means that regulation is urgently required in many of the more heavily exploited marine fisheries. The common-property status of the fish stocks in these fisheries makes regulation difficult unless a supernational authority can be set up and suitably empowered. In 1969, it may already be too late to do this for many bottom-dwelling stocks of valuable gadid species.

There is some hope in the fact that almost all the nations engaged in trawl fisheries in the North Atlantic are members of the North-East Atlantic Fisheries Commission (NEAFC), or the International Commission for the Northwest Atlantic Fisheries (ICNAF), or both. Although set up in 1959 and 1949, respectively, and although the catches of demersal fish from the North Atlantic have been somewhat controlled by their recommendations, these conservation regulations have proved difficult to apply on the high seas. Both commissions still (1968–69) merely have "under active consideration" methods for the international enforcement of regulations. Sadly, the reports of their discussions are reminiscent of those of the international whaling commission. Regulation of fisheries for pelagic, shoaling species is less immediately required, but must eventually be introduced if we are to move toward a rational exploitation of the maximum protein yield from the oceans. In the long run, it is probably more important that stocks of fish like herring, sardines, and anchoveta, feeding at lower trophic levels and with the resilience of short-lived stocks to the stress of moderate over-fishing, be preserved for the future nutrition of mankind.

# Productivity and evolutionary change

IT MAY BE HERETIC to claim—at the end of these two decades of the flowering of molecular biology—that basic studies on the organic productivity of aquatic environments are likely to contribute a great deal to our future understanding of evolutionary processes. I do so. A more predictive theory of evolution will only come from a synthesis of the seminal field of modern population genetics with two branches of bioenergetic ecology: population dynamics and physiological ecology. Our knowledge of, and theories about, the processes of natural selection stand in need of some revision, particularly as regards relative rates of evolutionary change and the plasticity of physiological response. Studies of population energetics and "field" physiology and acclimation in both freshwater and marine littoral environments are likely to be of major significance in this revision.

Darwinian natural selection involves differential survival of progeny, and hence a potential decrease in the genetically determined variability of the *steady-state* population under selection pressure. As usually defined, measures of Darwinian "fitness" involve relative ratios of surviving daughters to mothers or relative degrees of adaptedness to the immediate environmental circumstances. The "fitness" involved in simple selection is therefore short-term, and concerned with the relative proportions of the genotypes concerned in the gene pool of immediate succeeeding generations. On the other hand, evolutionary "progress" involves increasing the probability of surviving offspring after a large number of generations have elapsed. Evolutionary "success" over, say, $10^7$ years implies more than relative degrees of adaptedness, and almost certainly involves the maintenance of a repertoire of genetic flexibility. There is some empirical evidence on this paradox which can be gained from studies of physiological variation in populations of freshwater animals such as snails (see pages 167 and 215).

Neither the paradoxical aspects of evolutionary "success" nor any major questions of phylogeny seem likely to be resolved by studies in molecular biology or biochemistry alone. In particular, the optimistic claims that similarity in a given biochemical pathway—or in the mechanism of control of that pathway—would provide incontrovertible evidence of close phyletic relationship are somewhat suspect. Recent studies on the regulatory interactions of end-product metabolites upon the synthesis of various multiple forms of enzymes suggest that neither common enzymatic steps nor closely similar control patterns need reflect phyletic affinities. On the other hand, diversity in control patterns of biochemical pathways need not imply polyphylogeny. Recent discovery of extensive gene-enzyme polymorphism adds to the difficulties of drawing phyletic conclusions from biochemical data alone. Of course, data on actual amino acid sequences could provide evidence for phyletic relationships if obtained extensively, but the difficulties of collecting such crucial evidence of genetical and chemical identity make widespread utilization of this method seem unlikely.

It seems obvious that evolutionary biology cannot "go molecular" entirely, that all kinds of ecological studies must contribute, and that even the despised substantive knowledge collected laboriously from natural populations in the field is essential to its future. Construction of theoretical models of both populations and communities forms a necessary part of any analytic approach to ecology and evolution, but data from laboratory ecosystems are required to develop the more useful models, and data from field populations and communities to establish their validity.

As an unrepentant heretic in modern biology—a zoöcentric zoologist —I have a bias toward field studies involving two rather trite concepts. First, processes of animal evolution by natural selection have been involved with *whole animals* and their efficiencies as machines to make more of their own kind in immediately succeeding generations, while retaining sufficient flexibility of response (or, in a sense, machine inefficiency) to ensure persistence of the species through many generations. Thus, rather than single alleles, patterns of functional interdependence (largish bundles of integrated genetic material) are what I think to be important in making hypotheses about evolutionary matters, including phylogeny. Secondly, modes and rates of evolutionary change are largely determined by the spatial and temporal extent of steady-state populations. Continuity of any environment in space determines the size of a panmictic population, its continuity in time the number of generations that a population exists with its gene pool subjected to continued selection pressures. Bodies of fresh water provide "experimental" populations which have experienced varying degrees of spatial and temporal limitation.

It is impossible, given the limitations of this book and author, to make the remainder of this chapter an exhaustive survey of the possible impact of studies in aquatic ecology on evolutionary biology. Thus—even more than the rest of the book—it is culpably eclectic in its matter.

## Community structure and competition

One of the basic premises of the theory of natural selection is that the numbers of individuals in most species-populations remain nearly constant from generation to generation over long periods of time. At the level of a single population, generalizations based on model steady-state systems of single species have proved useful (see Chapters 9 and 10). A few workers have attempted to construct steady-state models of communities, and these have considerable evolutionary as well as ecological interest.

Unfortunately, some of the conceptual terms used—such as "niche" (for the part of the environment occupied by a species), "competition" (between species), and even "community" itself—have undergone semantic changes involving somewhat unprofitable controversy, which cannot be discussed here. In crude terms, however, conceptual models of community structure can be developed from G. F. Gause's "rule" that two species cannot live in the same place at the same time on the same resources. A great deal of data from field studies have been accumulated in the last two decades which suggest that natural selection promotes ecological divergence in closely related species living together in any environment. By far the most detailed laboratory studies on competition between species, and the only ones extensive enough to yield good statistics, are those of T. Park on flour beetles of the genus *Tribolium*. For these experimental interactions, P. H. Leslie was able to develop a mathematical model involving stochastic factors in predictions of the outcome of competition under different circumstances. More appropriate to this book—and giving considerably more attention to the energetics of food supply—have been the studies on competition between different species of *Hydra* by Lawrence B. Slobodkin. Among the experimental systems were several where the available food energy had to be partitioned between a brown species and a green species. Apart from complications introduced by the green species deriving a considerable part of its energy supply from the photosynthetic activities of its algal symbionts, the size of the food organism supplied would determine the outcome of competition. There are many interesting variants all related to food supply, individual size control, and rates of increase by budding in these competing populations of *Hydra*, and Slobodkin has shown that consideration of their adjustments in terms of a strategy to stay alive rather than in strictly mechanistic tactical terms can be revealing. This will be considered below (page 223), but meanwhile one particular type of experiment is relevant to the concept of steady-state communities. Normally, if fed in the light with relatively small food organisms (nauplii of *Artemia*) at a rate at which competition occurs in mixed cultures, the green species becomes more numerous and the brown one is eliminated after about forty days. However, by "predation" on the two populations of *Hydra* by removing a large fraction of the reproductive increase each day, the combined culture of the two species could be maintained in something approaching a steady-state.

As with so many other aspects of the "ecological theater" as a setting for the "evolutionary play," it was G. Evelyn Hutchinson who first pointed out certain regularities in the relative abundances of species found together. Starting from ecological theory, Robert H. MacArthur constructed certain species-abundance distributions, one of which was based on the assumption of the universal validity of Gause's rule. In the course of this he had to distinguish between what he termed opportunistic and equilibrium species, and it was with the latter that the relative abundances could be predicted on the basis that increase in one species-population results in a roughly equal decrease in the populations of the other species. Close correspondence of field data with the MacArthur hypothetical distribution could only be expected in a limited environmental area, with truly random sampling, and with fairly closely allied species of the same trophic level. Thus it is significant that one of the best fits to the theory so far described is the case of the cone-snails of the genus *Conus*, predatory carnivores in intertidal and subtidal tropical waters which have been extensively studied by A. J. Kohn. Application of MacArthur's best model, the one dependent on Gause's axiom of nonoverlapping niches, to more extensive communities of animals has proved somewhat disappointing. In most cases of data collected from more complex ecosystems, the common species proved to be more common and the rare species more rare than would be predicted by the model. This was pointed out in an early critical examination of data from natural communities by Nelson G. Hairston, and recently MacArthur has himself expressed considerable reservations about the validity of the model. Its importance has been that of any theoretical system: by setting up some predictions to be tested against field situations, it encouraged the collection and more rational examination of data on the species-abundance structure of natural communities. There is considerable evidence of pattern in these species-abundance distributions in nature.

It is safe to predict that more detailed faunistic studies in the oceans and in fresh waters will reveal further evidence of pattern in species-abundance distributions, and the need for further theoretical formulation will become more critical. As noted in Chapter 5, with modern sampling methods, workers like Howard L. Sanders and Robert R. Hessler have demonstrated an unsuspectedly high species diversity in deep-sea benthic faunas. There is no direct relation between total productivity and the level of species diversity found in bottom faunas. Like earlier workers, Sanders and Hessler found the common species to be excessively abundant in their samples, and the uncommon species excessively rare, when compared to the MacArthur model. It is highly significant that very great diversity may occur on the deep-sea bottom directly under relatively sterile tropical waters.

A closely related matter concerns the nature and extent of food-webs in natural ecosystems (see pages 29 and 141). In considering stream faunas with typically fluctuating and allochthonous basic food supplies, we noted empirically that the chances of starvation for any animal population at a higher trophic level were greatly decreased when that population was not restricted to a single prey species but had a choice of prey, not only at the level immediately below it but to a varying extent through several levels. Earlier we had seen, in the food-webs involving herring in the sea (page 84), a similar modification of the risks of population extinction. Intuitively, it would seem that such trophic conditions promoting population stability would also increase stability of the animal community as a whole. As noted earlier, there is abundant empirical evidence—though mostly from terrestrial communities—of the negative aspect of this hypothesis, and this has been carefully documented and summarized by Charles Elton in his studies of invasive species. The unstable ecological situations which can result from the irruption of new species into previously stable communities are well known. One particularly significant conclusion recorded by Elton is that "successful invasion" by a species is more difficult when invasion occurs into a more diverse community. As an empirical generalization, then, the stability of animal communities in time is somehow proportional both to species diversity and to food-web complexity. In turn, the level of species diversity in a community—and possibly the complexity of food-webs within it—is somehow directly related to the age of the community as such. Theories relating the number of links in the food-web of a community to its temporal stability have been put forward. However, community stability has not yet been satisfactorily explained in terms of a rigorous predictive model, in spite of continued efforts by theoretical ecologists. Once again, whether a model becomes available soon or not, more data on food-web complexity from aquatic environments are required. Both in this, and in certain other evolutionary problems such as the seemingly "conservationist" practices shown by some predators, freshwater communities have much to offer in the way of time-related "natural experiments." I believe that observations on the extent of physiological variation among populations in such communities can be related to some rather simple hypotheses about their age and extent.

## Evolution in fresh waters

In Chapter 6, two obvious features of the physical environment provided by fresh waters were summarized. First, lakes clearly lack the geographical continuity of the oceans and of the major land masses, and even the largest lakes are of relatively small extent; thus the bulk of freshwater faunas lives in, and has evolved in, relatively small units. Except for a few major river systems, there is little continuity of habitat for freshwater animals, since all coastal rivers and the majority of mountain streams are as isolated from each other as are closed ponds. Secondly, bodies of fresh water are relatively transient in a geological time-scale. Apart from a few ancient lakes (see Chapter 6), whose diverse faunas will not be discussed here, the duration of most lakes is of the order of $10^3$–$10^4$ years, and of ponds of $10^2$ years. By contrast, certain relatively constant environments may persist on areas of the continental land surfaces for up to $10^6$ years, and in the oceans for many times this period. Certain features of physiological and morphological variation which are shown by populations of some groups of freshwater animals seem likely to be related to those two features of the physical environment. My own observations on this have been largely concerned with freshwater molluscs.

The snails of fresh waters fall into two distinct groups. There are a few families of prosobranch snails—the so-called freshwater operculates—which are closely related to marine, gill-breathing forms of the littoral, and some of which are clearly the direct and recent descendants of such forms. The other and more extensive group consists of pulmonate snails with no gills and the former mantle-cavity (or chamber which enclosed the gills) modified to form a lung. These have as their closest relatives air-breathing, true land snails. In both groups, we find different degrees of adaptation to life in fresh waters coexisting and forming recognizable functional and morphological series. For example, the pulmonate snails of present-day freshwater environments range from marsh-dwelling forms, able to withstand occasional submergence but capable of being drowned, through those which feed and reproduce under water, but are really "divers," continually visiting the surface to breathe, to completely adapted, aquatic snails of two kinds. Some of the completely aquatic pulmonates have secondarily developed gills, which we term neomorphic because they are clearly not homologous with the typical respiratory structures developed in other molluscs. It is significant that the characteristic molluscan gill— the ctenidium—used by the vast majority of molluscs of all kinds living in the sea, and almost certainly possessed by the remote ancestors of these freshwater pulmonate stocks, is never regained in the course of this readaptation of an air-breathing land stock to aquatic life. Neomorphic gills are best developed in planorbid snails (of ram's-horn shape, often used in aquaria) and in the various stocks of freshwater limpets, including *Ancylus* in Europe and *Ferrissia* species in North America. Members of the other major line of completely aquatic pulmonates are without obvious anatomical modifications, but they can live successfully submerged by employing certain functional adaptations of the lung and by considerably modified behavior patterns. Such ubiquitous genera of worldwide distribution as *Lymnaea* and *Physa* are typical of this line.

Some years ago at Loch Lomond, I carried out a number of ecological and physiological studies on different populations of two such species, *Lymnaea peregra* and *Physa fontinalis*. The patterns of respiratory schesis differ from population to population. Some populations of each species living near the margin of the lake come to the surface regularly, but only when the water temperature is relatively high, and then much less frequently than in laboratory experiments. The need of these "diving" populations to visit the surface involves them in both seasonal and short-term migrations. At high water temperatures in littoral populations of *Lymnaea peregra* in Loch Lomond, I found that the respiratory needs of adult snails may result in their temporary starvation (by forcing migration onto near-sterile substrata), or may cause them to migrate away from young they have just produced. Other populations of both *Lymnaea* and *Physa* live up to 1 km offshore, though in Loch Lomond they have not been found in depths of over 6 meters. Even at this depth and distance offshore, periodic excursions to the surface are plainly impossible. In many populations, including some in relatively shallow water, the mantle-cavity or lung remains water-filled throughout life, and all respiration is cutaneous. In others the cavity contains a gas bubble, and micro-gas-analysis has revealed that in some cases the gas composition is such that the bubble could be used as an *exposed* physical gill. This is an ingenious method of gaining oxygen, employed much more extensively by aquatic insects, and depends on the maintenance of a bubble of relatively high nitrogen content from which oxygen is removed to the tissues of the snail as it diffuses into the bubble from the higher concentrations of dissolved oxygen in the water outside. In experimental tanks, snails with this respiratory pattern can remain submerged for much longer periods if they have been artificially supplied with a lungful of pure nitrogen rather than one of pure oxygen. In other populations where the lung contains a gas bubble, a relatively high carbon dioxide content and other features suggest that this use as a physical gill is unlikely, and a hydrostatic function as an internal bubble giving buoyancy is more likely. Further evidence on the hydrostatic function of the gas bubble in the lung in some species was gained by my former colleague Andrew E. Henderson, who showed that in certain populations of larger species (including *Lymnaea stagnalis* and *Planorbarius corneus*) the hydrostatic function apparently determines the amount of air taken in at surfacing and triggers the elaborate behavior patterns which end a dive. The major point to be emphasized about all this is that several distinct states occur in different populations of each species, and although the associated behavior patterns also differ and can be extremely elaborate, they are, under natural conditions, specific for each population. However, stocks brought into the laboratory always return to a pattern of relatively rapid visits to the surface to breathe, alternating these with relatively short dives. The fairly complex sequences involved in carrying out regular ventilation of the lung at the surface, and in controlling the extent of dives in relation to the exhaustion of oxygen from the bubble, are immediately assumed by stocks from the offshore bottom in Loch Lomond. Until being brought into the laboratory, such offshore stocks had lived all their lives with water-filled lungs, as had their parental stocks for many generations. In an overcrude generalization, the genetic basis for such elaborate behavior patterns must have been retained unused (and of no selective value) over several hundreds of generations.

A somewhat similar plasticity of growth rates and of reproductive behavior occurs in many species of freshwater snails, and has been investigated in Scotland and in the northeastern United States. Infraspecific differences between populations in many species involve only growth rates and the time and intensity of the breeding season. However, in *Physa, Lymnaea peregra, Ancylus,* and *Ferrissia,* interpopulation differences involve the seasonal course of the reproductive cycle (and the number of generations per year), as well as growth rates. Growth rates, fecundity, and one particular generation pattern and its controls are remarkably uniform within each population, and do not seem to differ from year to year in those populations more intensively studied. The onset of each breeding season in different populations involves both environmental factors (water temperature being the most important) and endogenous causes involving the growth rates of the snails. Perhaps the majority of the observed infraspecific variations in growth and fecundity can be explained as environmentally evoked, but there is good circumstantial evidence that certain of the interpopulation differences are genetically determined. Here again we have considerable adaptive plasticity of form and function in these freshwater species. Except for the genetically determined cases, the interpopulation differences within species imply possession of a genotype which allows phenotypic flexibility. Again in a crude generalization, the possession of such a genotype by a species allows the optimum utilization of the varying environmental conditions, both trophic and physical, found in different bodies of fresh water.

It would be inappropriate to recount further examples of infraspecific variation here, but such interpopulation variation has been found in feeding behavior, and in several aspects of growth which are reflected in the shell shapes of freshwater molluscs. In all cases where any detailed biometry has been done there is one consistent feature. The amount of variation within any single population is always very much less than the range of variation found for the species as a whole. Many kinds of interpopulation variation appear to be geographically random, with populations having the closest similarities often being far removed from each other. Recently, my colleagues and I have shown that there are considerable interpopulation differences in calcium uptake during growth in one species of stream limpet of the genus *Ferrissia* which occurs in a wide variety of creeks in upstate New York. These differences are not directly related to the calcium content of the waters in the creeks (which varies over sevenfold), and considerable differences in energy expenditure on active transport of calcium are involved among the several populations (see also Chapter 8). The populations are genetically isolated from each other, and environmental causes cannot be evoked to explain the differences in calcium metabolism. We have also found considerable variation in the secretion of shell proteins, again of random geographic distribution and apparently showing no relationship—compensatory or otherwise—with the differences in calcium metabolism found in the same range of populations. All evidence points to these being "physiological races" showing a rather random geographic dispersal. One final example where the variation is not likely to be phenotypic but almost rigidly genetically determined, was investigated by my former colleague A. D. Berrie, who carried out a biometric study of the proportions of certain lateral teeth in the radula (the chitinized tongue ribbon) of *Lymnaea peregra* in a series of populations all over northwestern Europe. He found once again that the variation within the populations was low (an investigation of museum samples showed that for some localities it had remained low for at least ten years), but that the variation among populations was very high and of a level of significance which would in some cases justify the setting up of subspecies. Again, the interpopulation variation was geographically random, with the biggest differences in some cases occurring between adjacent populations. Further, in certain of the ratios which varied, the least differences were between widely separated stocks; for example, a population just west of Glasgow in Scotland was found to be closest to a population in Swedish Lapland.

Similar results have accrued from modern revision of systematics within groups of freshwater molluscs. Such work on many groups of snails by Bengt Hubendick reveals a characteristically small number of species, almost worldwide in distribution, but with a high degree of infraspecific interpopulation variation both in their shells and in such other anatomical features as those of the reproductive system which are used in systematics. This is also broadly true of modern work on freshwater bivalves, although in this case, individual species are usually less cosmopolitan in spite of being widely distributed. Unfortunately, there are whole areas of the world—including North America—where the freshwater bivalve faunas have not yet received the careful revision of their systematics that D. F. McMichael has recently given to those of Australasia.

These features which the freshwater molluscs show—of interpopulation physiological variation and plasticity, and of a high degree of infraspecific variation within a very few cosmopolitan genera and species—are, I believe, also possessed by certain other groups in freshwater faunas. They are almost certainly characteristic of oligochaete worms, of freshwater ectoprocts, of certain fish genera, and of some arthropod groups. Obviously, they are *not* shown by the migratory fishes or by the great majority of freshwater insect forms. Significantly, these features are not found in any animal groups in the few ancient lakes like Tanganyika and Baikal (see Chapter 6).

The hypothesis we have evolved about these features is that they result from the temporal and spatial nature of the freshwater environment. The transience of most freshwater habitats limits the number of generations for which any separate population of freshwater animals can exist. But much short-term, small-scale isolation can occur, as freshwater habitats are geographically discontinuous and mostly of small extent. Genetic isolation can be sufficient to produce some interpopulation diversity, but even limited transfer of individuals between populations by passive dispersal usually results in sufficient gene exchange to prevent full speciation. This also puts a premium on those genotypes which can show phenotypic flexibility. It seems likely that a unit ecosystem rarely exists long enough in time for species separation into different ecotopes to occur. The short-term genetic isolation is limited by the rare gene-exchange of passive dispersal, but this gene-dispersal can be somewhat random in its results. Thus, a genetically determined character like the ratios in radular teeth investigated by Berrie is presumably without immediately significantly selective value, is nearly constant within populations, but varies greatly among populations in a geographically random manner. It seems possible that in the case of inheritable characters of selective value, infraspecific variation could form geographic clines; but, from our present knowledge, the appropriate interpopulation dispersal which could have allowed this does not seem to have occurred.

This hypothesis about the processes of evolution in molluscs living in fresh waters was put forward independently by Hubendick and me some years ago, on the bases of systematic studies and surveys of physiological variation, respectively. It has since been endorsed by other workers, including McMichael in a recent survey of Australasian molluscan faunas. An additional hypothesis concerns the physiological variation more exclusively. It is that the adaptive plasticity found in respiration, in reproduction, and in other aspects of the physiology of freshwater snails is itself of fundamental selective value. Particularly in species of freshwater pulmonates, selection has produced genotypes which can show phenotypic flexibility. What appears to have been most strongly selected *for* is the capacity to vary—the possession of adaptive plasticity.

Such evolutionary processes which are not involved with the selection of immediately advantageous characteristics (and which may perpetuate certain energetic inefficiencies) are of immense significance. They will be briefly discussed near the end of this chapter, but it is clear that they require further field study. The varying degrees of spatial and temporal limitation occurring in different small lakes provide "experimental" populations of great value for this, especially since the actual age of many lakes can now be more or less accurately determined.

Another evolutionary aspect of interpopulation differences within aquatic species concerns the rates of energy flow through individual organisms. Examples of markedly different growth rates, and of number of generations per year, involve not only the freshwater snail species discussed above but also the populations of *Calanus* in different latitudes discussed in Chapters 4 and 5. In these cases, and in many other similar ones in marine and freshwater environments, within a single species different populations can have markedly different rates of turnover (assessed as the ratio of productivity to mean standing crop). Although this can affect such processes as acclimation, little is known regarding possible effects on evolutionary rates. It is possible to speculate on this in more general terms.

## Rates of turnover and of change

It is obvious that systems with a high rate of turnover have a capacity for faster rates of change than can occur in low-turnover systems. Some biologists have extended this postulate to include rates of evolutionary change, and have claimed that high-turnover systems are favorable to accelerated evolution. This is less axiomatic. Here again, we must distinguish among levels of biological organization.

As already discussed, the open "'systems" of biological organization —all continually exchanging energy with their surroundings, and thus normally in a dynamic steady state—include individual living cells, whole living organisms, and the integrated communities of most ecosystems. The relation of rate of change of the system to rate of energy flow through it is: first, unlikely to be arithmetically direct; secondly, almost certain to involve homeostatic features; and thirdly, unlikely to be even similar at these three different levels of biological organization. We must distinguish among the levels. In the individual cell and, perhaps most obviously, in the still-differentiating cell of development, an increase in rate of energy flow through the system could well result in an acceleration of the genetically determined processes which establish certain metabolic pathways in preference to others and lead to the functional canalization of a specific histological cell type. Similarly, an increased turnover rate in a community of organisms could, through its effect on total numbers as well as on temporal aspects of lifespan and fecundity, result in a potentially more rapid change of the proportions of different organisms in that community, given suitably directional selective pressures.

It is less easy to generalize about whole individual organisms or about populations of single species. It has been claimed that rates of evolutionary change are accelerated in species with a high rate of turnover. Some of the pairs of species discussed in this context seem rather ineptly chosen, and involve major phyletic differences and thus significantly differently integrated patterns of animal machines. Perhaps less inappropriate than some is the oft-quoted comparison between a giant land tortoise and a hummingbird. They are both amniote vertebrates, comparable in gross developmental pattern and in major bodily organization. Crudely, both depend upon an input of energy and of information for their continuity, and both give rise to an output in terms of growth, activity, maintenance interactions, and voided waste products. However, the rates of energy flow through individuals of the two sorts are markedly different. In the giant tortoise, the input is erratic, small in proportion to the biomass of the individual, and occurring at considerable intervals of time. The output—a limited amount of slow activity—is likewise small, and the system as a whole is characterized as a low-turnover one. In contrast, the input to a hummingbird must regularly involve almost all of its waking hours, is large in calorific terms in relation to the bulk of the individual organism, and corresponds to an output at a similarly sustained high level of activity. The result is a high-turnover system. Unfortunately, we can have no direct evidence that the rate of evolutionary change is potentially greater in hummingbirds than it is in giant tortoises, but a few comments can be made.

Undoubtedly the physiological processes of the whole organism can respond to environmental changes, just as does the individual cell, by changes in the rate or nature of certain biochemical processes. In more highly organized animals, these changes can become effective within a fraction of the lifetime of the individual organism, and such processes of physiological acclimation have often been discussed. The rates of such changes obviously could be related to the overall rate of energy flow through the organism. However, since such changes do not involve the genetic constitution of the organism, they can have no direct effect on the rate of evolutionary change. However, one result of successful acclimation could be to increase the amount of time spent by the organism in environmental circumstances appropriate to that physiological change and—if this occurred before breeding—affect the relative rates of selection in a directional fashion. Of course, this is only a form of the pseudo-Lamarckian process of "organic selection" suggested by Lloyd-Morgan early this century, and later developed along with other seminal ideas in quantitative evolutionary studies by G. F. Gause.

In view of certain aspects of surface:volume ratios discussed earlier (see Chapter 4), the mere size difference between giant tortoise and hummingbird might affect the significance of the differing rates of energy flow through the two systems. In addition to homoiothermy in the bird, the relative fractions of the energetic input involved in homeostatic maintenance could be expected to differ considerably. However, the paramount effect on rates of evolutionary change resulting from differences in rates of energy turnover must lie in the effects on the time-courses of growth to reproductive maturity and of total lifespan. Obviously, one of the most important determinants of rate of evolutionary change is the frequency with which recombination of genetic material can occur. Since such recombination depends upon the cytological processes of chiasma-formation occurring during the maturation of gametes which precedes sexual reproduction, the extent of the time interval betwen sexual reproduction in succesive generations is of prime significance to the potential rate of evolutionary change. The extent to which the rate of growth to reproductive maturity is dependent on nutrition varies among different groups of animal organisms. Though the relationship is obscured by homeostatic mechanisms in most of the more highly organized animals, there is some relation between rate of nutrition and rate of maturation in perhaps the majority of lower forms. Thus, indirectly and certainly not arithmetically, an increase in energy flow through the individual organism could result in accelerated evolution in the species to which it belongs.

## A defense of teleology

In the professional training of biologists the need to avoid teleological explanation is often stressed. It is clear that the attribution of design or purpose to a biological phenomenon can, in many cases, stultify any attempt at an analytic explanation. The professionally required abjuration of teleology does not really result from this pragmatic disadvantage, but rather from historical conflicts with the revealed religions over the rôle of a creator in the middle nineteenth century, and with belief in "vitalism" even later. As mechanistic biologists, we can almost always translate a piece of teleological shorthand into a functional description in physicochemical terms with or without an added qualification on the "adaptive" value of the process described. To be completely mechanistic, such a qualification has to be couched in the population geneticist's terms of the probability of differential survivorship, or even of Darwinian "fitness." Mechanistic explanation has also to be extended to the historical level. For very many biological problems, it is much easier to discuss the adaptational significance of a process than to speculate on the history of the process in time (or how it had evolved), but some biological phenomena can be described in teleological phrases which are then extremely difficult to translate into mechanistic terms in this way. By drawing attention to such phenomena, teleology serves a useful purpose in biological speculation (and, in a few cases, use of more extensive teleology in an analog model would seem to be justified on pragmatic grounds).

As has appeared in a few places earlier in this chapter, some long-term evolutionary processes are among those where translation is difficult, largely because immediate adaptational advantage within an individual lifespan is not applicable as part of either the "differential survivorship" or "historical" levels of explanation.

Slobodkin's populations of *Hydra* whose adjustments of budding rates and size are most easily explained in terms of a strategy to stay alive rather than in terms of immediate mechanistic advantage, and my populations of snails living on the bottom of Loch Lomond and retaining over many hundreds of generations all the genetic components of an elaborate set of behavior patterns which are only of adaptive value in a very different environment, are but two examples of a broad group of problems. These include many where direct selection effects are obscured by complex coadaptation, by various forms of developmental canalization, and by maintained heterosis. I believe that initial teleological description is valuable when it attributes supposed foresight (conscious provision for remote descendants or for the survival of the population or species) to individual animals. Altruism and precognition are *impossible* as explanations, but such teleology underlines the need to develop for each case a more complex mechanistic model, involving more extensive considerations of the responses of the *individual* whole animal which, in an integrated hierarchy of behavioral and physiological shifts, are interposed (in time) between the animal and the environmental changes which could cause its early death or reduce its reproductive capacity. Effects of environmental changes on the life of *individual* animals are the only basis for the differential survivorship and the differential fecundity in *populations* upon which evolutionary change depends. J. M. Thoday was responsible in the early 1950's for a definition of biological persistence (or, as he then termed it, "fitness") as "the probability of leaving descendants after a given long period of time," which is relevant here. In teleological terms, it is obvious that many organisms have found ways of subordinating their responses which would give immediate energetic advantage after an environmental change to this overriding consideration of increasing persistence time. Such "subordination of aim" is widespread. Recently a number of authors have considered the possibility of using formal game theory to produce model descriptions of such long-term interactions between the organism and its environment. R. C. Lewontin, F. E. Warburton, and L. B. Slobodkin have been among those so concerned. Slobodkin, whose phrase "the strategy of evolution" expresses much of Thoday's concept of persistence, has rightly emphasized the importance of the increasing homeostasis of higher organisms. Clearly, it is possible that this internal constancy or homeostasis is not subject to the normal selection pressures on energy expenditure without immediate adaptive return. This could be regarded simply an extension of A. J. Lotka's principle of a tendency of organisms to maximize the energy flow through their systems. In several papers, Slobodkin has pointed out that any predictive theory of evolution must be able to take into account the possibly directional effects of a never-regressing capacity for homeostasis in stocks of higher organisms.

Once again, not only better models but more refined field data are required. Once more, I am heretic enough to suppose that not all our future understanding of such evolutionary problems will come from molecular biology, but that a significant part will come from studies of the physiological ecology of whole animals and on the bioenergetics of aquatic populations and communities.

# The finite nature of
# primary productivity

IN THE COURSE of the most significant debates of geopolitics—those which hinge on the increasing rate of human population growth—statesmen often describe certain world resources as immense, inexhaustible, incalculably large, or unlimited. The automatic response of scientists, technologists, and economists (all of whom should have a proper professional pride in quantifying things) should be to stress the ultimately finite nature of terrestrial resources, whether they be of fossil fuels, of metallic ores, or of agricultural land.

*World food production has tangible limits.* The doubling of present protein production which is thought necessary to provide a reasonable level of nutrition for the probable world population of even 1980 may or may not be accomplished by that time. Aquatic productivity must play an increasing part in this, and in particular, a larger fraction of the potential protein harvest of the sea must be exploited. Appropriate research effort on marine resources, and major effort on the development of techniques for exploiting them, could accomplish much within the next decade. However, any biologist, in giving a considered opinion on the possible technological advances which could increase the food available to man over the next few decades (including that gained from the sea), must stress the ultimately finite nature of all organic syntheses. The technological advances which are possible offer only a *temporary* respite from the main problem of the continuing acceleration in the rates of human population growth. The same is true of all actual or potential food resources, whether derived from maritime cropping, from conventional agriculture, from freshwater fish-farming, from microbial culture, or from energy-consuming "artificial" syntheses.

*It is vitally important for mankind to gain more protein from the*

**225**

*oceans over the next few decades. It is also vitally important that the educated public comes to realize that potential marine productivity is finite, and that its limits can be assessed.*

## Global carbon computation

Without any doubt, the marine phytoplankton constitutes the largest annual crop of green plants in the world. Without any doubt, this primary productivity of the oceans—made up of diatoms, $\mu$-flagellates, dinoflagellates, and coccolithophores—amounts to considerably more than half of the primary productivity of the entire world. Assessment of total primary productivity of the oceans can be based on two sorts of data. Observations on the amount of carbon fixed (that is, converted by photosynthesis into organic material from carbon dioxide) per unit area of the oceans can provide a basis for computation. Alternatively, calculations can be based on the limitations imposed by the amounts of solar energy available. The first method involves difficulties mainly arising from the need to extrapolate from insufficient and rather scattered data in preparing an estimated mean value for carbon fixation. Possible bias in the second method arises from uncertainties as to the overall efficiency of photosynthesis under field conditions. It is worth emphasizing that these uncertainties in the computations are not really important if our concern is—as it is in this chapter—to establish a probable *upper limit* for total primary productivity.

Before we attempt any quantification of total carbon fixation, it is worth recapitulating a few matters regarding marine organic productivity which have already been discussed. First, the extent of primary productivity in the seas is controlled by the availability of solar energy, on the one hand, and by the availability of soluble nutrient salts, particularly those of combined nitrogen and of phosphorus, on the other. Secondly, of the amount of carbon dioxide available—mostly in solution in seawater—only about 1 per cent is regularly turned over in organic productivity. Thirdly, the total amount of carbon fixed in the course of one year is greater than the total amount of organic carbon in the biomass at any one time. Fourthly, the level of biomass present at any one time is determined by the availability of the limiting nutrient salts and, since it does not represent accumulation of carbon fixed, cannot be related directly to the rates of carbon fixation.

Realistic estimates suggest that, in the ocean, 100–200 grams of carbon per square meter of surface is fixed each year (more concisely, 100–200 g/m$^2$/yr). Both the estimated mean values prepared by H. W. Harvey and the series of measurements carried out by Gordon A. Riley and his associates suggest this range as the most likely one for average values for all oceans. Some workers, including E. I. Rabinowitch, concerned with the energetics of photosynthesis would give slightly higher estimates. However, P. Steemann-Nielsen and his associates, from a series of widely dispersed but single (that is, nonseasonal) observations of photosynthetic rates in the open oceans, compute values in the range 20–35 g/m²/yr. Recent careful revision of the available data has been made by John H. Ryther incorporating his own seasonal data on gross and net production for several sea areas. A conservative estimate (that is, a likely lower level for production based on this revision would be about 50 g/m²/yr of carbon, a figure which is still about twice Steemann-Nielsen's average values. At first sight, these estimates may seem to vary rather greatly. However, it is important to remember that there are wide variations in the rate of phytoplankton production in different parts of the oceans and at different seasons, and much bias can be introduced into calculations by attempting appropriate weightings in producing average values. Some differences have also come from the nature of the techniques employed by different workers in assessing rates of carbon fixation. The early—but still highly significant—results gained by Gordon A. Riley and his associates in Long Island Sound were based on the use of Gran's light and dark bottles (see page 37). Changes in oxygen tension were used to prepare assessments of net plant production, but analyses of chlorophyll and of total carbon were also employed in estimating gross annual production. Yet another assessment of net production made by Riley was derived from the differences in both dissolved phosphates and dissolved nitrates which arose between light and black bottles. Subsequent investigations by Bostwick H. Ketchum suggested refinements necessary in computations based on changes in nutrient concentrations because of the ability of diatom and other photosynthetic cells to go temporarily into a state of either phosphorus or nitrogen deficiency (see also page 156). Use of radioactive tracers may further clarify the relationship of nutrient turnover to carbon fixation in similar experiments, but disappointing results obtained with radioactive phosphorus ($^{32}$P) suggest that using radioisotopes of some of the minor but essential constituent elements will prove more profitable. E. Steemann-Nielsen introduced the use of radioactive carbon ($^{14}$C) for assessing plant production in similar bottle experiments. Particularly in the tropical oceans of the world, assessments made in this way with $^{14}$C were markedly lower than those which had earlier resulted from measurements of oxygen changes in paired bottles. The low tropical results may reflect the high sustained respiration rates of plants under these conditions (and thus large differences between *gross* and *net* production). More recently, the work of John H. Ryther and associates on such nutrient-poor tropical sea areas as the Sargasso Sea has elucidated the seasonal variations which occur and resulted in somewhat higher assessments than those of Steemann-Nielsen (which were based on single observations rarely encompassing seasonal maxima). Given all the uncertainties, the estimates are actually surprisingly similar and, our purpose here being to establish the finite nature of productivity, we had best avoid the bias of the conservative estimate and adopt for most of our computations an "average upper" level of 200 g/m²/yr of carbon fixed. The fourfold reduction which would correspond to the conservative estimate of 50 g/m²/yr can be considered more briefly.

Of the Earth's surface, 70.8 per cent is covered by the oceans, amounting to 361.1 million square kilometers. As is shown diagrammatically in Figure 12·1, much of this ocean coverage is of considerable depth. Somewhat over 88 per cent of the area of the oceans is more than 1000 meters deep, and over 77 per cent 3 km (nearly 2 miles). To put this another way, 62.3 per cent of the Earth's surface has a kilometer of seawater lying over it, and more than half the world (54.5 per cent) lies under at least 3 km of ocean depth. The volume of the ocean is thus large, amounting to a little over 1370 million cubic kilometers (or $13.7 \times 10^{17}$ cubic meters or approximately $10^{18}$ metric tons of seawater). Obviously, the surface:volume ratio is relatively small. If we apply, somewhat incorrectly, the bathymetric standards used to predict the trophic condition of lakes (see Chapter 6), then, taken as a whole, the oceans would correspond to an extreme condition of lacustrine oligotrophy and, on a volume basis, approximate conditions of near sterility. For the purposes of our computation of annual carbon fixation, we must exclude the ice-covered part of the Arctic ocean and some other marginal waters, leaving a photoproductive area of about $3.5 \times 10^{14}$ square meters.

Combining our upper assessment of 200 g/m²/yr of carbon fixed with this working area of $3.5 \times 10^{14}$ square meters, we have an estimated annual fixation of carbon in seawater amounting to $7 \times 10^{16}$ grams or $7 \times 10^{10}$ tons of carbon per year. This corresponds to a utilization of $2.6 \times 10^{11}$ tons of carbon dioxide, and an output of $1.9 \times 10^{11}$ tons of oxygen during photosynthesis. These figures represent between 75 and 80 per cent of the world's organic productivity, so that the total annual turnover amounts to about $8.7 \times 10^{10}$ tons of carbon and $2.4 \times 10^{11}$ tons of oxygen. If we had employed the conservative value for marine fixation of 50 g/m²/yr of carbon, then our estimates for productivity and turnover in the oceans would be a quarter of those set out above and the total marine fixation would correspond to $17.5 \times 10^{9}$ tons of carbon per year.

If we allow that the initial formation of organic matter will have the protein content, and hence the **C:N** ratio, of rapidly dividing cells (see Chapter 8), then we can estimate the amounts of combined nitrogen and of phosphates which are involved in these levels of annual primary

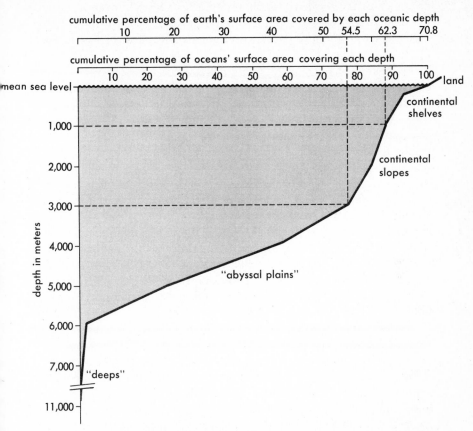

**Figure 12·1. The extent of deep ocean.** The fractions of the Earth's and of the oceans' surface areas covered by each depth of water can be read off from this diagram. Note that over half the world (over 77 per cent of the area of the oceans) is covered by more than 3000 meters of water.

productivity. Our "upper level" value of $7 \times 10^{10}$ tons of carbon fixed annually would require nitrogenous salts corresponding to $1.4 \times 10^{10}$ tons of nitrogen and $2 \times 10^9$ tons of phosphorus. Such requirements are in excess of the amounts of soluble nitrogen and phosphorus compounds in the oceans at any time. As already discussed, the concentrations of these nutrients in the surface waters of the oceans are always low, and are extremely variable both from place to place and seasonally. If we employ the figures for concentrations of soluble nitrogen and phosphorus compounds which have been assembled by H. W. Harvey, and relate them to the above computation for carbon fixation, it would appear that every year the nitrate-nitrogen content of the surface layers of the oceans must be turned over from five to fifty times (in different areas), while available phosphorus is turned over from three to about twenty times (again in different areas). Most of the considerable nutrient content of the deeper waters of the oceans is not involved in this very rapid cycling.

The extent of nutrient recycling again serves to emphasize that the total amounts of carbon fixed in one year cannot accumulate, and that the total amount of organic matter forming the biomass in any sea area at any one time is determined by the local availability of such nutrient salts as nitrates and phosphates. Some of the most significant results which are likely to emerge from expanding research on global oceanography in the next few years are those which will allow us to make a more sophisticated assessment of the rates of turnover of combined nitrogen and phosphorus in different parts of the oceans. Pragmatically, the need for more data is urgent, and the rational exploitation of the sea will depend on their availability. One likely source of such data could be from experiments (further modified by the use of radioactive tracers) like those of one of Gordon A. Riley's modifications of Gran's light and black bottle technique which involved assessing the differences in phosphate and nitrate contents between the bottles.

Carbon cannot accumulate in the oceans under the actual conditions of availability of assimilable forms of nitrogen and phosphorus. However, it is still worth examining the limitations that would be imposed by the energy source if sufficient nitrogen and phosphorus could be supplied artificially. Of course, this is entirely hypothetical. There are geochemical and energetic reasons making *sufficient* supply of nitrogenous salts completely impossible (see also Chapters 8 and 15).

## Global energy computation

In attempting to calculate the upper limit of marine productivity as determined by the solar energy available, we have relatively good data on the quantities of energy reaching the Earth's surface, but there are considerable uncertainties as regards the average efficiency in photosynthesis of energy incorporation. Reliable estimates suggest that the solar radiation reaching the upper atmosphere of the Earth amounts to $5 \times 10^{24}$ joules per year. There are considerable geographic variations in the amount of scattering by dust particles or water droplets, but on average about 40 per cent of the radiant energy penetrates the atmosphere. Thus about $2 \times 10^{24}$ joules reaches the Earth each year. About half of this is in the form of infrared radiation, which is not used in photosynthetic processes in normal green plants. If we also allow for some 20 per cent absorption by nonphotosynthetic areas and reflection by ice and snow, there remains $8 \times 10^{23}$ joules which is directed at potentially photosynthetic areas including the oceans. Because of additional absorption and reflection losses perhaps $6 \times 10^{23}$ joules is available for photosynthesis. The field efficiency of photosynthesis varies considerably, but seems rarely to involve as much as 5 per cent of the absorbed energy in the resultant chemical energy of the plant tissues. Some measurements have shown that as much as 95–99 per cent of the energy absorbed by photosynthetic surfaces of plants is almost immediately lost in the form of sensible heat energy and as heat of evaporation. Thus only 1–5 per cent is used in photosynthesis, and much circumstantial evidence suggests that an average value of 2 per cent efficiency for photosynthesis under field conditions will be most valid. Thus we have to conclude that, at most, $1.2 \times 10^{22}$ joules per year can be utilized for photosynthesis. This can be converted to heat units, a mean conversion factor to calories being 4.186. Thus there can be a little under $3 \times 10^{21}$ calories involved annually in biosynthesis. The fixation of 1 gram of carbon requires approximately $9.5 \times 10^{3}$ calories. Thus, if the above estimates of energy losses are approximately correct, we can have a maximum annual fixation of $32 \times 10^{16}$ grams, or $32 \times 10^{10}$ tons, of carbon in global primary productivity. If we again assume that 80 per cent of this fixation occurs in the oceans, the maximum annual marine productivity would be limited by energy available to a level of $26 \times 10^{10}$ tons of carbon. We can compare this with the estimates made above of total carbon fixed annually at present in the oceans. Our upper level estimate of $7 \times 10^{10}$ tons of carbon fixed annually corresponds to about 27 per cent of the limit set by energy input. Our conservative estimate of $17.5 \times 10^{9}$ tons of carbon per year would amount to approximately 7 per cent of the energy-set limit. Considering the uncertainty of these figures we can conclude that the present primary productivity of the oceans lies between 5 and 30 per cent of the limiting level set by the available energy input. The fact that, on average, only one order of magnitude separates the estimated figure for actual marine carbon fixation from that of the theoretical maximum based on available energy should be impressive. However much they may prove faulty in detail, these computations emphasize the finite nature of the resource provided by annual primary productivity.

Before we leave computations of global energy resources, it is worth comparing the values for incident solar energy at the Earth's surface (corresponding to $48 \times 10^{22}$ calories per year) and for maximum energy available for photosynthesis ($3 \times 10^{21}$ calories per year) with the present annual energy turnover of man-made machines. This last is difficult to sum, and increases annually, but is in 1969 probably close to $12 \times 10^{18}$ calories per year. Thus the annual fuel-energy consumption by machines amounts to about 1/70 of the energy actually used annually in photosynthesis, about 1/250 of the annual energy available for photosynthesis, and less than 1/40,000 of the annual solar energy input to the Earth's surface. Of the present annual fuel consumption, 96.4 per cent is drawn from the biologically formed "fossil fuels"—coal, oil, and natural gas. These resources also are finite.

In the next chapter it will be shown that probably between 3.3 and $6.7 \times 10^8$ tons of carbon was being cropped as fish in 1967. If allowance is made for a trophic transfer efficiency of 8 per cent, then about a twofold increase of conventional fisheries may be possible. If the average ecological efficiency in established marine communities proves to be as high as 15 per cent (see Chapter 9), then fisheries yields could possibly be increased about 18.5 times. Before we discuss this, it is worth briefly considering the slight possibilities of actually increasing the primary productivity of the oceans.

## Increase in primary productivity

Given the premises outlined in the last two sections, increase in primary productivity in the seas could be brought about in two ways. The chances of either becoming important to human nutrition in the near future are low. The first method—more fundamental, but extremely unlikely to become possible within the next few decades—is to increase the efficiency of the photosynthetic process in marine plants like diatoms or flagellates. The second—of more limited value, but slightly more feasible—is to increase total algal productivity by modification of the present nutrient limiting factors (that is, by narrowing the gap between actual present productivity and the maximum allowed by radiation capture).

As regards the efficiency of photosynthesis, the present field level seems to be about 2 per cent, and if conditions could be created under which carbon dioxide is reduced and fixed more efficiently, a considerable increase is theoretically possible. There are even some empirical data on this from work on algal cultures. A number of studies have been concerned with assessing the quantum yield, that is, the efficiency of the photosynthetic process in terms of carbon fixed per quantum of light-energy. T. Tanada, working with the diatom *Navicula minima,* made data available on the quantum yields at different wavelengths for the entire visible spectrum. John H. Ryther recalculated these data of Tanada, taking into account the differences in energy per quantum at different wavelengths and certain other factors, averaged them, and calculated the mean efficiency for the entire visible spectrum; he believes that a value of 17.5 per cent efficiency of photosynthetic utilization is appropriate (as long as we are concerned with intensities *below* saturation values; see page 52). Other recent studies, more particularly of higher plants, assessed the effects of various wavelengths of light—alone and in combinations—on photosynthesis, and revealed the existence of processes of additive efficiency which have been termed "photosynthetic enhancement." The mechanism of photosynthesis in higher green plants involves two kinds of chlorophyll, each with a specific role in a cyclic chain of electron transport. They differ only slightly in structure and absorption spectra, and it appears that both are required for normal processes of capture of light-energy. At least one other kind of chlorophyll is important in algal cells, and it is clear that chlorophyll molecules are not the only ones concerned in the absorption of light-energy in lower plants. The intensely colored carotenoids may supplement or replace chlorophyll as primary light-absorbers in some plant cells, though the light-energy they absorb must be passed to chlorophyll before it can be used for the photo-chemical work of carbon fixation. Details of the molecular energetics are likely to be elucidated within the next few years, and obscure features—including the energetic details of the water-splitting reaction —may become better understood. There is a slight possibility that a more complete conception of the processes of physical chemistry in-volved could allow us to influence the efficiency of green plant popula-tions in nature and thence to increase primary production.

The computations set out earlier in this chapter suggest that present marine productivity is already within an order of magnitude of the limit of productivity as determined by the utilizable sunlight reaching the oceans. Therefore, the second possibility of increasing primary production, modification of the supply of nutrients which are presently limiting, could only involve a maximum fivefold increase, but it may be a more immediately valuable approach in certain sea areas of the world. Considered economically, provision of sufficient phosphates or nitrates to modify their concentration in entire oceans is very im-probable, even in the unlikely event of abundant and cheap energy sources becoming available (see Chapters 13 and 15). However, more *local* application of inorganic "fertilizers" to limited areas of the sea is feasible. In this connection, it is important to remember that biological fixation of nitrogen in the open ocean is either completely absent or negligible and that, apart from the recycling of available nitrogenous salts from decomposing bacteria, the supply of combined nitrogen in the oceans is dependent upon the very small amounts carried in from land and precipitated as oxides of nitrogen from the atmosphere through electrical activity. Estimates of the total nitrogen involved in oceanic productivity suggest that river drainage accounts for somewhat less than 1 per cent of the total nutrient requirements each year. Thus the effects of nutrients derived from land or fresh water are only locally important in coastal seas. The great bulk of nitrogenous nutrients involved in marine primary productivity has resulted from recycling. As explained in Chapter 3 and elsewhere, phytoplankton cells can probably never maintain high rates of photosynthesis, growth, and reproduction in any given water mass because their growth rapidly reduces the local availability of nutrients in solution. In many cases, water movements which might bring nutrient replenishment, such as vertical turbulence or lateral flow, could at the same time involve dispersal of the photosynthetic cells into levels of less appropriate illumination. It is obvious that waters of high and sustained levels of primary production (such as mildly polluted inshore waters, some coral reefs, and regions of continuous upwelling of deep nutrient-rich waters in the tropics) must often involve continuous or regularly recurrent systems of water flow that bring about continuous replenishment with recycled nutrients. In some cases of high but *temporary* productivity, including the "red tide" outbreaks on the Gulf coast of North America which involve very dense concentrations of dinoflagellates, the rich production must depend upon the opposite condition. As was elucidated some years ago by work of Lawrence B. Slobodkin and others, such local "blooms" can only result from physically *reduced* exchanges between a nutrient-rich water mass containing the rapidly producing cells and the surrounding more sterile waters. Increased understanding of the mechanisms which govern the formation and disappearance of algal blooms in general could undoubtedly contribute to our ability to influence primary productivity by *local* application of nutrient salts.

During and just after the Second World War, large-scale experiments on the crude fertilization of sea inlets were carried out at Loch Sween in Scotland by Fabius Gross and a group of associates including Sheina M. Marshall, A. P. Orr, and J. E. G. Raymont. Nutrient salts were added regularly (in the form of the agricultural fertilizers sodium nitrate and superphosphate), and the effects on plankton, benthic animals, and fishes assessed. Lack of clear control conditions made it difficult to evaluate the results, but it was obvious that both phytoplankton and zoöplankton were enriched, the total biomass of bottom organisms increased, and the growth rates of flatfish (plaice and flounders) doubled or tripled. On the other hand, the expense of the nutrient salts used was far greater than any increase in cropping. One significant feature in this was the great utilization of the fertilizers by attached seaweeds round the shores of the inlets (which did not contribute to fish food). Another disadvantageous result of the rich plant growth was the marked increase in alkalinity (even occasionally reaching a pH value of 9), which probably had an adverse effect on the zoöplankton and other animals. As already discussed (see Chapter 5),

it is probable that a far more effective increase in productivity by fertilization has been brought about in the southern part of the North Sea
and in some regions of Long Island Sound by the slow addition of
sewage effluents from dense urban populations. In certain fresh waters,
including some kinds of fish-ponds in Germany and America, suitable
addition of nutrient salts has resulted in an increased fish crop (see
Chapter 15). Marine conditions, even in relatively small inlets, are
more complex and, while primary productivity may be increased, it
may be difficult to ensure that all the enhanced plant growth is of a
sort suitable to pass into an appropriate food-chain and thence to
increase the catch of commercially valuable fish. Fertilizers may more
readily be used to increase primary productivity passing to shellfish
stocks, and some oyster-farming in Japan already involves added
fertilizers (see Chapter 15).

The first successful use of added nutrient salts to increase marine
productivity is likely to occur in some semienclosed inshore waters
(perhaps part of an estuary) where water flow-patterns provide better
conditions for the *controlled* addition of nutrients. In theory, the
"steady-state" system of relatively high productivity could be developed.
This would involve application of our knowledge of the effects of
nutrients on population dynamics in plant cells which has resulted from
laboratory studies making use of steady-state culturing devices such as
the chemostat or the turbidostat.

Another aspect of the possibility of increasing primary productivity
in the more extensive estuary systems of the world lies in the fact that
harvesting of larger plants from shallow water or salt marshes is now
technologically possible. Even under natural circumstances, the primary
production rates of the higher plants in some warm-water estuaries
already approach the highest levels of intensive agriculture, as comparisons by Eugene P. and Howard T. Odum have shown. A factor
which may be of some importance has resulted from British studies on
the species of blue-green algae living in a salt marsh. It appears that a
considerable proportion (perhaps even one-third) of these estuarine
species can fix atmospheric nitrogen, and this contrasts with most
oceanic waters where biological fixation of nitrogen is negligible. The
parallel with agricultural production of leguminous crops may be close,
and addition of fertilizers containing phosphorus and sulfur but *not*
nitrogen should provoke increased activity of the nitrogen-fixing algae
and ultimately increased protein production in the young shoots of the
higher plants whose root systems are in contact with the blue-green
mats. (It is instructive to note that the high yields from lowland or
"wet" rice cultivation depend on blue-green algae on the soil surface
of the "paddy fields," and the Japanese have developed miniature rural

factories where nitrogen-fixing blue-green algae are grown in warm culture tanks, and then used as a living fertilizer to be spread twice yearly over the rice fields.)

As regards the potentialities of estuaries, a major change in man's exploitation could come from deliberate husbandry of some specific higher plants in salt marshes and shallow estuaries. This could include further development of salt-tolerant varieties of existing food and fodder plants, or deliberate breeding of useful strains from existing species which occur naturally in these conditions (for example, the development of strains of *Spartina* which could be utilized as animal fodder). A possible relation of this to inshore "sea-farming" is discussed in Chapter 15. The rate at which applied genetic work on such plants can be carried out has greatly increased and such breeding development is certainly possible within two decades.

Finally, it is worth briefly considering a future possibility of modifying the availability of nutrient salts in certain tropical and subtropical waters. As already discussed (see Chapter 5), many areas of the sea in the tropics and in low latitudes are relatively unproductive, in spite of the greater amounts of solar energy which they receive annually. This is largely due to lack of available salts of phosphorus and nitrogen in the euphotic zone, although at greater depths in these seas, such nutrient salts are usually available. It is this disparity that gives such great biological significance to regions of upwelling in the oceanic circulation. If it were possible to create artificial upwelling in topographically suitable situations, enormously enhanced productivity would result from the flow of water rich in nutrient salts into well-lit surface waters. In a suitable situation, if a nuclear reactor were placed on the sea floor and used to raise the temperature of a column of seawater by a few degrees, this could create an upwelling. The process would involve a relatively efficient utilization of the heat energy produced by the reactor if compared to the nuclear power stations of the 1960's. If the situation were carefully chosen, little mechanical channeling of the water column would be necessary since, as we have seen (page 42), water masses at different temperatures (that is, of different densities) do not readily mix. It is precisely where the need for increased food production is likely to be most acute, off certain tropical coasts, that conditions for such creation of artificial upwelling and hence high productivity are most practicable.

# The finite biomass and
# human nutrition

THE SIMPLE FACTS of organic cycles and trophic levels outlined earlier can be applied on a global scale. All food-chains depend ultimately on green plant production. This primary productivity in the oceans—and elsewhere throughout the world—is of limited extent, not an "inexhaustible resource." The computations of the last chapter set out both the probable upper limit of global productivity and an estimate of the present annual carbon fixation in the world's oceans. The potential upper limits of productivity at higher trophic levels can be derived from these. This is done below, and the results related to the growth of world fisheries and to the total availability of protein for human nutrition.

Before we go into the details of the finite animal biomass of the world, there are a few background statistics on human population growth and on the world yield of fisheries which must be borne in mind during the ensuing discussions. First, the present yield of world fisheries is about 60 million tons annually (based on 1967–68 figures, the probable annual increase will be about 8 per cent). Secondly, although this amounts to only about 1 per cent of the annual food intake of man, it corresponds to a little more than 10 per cent of the animal protein consumed. Thirdly, a conservative estimate of the world population in 1968 is 3.2 billion. Fourthly, increasing population growth rates have now (1969) reduced the number of years required to double the Earth's human population to thirty-five, and conservative population estimates for the years 1975 and 2000 are 4 and 8 billion, respectively. We will consider the relation between human population growth and nutrition in the last chapter, after this assessment of the finite nature of animal productivtiy and a brief consideration (in Chapters 14 and 15) of the future exploitation of the oceans.

## Finite animal stocks

In Chapter 12 our "high" estimate of the fixation of carbon in marine plants amounted to $7 \times 10^{10}$ tons of carbon annually, and our conservative estimate was $1.75 \times 10^9$ tons of carbon fixed per year. The dry-weight biomass of plants would—if skeletal materials were excluded—amount to more than double these figures. Given the fact that the total amounts of carbon fixed do not accumulate, there are many difficulties in setting up the relationship between total annual carbon fixation and the net particulate production of the phytoplankton which is available as food for the herbivorous zoöplankton of the second trophic level. Circumstantial evidence suggests that a fair level of net particulate production would be 30 per cent of the total carbon fixation, and thus for our upper level of estimated productivity we would have a net available production of $21 \times 10^9$ tons of carbon. It will be best to use for the computation an average value of 8 per cent for the gross ecological efficiency, or transfer rate between trophic levels (but see Chapter 9 and below). Thus the annual production of zoöplankton at the second trophic level would be $17 \times 10^8$ tons of carbon, and this value would represent the maximum level of animal productivity in the world's oceans. Similarly, production of plankton-feeding fish can amount to $14 \times 10^7$ tons of carbon, and of the fourth-trophic-level fish feeding on these to $11 \times 10^6$ tons of carbon annually. Human fishing activities involve both these trophic levels of fish, and if we assume that half the potential human crop is derived from each level, then the potential productivity of the fish which can be harvested has a maximum value of $75 \times 10^6$ tons of carbon annually. This would correspond to a wet weight of fish of about $9 \times 10^8$ tons annual productivity. Perhaps a third of this involves fish species which could never be harvested, leaving $6 \times 10^8$ tons of fish production. An admittedly crude estimate would be that half the production could be cropped while maintaining the total resource, and this would set a maximum level of annual fish crop for man and all other predators of $3 \times 10^8$ tons annually. (If, as discussed near the end of Chapter 9, the efficiency of transfer in established marine communities proves closer to 15 per cent, then the maximum level of fish crop could be 3.7 times greater.) Once again, the *finite* nature of the fish resources of the world is obvious. In relation to the present estimated fish crop of $6 \times 10^7$ tons wet weight of fish, then a fivefold increase in fish-cropping is, at least theoretically, possible. Recent developments in world fisheries, and their relation to future expansion, can now be considered.

# The growth of world fisheries

Since the end of the Second World War, the rate of growth of marine fisheries has been consistently somewhat higher than the rate of growth of the world's human populations. It has therefore been much higher than the rate of growth of agricultural food production. In fact, since the 1950's, each year's world fish catch has set a new record. Although the annual returns from individual nations have varied considerably, the summed totals for the world as a whole showed an annual rate of increase of 4.5 per cent through the 1950's and of 7 per cent from 1959 to 1968. The world catch had increased rather slowly in the earlier years of the century, reaching a value of 21 million tons in 1938. Catches dropped during the war (with interesting effects on some fish stocks; see page 195), but by 1948 they had recovered to a level of nearly 20 million tons. Thus the world catch figures for the year 1967, totaling 60 million tons, represent a tripling of the fisheries harvest in two decades. As shown in Figure 13·1, the commercial crop of marine fishes, after deduction of the smaller quantities of shellfish and of

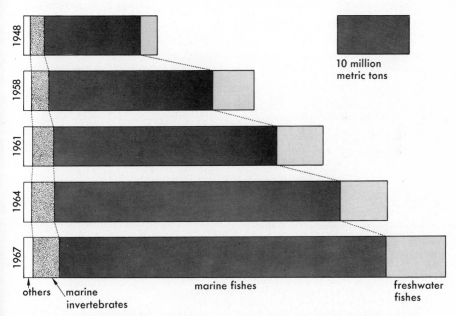

**Figure 13·1. The recent expansion in world fisheries** (a threefold increase in 1948–1967). This rate of growth has been somewhat higher than the rate of growth of the world's human populations and much higher than the rate of growth of agricultural food production over the same period. [Modified from figures in the *Yearbook of Fishery Statistics* for 1967 published by the Food and Agriculture Organization of the United Nations, Rome, 1968.]

freshwater fish from the total fisheries returns, rose from 14.7 million tons in 1948 to 46.9 million tons in 1967. For a number of reasons, world fisheries statistics are almost certainly too low. Different methods of recording "catches" and "landings" are employed, and for some countries landing statistics are incomplete. The Food and Agriculture Organization of the United Nations (FAO) collates the national returns and compiles the series of fisheries statistics yearbooks. At the time of revision of this book (spring, 1969), the yearbook for 1967 had just become available, and data from it are used in Figure 13·1, Table 13·1, and elsewhere in this section.

### TABLE 13·1
### Major Fishing Countries

(Ranked by 1967 production, annual totals reduced to millions of metric tons, with approximate percentages of world catch for each year.)

| | 1948 Total | 1948 Per cent | 1958 Total | 1958 Per cent | 1961 Total | 1961 Per cent | 1964 Total | 1964 Per cent | 1967 Total | 1967 Per cent |
|---|---|---|---|---|---|---|---|---|---|---|
| WORLD TOTALS | 19.6 | 100.0 | 33.2 | 100.0 | 43.4 | 100.0 | 52.7 | 100.0 | 60.5 | 100.0 |
| Peru | 0.1 | 0.5 | 1.0 | 3.0 | 5.3 | 12.2 | 9.1 | 17.3 | 10.1 | 16.7 |
| Japan | 2.5 | 12.8 | 5.5 | 16.6 | 6.7 | 15.4 | 6.4 | 12.1 | 7.8 | 12.9 |
| China | 0.9[a] | 4.6 | 4.1 | 12.3 | 5.8[b] | 13.4 | 6.0[b] | 11.4 | 6.2[b] | 10.2 |
| U.S.S.R. | 1.5 | 7.7 | 2.6 | 7.8 | 3.3 | 7.6 | 4.5 | 8.5 | 5.8 | 9.6 |
| Norway | 1.4 | 7.1 | 1.4 | 4.2 | 1.5 | 3.5 | 1.6 | 3.0 | 3.2 | 5.3 |
| U.S.A. | 2.4 | 12.2 | 2.7 | 8.1 | 2.9 | 6.7 | 2.6 | 4.9 | 2.4 | 4.0 |
| South Africa | 0.2 | 1.0 | 0.7 | 2.1 | 1.0 | 2.3 | 1.3 | 2.5 | 1.6 | 2.6 |
| India | 0.8[c] | 4.1 | 1.1 | 3.3 | 1.0 | 2.3 | 1.3 | 2.5 | 1.4 | 2.3 |
| Spain | 0.5 | 2.6 | 0.8 | 2.4 | 1.0 | 2.3 | 1.2 | 2.3 | 1.4 | 2.3 |
| Indonesia | 0.2[c] | 1.0 | 0.7 | 2.1 | 0.9 | 2.1 | 0.9[d] | 1.7 | 1.2[e] | 2.0 |
| Canada | 1.1 | 5.6 | 1.0 | 3.0 | 1.0 | 2.3 | 1.2 | 2.3 | 1.3 | 2.1 |
| Chile | 0.1 | 0.5 | 0.2 | 0.6 | 0.4 | 0.9 | 1.2 | 2.3 | 1.1 | 1.8 |
| Denmark | 0.2 | 1.0 | 0.6 | 1.8 | 0.6 | 1.4 | 0.9 | 1.7 | 1.1 | 1.8 |
| U.K. | 1.2 | 6.1 | 1.0 | 3.0 | 0.9 | 2.1 | 1.0 | 1.9 | 1.0 | 1.7 |
| Iceland | 0.5 | 2.6 | 0.6 | 1.8 | 0.7 | 1.6 | 1.0 | 1.9 | 0.9 | 1.5 |

[a] Fair estimate based on actual catch reported in 1950.
[b] Very doubtful estimates, based on catch reported in 1960.
[c] Fair estimates based on actual catches reported in 1950.
[d] Fair estimate based on actual catch reported in 1963.
[e] Fair estimate based on actual catch reported in 1966.
Source: Data on annual totals are extracted from tables in the Yearbook of Fishery Statistics (FAO) for 1967, collated and published late in 1968 by the Food and Agriculture Organization of the United Nations in Rome, and from earlier Yearbooks.

A closer look at the fish stocks involved in, and the countries responsible for, the threefold increase in fisheries in the 1950's and 1960's can be of value in attempting to forecast the future of marine productivity. As a whole, this growth of world fisheries has resulted from two factors. First has been the new exploitation of fish stocks (such as the anchoveta off the coast of Peru) which had not previously been harvested, though occurring in some of the most highly productive areas of the warmer oceans. A second cause of the increase involved the introduction of more modern fishing and fish-handling methods; including stern-trawlers, more efficient mid- and deep-water trawling, more efficient methods of fish-finding, and increased use of factory ships for processing at sea (some of these are discussed in Chapter 14). Annual returns for selected years are set out in Table 13·1 for the fifteen major fishing countries. The columns for 1948 illustrate national catches after recovery from wartime conditions, and those for 1958, 1961, 1964, and 1967 cover the years of maximum growth. Certain changes for individual countries have distinctly different kinds of significance. The case of Peru, whose contribution to world fisheries increased a hundredfold over the period to exceed $10^7$ tons in 1967, represents the new exploitation of a rich fishery. Much of this crop is anchoveta, with smaller quantities of tuna and bonito, and the greater part of the production is exported as fish-meal (see page 100 and page 250 below). The cases of Chile and of South West Africa are similar. Chile is only beginning to share in the rich fisheries of the Humboldt upwellings, and the still-growing fisheries of South West Africa exploit similar fish stocks in the Benguela current (see page 99). The case of Japan is different and represents steady growth in a wide variety of fisheries. It reflects the acute need for animal protein for a burgeoning population which drove this country to remain the premier fishing nation from the 1930's until 1962, but it also demonstrates the results of an industrial capacity to re-equip the fishing industry with some regularity and a fishing labor force willing to work, essentially, round the world. Japan's threefold increase in fisheries harvest over these two decades is well earned. In contrast, India's need for animal protein is as great as Japan's, but growth of fisheries has been slow, neither Indian industrial backup nor Indian fishermen being capable of a parallel growth. Certain other countries, including Norway, Denmark, and West Germany, have notably modernized their equipment over these years, and also extended their fishing to more distant waters. In the case of Norway, the decline of Antarctic whaling after 1963 has undoubtedly influenced increased growth in other fisheries. The cases of the United States and of Britain are remarkably similar, United States returns having remained around 2.5 million tons over these years of expansion and Britain's fishery crop remaining around 1 million tons annually. During the period, because of increased cropping by other countries, the United States dropped from second to sixth place and the United Kingdom from fifth to fourteenth. For both countries, re-equipment with modern ships and gear has been slow, and—in spite of the long fishing traditions of both countries—recruitment of suitable new labor poor. In both countries, the period from 1963 to 1969 has seen some legislation which could lessen the cost to the fishing industry of building modern vessels, and thus offset the subsidies paid by many European and other governments to their fishing industries. In Table 13·1, the case of Russia demonstrates a sustained and steady growth somewhat greater than that for the world as a whole, and represents, of course, not merely governmental subsidy beyond economic returns but also total paramilitary control. The worldwide distribution of Russian trawlers and factory ships over the last decade or so is not unconnected with that country's emergence as a major naval power.

The changing proportions of different kinds of fish in the world crop through this growth period are also revealing. If we consider only the period from 1957 to 1967 (see Figure 13·2), the total world catch of marine fishes rose from 22.8 to 46.9 million tons. One major category of fishes, the gadids (cod, hake, haddock, whiting, and so on) increased from about 4.5 million tons to just over 8 million tons, probably

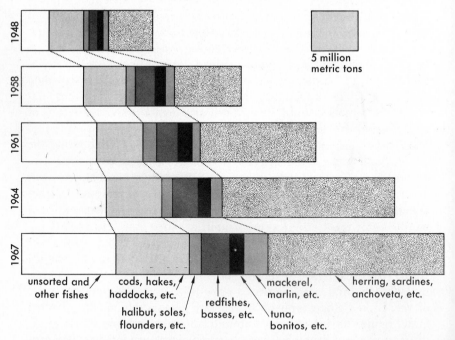

**Figure 13·2. Composition of the catch in world fisheries** during the recent expansion (1948–1967). For further discussion, see text. [Modified from figures in the *Yearbook of Fishery Statistics* for 1967 published by the Food and Agriculture Organization of the United Nations, Rome, 1968.]

reflecting better gear but also greatly increased fishing effort, yet not being proportional to the overall world increase in fisheries in the period. Certain smaller categories, including redfishes and basses on the one hand and tuna and bonitos on the other, showed a similar slow increase in returns. Another minor category, the flatfish (including flounders, halibuts, soles, and so on) showed something of a decline— doubtless a reflection of over-fishing—in the 1960's. The great bulk of the increase in world fisheries came from the category of herrings, sardines, and anchoveta, which rose from about 7 million tons to an annual crop of nearly 20 million tons between 1958 and 1967. A similar but smaller increase was shown by the category of mackerel and marlin. In view of discussions in Chapters 4, 10, and elsewhere, the reasons for the predominance of fish stocks of short life-cycle, feeding largely on plankton, should be obvious.

The theoretical computations earlier in this chapter suggest that a further fivefold growth of marine fisheries could be possible. It is more reasonable to think of a further doubling of world fisheries over the next ten years or so, largely resulting from further improvements and extensions of conventional methods of fish capture. It is worth speculating on the sea areas and fish species likely to be involved in this continued growth. There are some parts of the oceans in which almost all suitable fish are already overexploited, and these include the seas around the Japanese islands and the Mediterranean. From such waters, we cannot expect increased yields and may face decline in certain fisheries. In regions such as the North Sea and northeast Atlantic the bottom-dwelling fish are grossly overexploited, but some stocks of pelagic fish such as mackerel and pilchard are not yet cropped at an optimum level. Further, there are several areas of the sea where a wide variety of fish stocks are at present under-fished. These include parts of the North Pacific and South Atlantic and the Australasian side of the Indian ocean. Similarly, except for the waters near Peru, there are many areas around the South American continent with under-fished stocks. There are probably a number of cases of sea areas where one fish species has been subjected to continued over-fishing, while related forms of equivalent nutritive value, but perhaps less marketable, are not yet intensively fished. In the western North Atlantic, for example, there are probably several stocks of hake which are under-fished, although several other related species have declined through over-fishing. In many areas of the open ocean, stocks of tuna are probably overexploited (almost always by Japanese vessels), while in some of these areas stocks of bonitos are not yet cropped so intensively.

In general, however, it seems likely that at the present rate of development, most unexploited stocks of fish which can be cropped by conventional methods of capture will become intensively fished within the next twenty years. Thus the need for international conservation and uniform legislation aimed at obtaining the maximum sustainable catch will become increasingly urgent. Over-fished stocks are becoming more common, and this will continue.

An important aspect of these trends is the increased intensity of exploratory fishing, an activity rather distinct from the rest of applied fishery research on the biology of fish populations. Although the amount of exploratory fishing carried out by the "traditional" fishing nations, such as the United States and Britain, is very small, in every part of the world's oceans, Japanese and Russian vessels are presently engaged in this kind of trial or exploratory fishing which disregards immediate commercial returns. The world lead in this type of activity seems to have been taken by the USSR, with more than forty vessels, including some submarines, known to be involved in scientific exploration for new fisheries. These are in addition to the vessels which regularly scout in advance of the main Russian fishing fleets. Again, a more balanced international effort on exploratory fishing, with perhaps the FAO as a "clearing house" for information, seems desirable. The recent growth in world fisheries has made a real contribution to world nutrition, but again there are highly significant differences in the global distribution of the crop.

## Protein availability

It is possible to state—with some inhumanity but fair accuracy—that relatively few people are dying from starvation in the world of 1969. It is possible to believe comfortingly that a few shiploads of surplus grain can help "deal" with areas of recurrent famine. However, the *whole* truth regarding world nutrition must include some statement on the widespread protein deficiencies which exist, and this cannot be comforting to any member of our species. The diets of more than half the world's population at present are nutritionally unbalanced and consist mainly of cereals and starchy foods with only a small proportion of animal protein. The majority of these unfortunates actually have an adquate food intake in terms of total calories, but most of it is carbohydrate, and the $C:N$ ratio of their diets is impossibly high (see Chapter 8). Unfortunately, merely bringing the $C:N$ ratio below the critical level of 17:1 by increasing, for example, the proportion of plant protein, such as that provided by soybeans in the diet, is not enough. Adequate human diets must contain, in appropriate relative concentrations, ten essential amino acids (lysine, arginine, histidine, leucine, isoleucine, valine, threonine, methionine, phenylalanine, and tryptophane). Almost all animal protein foods, including marine and freshwater fish, provide a balanced repertoire of these building blocks for human proteins and also other required constituent elements and presynthesized vitamins. Most protein-deficient diets can be made adequate by supplying a supplement of animal protein amounting to as little as 15 grams (dry weight) on average per head per day. This corresponds to an annual per capita supplement of animal protein amounting to just under 5.5 kg, or about 12 pounds—a relatively small quantity of meat or fish by the standards of Europe or North America.

Even a relatively crude measure, such as the percentage of animal products in the diet, can reveal the geographical distribution of nutritional deficiencies. Animal products make up only 6 per cent of the average human diet in the countries of the Far East and 7 per cent in Africa, but amount to 22 per cent in western Europe and 36 per cent in North America. The average protein intake of citizens of such countries as the United Kingdom and the United States is about double the "balanced" requirement. Taking the world as a whole, approximately 69 per cent of the present consumption of protein is derived from plant sources (mainly legumes, see Chapter 8), and approximately 31 per cent from all animal products consumed. At present, fish contribute about 11 per cent of the animal protein (that is, about 3.5 per cent of the total protein). A surprisingly high (13.6 per cent in 1967) but decreasing fraction of this fish protein comes from fresh waters (see Figure 13·1).

If mankind is to cope with the present protein deficiencies and the nutritional needs of a rapidly expanding global population, then not merely more equable distribution of present protein production is required but also considerable additional protein resources. There is but little hope that agriculture, microbial culture, or chemical synthesis can provide any of this additional protein, and thus it *must* come from marine and freshwater productivity. This summary dismissal of the potential of all protein crops other than aquatic may seem overpessimistic, but it hinges on the limitations of space and of energy resources, and can be defended. As regards conventional systems of agriculture, there is not much more suitable land which can become available. Until relatively recently, there were optimistic estimates of the agricultural potentiality of the large areas covered with tropical rain-forest in South America and in central Africa. Attempts to introduce intensive agriculture after clear-felling of the forest have mostly resulted in failure, with in a number of cases nutrient-sterility and massive soil erosion. It is inappropriate to try to cover all the reasons here, but they include the high $C:N$ ratio of the virgin forest cover and its soils, the lateritic nature of these soils in most rain-forest areas, the fact that the "boundless fertility" of rain-forest represents a high ratio of standing crop to turnover, and finally the effects of tropical sun and rain in destroying the organic content and bacterial flora of lateritic soils when they are exposed by tilling. Even if erosional difficulties could be bypassed, nitrogenous fertilizers and lime would be required on these soils to such an extent that their transport costs alone would outweigh the economic returns of intensive agriculture. Local populations in such areas in Africa have long practiced shifting cultivation, leaving large trees standing, clearing small patches for a few years, using leguminous plants extensively, and allowing a "fallow period" of return to jungle vegetation for about fifteen years between each two- to three-year period of cultivation. The only successful "intensive" cultivation of lands in these areas has been tree-agriculture involving the production of crops like oil-palm, rubber, cocoa, and certain nuts. The annual organic yield of such crops is rather low. Neither shifting cultivation nor tree-agriculture can make much contribution to the world's food supply, and it is likely that the majority of undeveloped lands in the wet tropical zones could not be "developed" to more intensive cropping.

It is barely possible that the productivity of present arable lands could be tripled in a few decades by an extension of present trends including catch-cropping, increased input of fertilizers, and the development of high-yielding crop varieties including hybrids. A doubling is more likely. As already discussed (see Chapter 8), high crop yields generally mean low $C:N$ ratios; thus most agricultural expansion of this type would help provide food calories for an expanding human population, but would be unlikely to yield more plant protein. A more productive conventional agriculture could result in more widespread dietary imbalance in the world. Further, surveying the next two decades in 1969, some agricultural authorities have suggested that the production of meat may actually have to be curtailed because of feed availability and space limitations. The production of animal protein of terrestrial origin may, within a human generation, be even less than it is at present.

Even the possible doubling of production of crop plants would demand vastly greater quantities of fertilizers. Provision of phosphates, potassium salts, and sulfates even at present levels will require that steadily increasing amounts of energy be expended in their extraction, manufacture, and distribution. Resources of phosphorus and sulfur are finite, but immediate scarcity of either need not complicate the world's food problems for at least a half-dozen human generations. Long before this, available energy supplies may limit the use of such fertilizers. Here, as in other cases, it is not a true and complete exhaustion of the resources which may limit man's use of them but the level of depletion at which it becomes uneconomic (in fuel-energy terms) to extract, process, and transport them. Provision of nitrogenous fertilizers provides an even better example of ill-informed optimism on the future of human nutrition. Man's future food supplies *do* need an increased proportion of nitrogenous organic materials (that is, more protein fraction, or a lower **C:N** ratio), and nitrogenous inorganic salts *can* be prepared by "synthetic" fixation of atmospheric nitrogen, reserves of which are vast. These facts would be grounds for optimism but for two difficulties which have already been briefly noted (see Chapters 8 and 12). First, the synthesis of nitrogenous salts from gaseous nitrogen requires considerable energy expenditure and, in our present fossil-fuel economy, we simply consume large quantities of organic carbon (oil or coal) from *finite* stocks of these fuels to create nitrogenous nutrients. Once again, provision of a moderately increased amount of nitrogenous fertilizers is well within the future energy budget of world industry for a few decades, but known energy resources could not possibly sustain, for example, a tenfold production increase for a century. Secondly, provision of increased nitrogenous salts to agricultural crops does *not* result in increased protein yields (except in the rare cases where the crop consists of the actively dividing tissues of young plant shoots), but rather in increased carbohydrate (or more rarely fat) yields. Around the end of last century, the work of J. B. Lawes and others (see page 54) had already emphasized that the characteristic effect of nitrogenous fertilizers (in nonleguminous crops) was to increase yields per acre of nonnitrogenous constituents. It has since been shown for crops of legumes that increased application of nitrogenous salts does not increase gross protein yield, but merely results in a decrease in the proportion of nitrogen fixed by the bacteria in the root nodules. The only way to increase protein yield in leguminous crops (such as soybeans or fodder crops) is to provide the other fertilizers, including phosphates, sulfates, calcium, and potassium in abundance, but *not* provide nitrogenous salts, thus encouraging the maximum activity of the nodule bacteria. Thus it is clear, that even with an improbably rapid development of new and cheap energy resources, increased fixation of atmospheric nitrogen cannot be the panacea providing the needed increase in protein supplies.

Optimistic press statements regularly appear suggesting that the global protein deficiency is about to be solved by mass production of "artificial" or "synthetic" foods. Almost all have a basis in technologically feasible methods, but none can promise more than a small fraction of the required protein in return for enormous energy expenditure. This is particularly true of processes of chemical synthesis. Of the ten essential amino acids only methionine has been synthesized on a commercial scale and lysine in smaller quantities. While it seems likely that the other eight amino acids will be prepared synthetically within the next decade or so, it is much less likely that a major fraction of human nutritional requirements can be provided in this way within the global energy-budgets which are likely up to at least the year 2000. A relatively more likely prospect—but still only involving a fractional contribution —lies in increased returns from various methods of microbial mass culture. Most of the techniques involved are essentially similar to those of modern brewing. Commercial production of lysine for use as a "vitamin-like" food additive depends on a method of this sort. If we assess the likelihood of extension of fermentation-culture processes, three points should be noted. First, energy costs are high: in providing some constituents of the media; in excluding contaminant organisms by maintaining nearly aseptic conditions; and in running elaborate pumping, temperature-control, and extraction equipment. Secondly, the raw materials for such factory processes—the substrates for the microörganisms to grow upon—are themselves organic materials ultimately of green plant origin. No matter how inexpensive (and the possible substrates for bacteria and yeasts include paper pulp wastes, sewage, dead leaves, lumbering wastes, and even crude petroleum and coal), these materials are part of *finite* resources of organic materials. Thirdly, as yet no single species of "fermenting" (that is, nonphotosynthetic) microörganism has been cultured, nor has a controlled mixed culture been designed, which can produce all the essential amino acids in appropriate proportions for human protein nutrition. Mass algal cultures and the hydroponic culture of higher plants can be considered together. Both are technologically possible, both can provide a balanced protein diet, and both are already being practiced. However, they are inordinately expensive, whether accounted for in currency terms or in any real measure of energy expenditure, and can only be carried out in circumstances where cost is of no concern. An obvious example is the provision of fresh vegetables for the unit of the U.S. Air Force on the isolated Ascension Island in the Atlantic. Many other optimistically promoted "artificial" human foods involve high protein content of normal organic origins such as cottonseed cake or fish-meal. Since most such are already employed as feedstuffs in intensive agriculture, producing meat protein for man, direct incorporation of them in human diets could represent movement to the next lower trophic level in each food-chain involved. As discussed earlier (see Chapters 4 and 5), the potential gain in protein input to our species is about one order of magnitude.

Any application of accountancy principles (a procedure appropriate to a canny Scots view of world problems) to matters of aquatic productivity, as well as to any of these other nutritional prospects, must hinge upon the necessary budgeting of global energy expenditure, and the signficance of the fossil fuels as a *finite* resource or as nonrenewable capital assets. As noted in the last chapter, the present annual fuel-energy consumption by machines must be about $12 \times 10^{18}$ calories per year. This was about 1/250 of the annual energy available for biological photosynthesis. The most carefully considered projections for human fuel-energy turnover in the year 2000 all lie around three times the present energy consumption by man-made machines. What is not often publicized is that almost all this increased artifact-energy turnover must come from fuels such as coal, oil, and natural gas. In 1968–69, hydroelectric sources provided about 3.5 per cent of our annual energy consumption and although increased construction is expected to bring about a 60 per cent increase in available power of this kind during the next three decades, this source will provide only about 2.1 per cent of needed energy in the year 2000. Even the most optimistic estimates of increasing availability of atomic power only suggest a twentyfold increase in available harnessed energy from nuclear-fission processes in the period between 1970 and 2000. This would suggest that nuclear sources *could* provide a maximum of 4.7 per cent of the world's energy requirements in 1980 and still only 14 per cent of the increased re-quirements in the year 2000. The prospects for the development of controlled nuclear fusion within the period are thought to be very low. Similarly, within this period, the direct utilization of solar energy and the harnessing of energy from geothermal sources will have consider-able local value for specialized needs, but will only make a very minor contribution to global energy requirements. Thus the fossil fuels, which at present provide for 96.4 per cent of our annual fuel consumption, will in the year 2000 still have to provide over 83 per cent of the energy required, or about 2.6 times the present level of consumption. Further, it is rarely pointed out that provision of nuclear energy has made, at least in its initial stages, enormous demands on fossil fuels. This can be illustrated by the growing atomic-industrial complex of eastern Tennessee, and presumably by less-known Russian equivalents. Oak Ridge was chosen as the site of a major part of the United States war-time effort on nuclear fission because of the then recently developed surplus hydroelectric resources of the area (the TVA). The greatest concentration of new power plants built in the United States over the last quarter-century—almost all coal-fired steam-generating stations—had subsequently to be built in that same area, largely to supply the energy needs of developing atomic power. Obviously, over the next few decades, the *net* energy gain from nuclear power stations will be markedly less than their rated *gross* output.

It is notoriously difficult to assess the world reserves of fossil fuels. They are *finite,* and with steadily increasing consumption the reserves will decrease exponentially and become increasingly difficult to exploit. Within an assessable number of years, the energy expenditure required to gain any given quantity of fuel will gradually approach the energy content of the fuel gained. The reserves will thus never be completely exhausted. In terms of a somewhat imperfect money analogy, we are consuming not interest but capital and our rate of consumption can only continue to increase as though at a compound interest rate for a limited number of years. There is good geochemical evidence to suggest that the initial supply of fossil fuels (almost untouched by man before 1800) was proportionately made up of about 69 per cent coal, 14 per cent petroleum and natural gas, and about 17 per cent tar sands and oil shales (the proportions reduced to heat-energy units). Moderately optimistic assessments of reserves suggest that the peak of petroleum and natural gas production will be passed in under forty years, while that of coal need not be reached for two centuries. Here again, the outlook is increasingly bleak if human population expansion continues for more than a couple of generations. In terms of our immediate concern—the supply of adequate protein to the expanding world population—this discussion of fuel-energy resources can only underline man's continuing need to rely on the vastly greater annual energy turnover of green plants for provision of food. It is most likely that this reliance has to continue for the few decades of the foreseeable future.

Some recapitulation may be appropriate. The possible doubling of conventional agricultural production during the next decades would not necessarily supply a proportional increase in protein-rich foodstuffs. Optimism with regard to the extension of conventional agriculture in tropical areas is misplaced. Assessment of the energetics of the processes involved implies that the contributions to world food supplies from chemical synthesis, microbial fermentation, or mass algal culture are not likely to be great in the next decades. In turn, this implies that greatly increased protein crops must be gained from aquatic productivity.

As already discussed, further development of conventional methods in marine fisheries could produce at least a doubling of present yields, within a few years. Much of this will have to come from stocks of smaller pelagic fishes with short life-cycles which feed directly upon zoöplankton: fishes like herring, sardines, and anchoveta. Much will probably be processed into fish-meal and fish oils. It is to be hoped that the bulk of these concentrates can be employed directly as food supplements to relieve protein malnutrition in underdeveloped countries; their employment as animal feeding-stuffs, at even the present levels, would constitute grave global injustice. The shift to direct human use will require some changes in handling and processing, but these have already been developed. At present, the processing of menhaden into fish-meal for animal feed results in a product which is always unpalatable to man, and occasionally would be unsafe.

Two United States agencies, the Bureau of Commercial Fisheries and the Agency for International Development (AID), are concerned in the development of fish protein concentrates (FPC) for supply to, and eventual production in, tropical countries with protein deficiencies. Some statistics regarding the Bureau of Commerical Fisheries' product are worth examining. As already noted, hake stocks in the western North Atlantic are underexploited since they are rarely marketed fresh in the United States. From each ton of hake caught, processing yields about 145 kg of concentrate containing about 114 kg of protein at a total cost of about $63 per ton of wet fish. If it is remembered that a daily supplement of about 15 grams of high-grade animal protein is usually sufficient to overcome acute protein deficiency, and that slightly less will provide enough animal protein to meet the daily minimum requirements of a growing child, then FPC could be supplied in the required quantities at a cost of just over $2.50 per head per year. The costs for processing some fish species might be slightly higher, but these figures for hake could represent the average costs and average yield on a commercial scale. The existence of protein malnutrition in the present day results from inequable distribution of existing fish and meat production. This is emphasized if one considers that, if the world catch in 1967 of 60.5 metric tons had all been converted to FPC at the rates for the experiments with hake (this was impossible technologically at the time—even if desirable), it would have yielded an appropriate annual protein supplement for just over 1.5 billion humans. This number is a bit under 50 per cent of the world population at the time, and corresponds surprisingly closely to the estimated number then suffering from any level of protein deficiency. Assuming that a more equable distribution of high-protein plant products could have been made in 1967 than actually occurred, the world's dietary requirements in that year could have been filled without involving the meat production from cattle (amounting to 36 million metric tons after processing in 1967). Politically and economically, this sort of distribution was and *is* impossible. To deal with existing malnutrition, and to prevent its involving greater numbers of mankind in the next decades, will require both some redistribution of the annual protein crop and some crop expansion, particularly in fisheries.

With the present small production of fish protein concentrate (FPC), there are already indications of its many advantages and one disadvantage in attempting to overcome protein malnutrition in some tropical countries. Only about 4.6 kg per head would be required annually, a quantity readily transported and stored. In contrast with the difficulties of distribution of fresh meat and fish, the dangers of bacterial and other spoilage are low and there is no need for refrigeration. Although highly nutritious, FPC itself is almost without taste or odor and thus can easily be added to a number of prepared foods such as various cereal mashes and forms of bread which are dietary staples in countries with extensive protein malnutrition. Its disadvantage lies, of course, in the cultural, social, and theological problems which could arise on the introduction of a food product of this sort prepared in this manner.

In spite of this, expansion of conventional fisheries for small pelagic fishes and the processing of the catch as FPC together offer the best chance to overcome protein malnutrition in the next few years. For reasons outlined above in discussing the limited potentials of conventional agriculture and of "artificial" foods, the even greater protein needs anticipated for the last two decades of this century have to be met from marine and freshwater productivity. This will involve not only extension and greater sophistication of conventional fishery techniques (see Chapter 14), but also the expansion of freshwater fishculture and the development of maritime farming (see Chapter 15). The above rapid survey of the *finite* nature of the world's animal biomass almost certainly involves several errors of fact and interpretation, but two conclusions are unlikely to be altered by even the grossest miscalculation. These are, first, that only aquatic productivity is capable of great expansion to provide more protein for mankind and, secondly, that even the potential productivity of the oceans is limited. All organic productivity is *finite*.

# Future marine exploitation (A): Improvements in a "sea-hunting" technology

IT IS OFTEN POINTED OUT that present human exploitation of the productivity of the oceans is analogous to that of the hunter on land rather than that of the farmer—this in spite of the enormous value of marine food already gained. Methods of finding fish and of processing them once they are caught have continually been improved, as has been the sophistication of fishing vessels themselves. On the other hand, the actual types of gear used in fish capture are essentially similar to those in use at the end of last century, and differ only in scale from those in use for at least three centuries earlier. There are four main categories of gear: lines with hooks, drift- or gill-nets, seine- or purse-nets, and trawl- or drag-nets. This brief chapter discusses some implications of recent trends in conventional fishing in relation to its future expansion. For convenience, the continuing improvements are summarized in three categories corresponding to the successive stages of finding the fish, capturing them, and processing the catch.

Before we pass to this summary, it is worth noting again the ecological significance of the kinds of fish and other animals which are the objects of conventional commercial fisheries. In all cases, man has found it economic to pursue only animals which represent local concentrations of the originally widely dispersed marine productivity. The simplest cases of local concentration are in large fishes such as tuna and bonito, and in whales, where the large size of the individual unit captured makes seeking such units over a wide area of sea an economic process. Local concentration can be behavioral, involving smaller units, and thus it is profitable to net the large shoals of such small fishes as sardines or anchoveta. A third type of local concentration of production is on the sea bottom in such fish species as cods and plaices. Perhaps a negative example will make this clear. A small nonshoaling fish species living in the middle depths of the open oceans is unlikely to become the object of an economic conventional fishery. To put it another way, all fisheries involve the concentration of animal biomass from a large volume of the ocean into the much smaller volume of the fish hold of the vessel and, up to the present, the exploited fish stock has always represented a considerable reconcentration of biomass. The originally dispersed primary productivity of the sea, and the secondary productivity of the zoöplankton herbivores, have to be concentrated by the shoaling behavior of sardines or by incorporation into a large efficient filter such as a whalebone whale before the value of the food energy gained becomes sufficiently greater than the cost of fuel and human energy expended in the fishing process for a "profitable" fishery to exist.

## Fish-finding and prediction

As Alister C. Hardy has noted, the trite phrase "won from the sea" is no exaggeration. He was referring to our piecemeal, and in considerable part chance-determined, sampling of the ocean environment for scientific purposes. It is equally true of commercial fisheries even today. Electronic methods of fish-finding, aerial spotting of shoaling fish and whales, and short-term biological prediction have all begun to reduce the "gambling" odds in favor of the fisherman. However, in most commercial fisheries, the chance of hauling empty nets or lines with some frequency is still high. It is important to realize that even the most useful fish-finding tool—sonar or echo-sounding—has only become important in fisheries since the end of the Second World War. Before that time the "lucky" fishing skipper found the fish stocks by his closely guarded appreciation of "signs" (including seabird movements and, quite literally, the taste of the water), and his vessel was followed by all those whose skippers had no reputation for "luck." Such had fish-finding been for centuries, and such it still was in 1938 when I was allowed as a boy to watch commercial herring fishing for the first time, from the deck of a ring-netter in Loch Fyne in Scotland. Twenty years later the capture methods were still the same, but echo-location of shoals was reducing the frequency of "clean shots" (when after shooting the nets, they are hauled empty of fish). In 1958, several experienced herring skippers had already computed that use of echo-sounders brought about more than a doubling of their "catch per shot." Marine electronics and sonar have become even more extensively used throughout world fisheries in the period from 1958 to 1969. The trend to greater sophistication in their use will continue through the next decades and their further development may modify some techniques of fish capture. This is already happening.

Conventional echo-sounding, in which sound impulses emitted from a transducer fixed under water on the vessel's bottom are echoed back from the seabed (the time taken for their return accurately indicating the depth), will also indicate the presence of shoals of fish, and the depth at which they occur, in intermediate depths. An important modification of the presentation of the echo-sounding record (or echogram), termed the white-line technique, was introduced in 1957 and allows a clear distinction between fish, or any other objects on or near the sea bottom, and seabed itself. The recording part of the equipment is arranged to show the seabed contour as a thin, dark line with a thicker white line immediately below it on the record, so that anything displayed on or above the dark line corresponds to something other than the seabed. Even a thickening of the line (see Figure 14·1A) can mean bottom-dwelling fish. This relatively small modification of echogram display has proved to be of immense importance to trawlers and long-liners, both in fish-finding and in enabling them to shoot their gear with the minimum risk of damage from irregular projections, or wrecks, on the sea bottom amid the potential catch. The record shown in Figure 14·1A is somewhat peculiar since it was made by a fisheries research vessel moving on the opposite course to the fishing vessel whose trawl-warps and -net are recorded as they approach the concentration of bottom fish. In normal echo-sounding procedures, a fishing skipper does not "see" his own trawl. It is rather different with the movable transducers of search sonar, which can be trained at various angles to the surface and to the course of the vessel.

Developed from the sonar used by antisubmarine vessels in the Second World War, angled search sonar has become very important in a wide variety of fisheries during the 1960's. A fairly simple record is shown in Figure 14·1B where first one and then two schools of fish near the bottom are recorded by sonar, the transducer being directed at a low angle ahead of the trawler. As the vessel closes with the schools, the traces corresponding to them move up toward the top of the sonar record. In this case the trawler then switched over to conventional depth-sounding, with the white-line technique, and Figure 14·1B also shows a conventional echogram of the two shoals on the bottom. Sonar is perhaps even more valuable in the capture of pelagic shoaling fish from middle depths in the open sea. Figure 14·2A illustrates its use by a trawler. Fish concentrations can be detected at distances of over a mile, and with most modern sonar equipment, the transducer can be set to scan automatically ahead and to the sides of the vessel. If fish are located to one side, the vessel can change course and move toward them, at the same time shooting the midwater trawl.

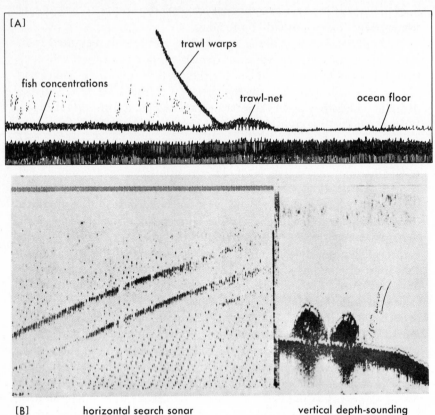

[B]　　　　　　　horizontal search sonar　　　　　　　vertical depth-sounding

**Figure 14·1. Echo-sounding techniques in fish-finding. A:** The white-line technique introduced in 1957 allows a clear distinction between the thickened line denoting a concentration of bottom-dwelling fish (with the approaching trawl) and the *thin* dark line above the thicker "white-line" which shows the seabed contour alone. **B:** In this pair of echograms, the first shows two schools of fish located by search sonar, the transducer being directed ahead of the trawler at a low angle. The traces move toward the top of the sonar record as the trawler moved closer to the schools. The trawler then switched to conventional depth-sounding (with "white-line") and in the second echogram we "see" the same two shoals on the bottom. [From echograms provided by the Simonsen Radio Company, Oslo, Norway, © Simrad.]

The sonar beam is tilted downward as the trawler approaches closer until, when the vessel passes over the school of fish, it is acting as an echo-sounder and gives an accurate measure of the depth of the school. The trawler continues to steam forward but adjusts its trawl to the correct depth so that it tows the net through the school. This process can be "watched" with the sonar before the trawl is hauled on board.

The rather different procedure using sonar in open water, in purse-seining, is illustrated in Figure 14·2B, which again begins with the

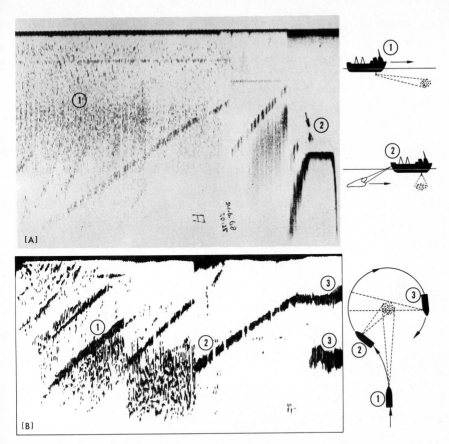

[A]

[B]

**Figure 14·2. Echo-sounding techniques in midwater trawling and in purse-seining. A:** In midwater trawling, a school of fish can be detected at a distance of over a mile. The vessel can change course to line up with the school (1) while moving closer to it, and while the pelagic trawl is being prepared and shot. The low-angle transducer is still facing ahead as the range on the recorder is twice changed, but then is pointed downward (like a conventional echo-sounder) as the trawler passes over the school (2) while the depth of the trawl is being adjusted to tow through the school. **B:** In modern purse-seining, the procedure again begins with the detection of a shoal of fish. The vessel is then steered closer through a series of range changes (1) with the transducer pointing ahead. At about 80 meters from the shoal the vessel turns broadside on to the shoal and begins to lay the circle of net (2) meanwhile "watching" the shoal. When the net is set halfway round the shoal, the echogram (3) shows both the shoal and more distantly (lower on the echogram) the other side of the "ring" of the purse-seine net. In both these fisheries, such recent sophistication in the use of sonar has led to reduction of the frequency of "clean shots" (that is, net hauls empty of fish). [From echograms provided by the Simonsen Radio Company, Oslo, Norway, © Simrad.]

detection of a shoal of fish about a mile distant. As the vessel approaches the shoal, the trainable beam of the sonar can be used to estimate its width and direction of movement. At a distance of perhaps 300 feet, the purse-seining vessel will begin to lay its net and steer in a circle around the shoal, training the sonar beam to the side of the vessel so that the shoal's movements can be followed. When the purse or "ring" is more than half set, then the vessel's skipper is able to "see" his net on the other side of the shoal. As the bottom rope of the purse is tightened, the depth of the shoal in the net can be checked.

Another development of the last few years has been to fit a transducer on the head-line of a trawl so that it records downward through the trawl opening to the seabed and thus allows a "view" of the fish as they are actually being caught, allowing the best time to be determined for hauling the trawl back on board. Figure 14·3 shows a record made

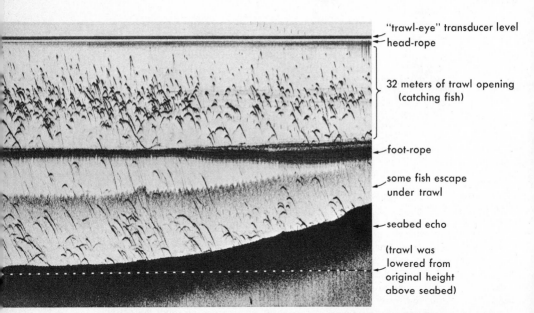

**Figure 14·3. Echo-sounding techniques: the sonar "trawl-eye."** In this procedure, the sonar transducer is attached to the middle of the head-rope of the trawl and allows a "view" of the fish as they enter the mouth of the trawl. The echogram reads from left to right, and towards the right the trawl was lowered (in the echogram the seabed echo moves up). There is a greyish "false echo" from the seabed which parallels the bottom (below the foot-rope echo), but the numbers of fish entering the trawl opening can be clearly distinguished as can the few escaping under the foot-rope. This record was made by the stern-trawler *Ottar Birting* fishing a pelagic trawl at about 2.5 knots to catch medium-sized cod in the Barents Sea in March 1969. [Echogram provided by the Simonsen Radio Company, Oslo, Norway, © Simrad.]

with this "trawl-eye" equipment in the spring of 1969 by a stern trawler using a midwater trawl to catch cod in the Barents Sea. The echogram reads from left to right, and the top zero line represents the head-line of the trawl where the transducer is located. The foot-rope is seen some 30 meters below and the seabed about 30 meters below that again. The cod are frightened away from the head-rope and foot-rope and concentrate in the middle of the trawl opening with a few escaping downward under the foot-rope. Toward the right of the echogram the trawl has been lowered to within 20 meters of the seabed, and at this part of the record the foot-rope is recorded thick and uneven because of the slower towing speed. Once again, it is obvious that this type of "electronic picture" of what is actually going on at the mouth of the trawl as it is being fished will help reduce the number of times that a fishing vessel need pull an empty trawl to the surface. Lastly, Scottish fisheries scientists announced in 1969 their development of a sonar capable of counting the numbers of individual fish in a "target" shoal. Their equipment involves a very high-resolution echosounder, a pulse analyzer sorting the echoes into 400 range-amplitude categories and recording this information, and a computer programmed to transform these records into a "count" of individual fish.

Aircraft of various sorts have been used in wider fish-searching for a number of years. In the last years of intensive Antarctic whaling, helicopters were used extensively; operating from the "mother" factory ship and directing the smaller whale-catcher vessels to their prey. Light aircraft have long been used in spotting shoals for the menhaden fishery of the Atlantic and Gulf coasts of the United States. Currently aerial spotting is limited because of its dependence on human visual detection of whales or shoaling fish. However, both photographic and remote electronic methods already exist for the detection by airborne cameras or sensors of variations in the surface temperatures of sea areas. Remote sensing and spectral analysis of reflected radiation can already allow aerial recognition of different types of land vegetation and crops. Similar aerial recognition of specific algal blooms within the *surface* waters is technologically possible. If the next decades were to see the (somewhat unlikely) development of surface-penetrating methods analogous to airborne radar, this could revolutionize distant detection of fish shoals. Meanwhile, there is already a most promising development in observations from satellites.

Many single color photographs taken from orbit during the Gemini and Apollo series of space flights show small darker patches in the oceans, which almost certainly correspond to known upwellings of colder water. In the course of the last few years (1967–1969), satellites maintaining a fixed position in space relative to the Earth have made it possible to monitor specific geographic areas continuously from

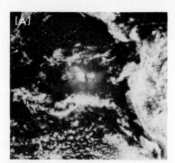

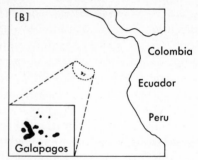

**Figure 14·4. Satellite detection of upwelling. A:** Photograph from an ATS satellite on 27 March, 1968 of an area of the Pacific Ocean to the west of Peru. Such satellites, at an orbiting height of approximately 36,000 km, maintain a fixed position in space relative to the Earth. The arrow in the key diagram **(B)** indicates a bright specular reflection within which the principal islands of the Galapagos can be distinguished. The photograph is one of a series over about an hour and a half showing a sunglint sequence, dark-bright-dark, which indicates that this area around and to the west of the Galapagos was then one of relatively calm surface conditions. This is known to have corresponded closely to an area with an upwelling of colder, nutrient-rich water at the time of the satellite observations. Satellite detection of this sort of upwelling could provide "predictions" of areas where enhanced productivity might be expected. [A: Photo from C. J. Bowley, J. R. Greaves, and S. L. Spiegel in *Science*, 165:1360–1362, 1969, © 1969 by the American Association for the Advancement of Science; photo-print provided by Dr. James R. Greaves.]

heights of about 36,000 km. Diurnal changes, including those in sunglint patterns, can allow detection by television camera of areas of the sea where there are transient or continuous upwellings of colder (and usually nutrient-rich) waters (see pages 99 and 241). Satellite photographic data of this sort (see Figure 14·4) could readily be used to provide "predictions" to the fishing industries of areas where enhanced secondary productivity could some weeks later become commercially significant.

Like electronic and aerial fish-finding, biological prediction of fisheries may become increasingly important in reducing the chance element in fishing returns. First, in certain fisheries, crude biological predictions regarding catch levels and the nature of the catch have been possible for some time. For example, extrapolation from data on year-classes in stocks in European waters of several gadid fish species and of herring could give some prediction of the dominant size groups in the next year's fishery. As noted in Chapter 5, annual differences in the productivity of such fisheries can result from differential survival of young, with the result that one or a few year-classes dominate the population for a number of years. Through the 1930's and again for a period after the Second World War, Dr. W. C. Hodgson of the Lowestoft fisheries laboratory in England was able to forecast the expected quality of the herring in the autumnal fishery in the North Sea by studying the age composition of the shoals from year to year. This allowed the processing part of the seasonal herring industry to know in advance the relative proportions of large and small fish which would have to be dealt with after landing.

Secondly, some measurable aspects of water circulation affect nutrient supply and thence primary production, and can allow predictions of subsequent productivity at higher trophic levels including fish. As noted earlier, the water masses of the North Sea and English Channel are of mixed origins. Proportionately more northern Atlantic water (that is, water with the indicator species *Sagitta elegans;* see page 78) off Plymouth in winter means more phosphates and other nutrients available in spring, and—as F. S. Russell has demonstrated over at least twenty years—corresponding increases in the numbers of young fish surviving from their early larval stages in each year. In many other parts of the world, variations in productivity in a sea area result from changes in the proportions of water masses of different origins moving into it, and it seems likely that much future predictive work on fisheries will involve assessment of this, possibly making use of sampling for indicator species such as those of the arrow-worm genus *Sagitta.* As regards the long-studied situation in the English Channel, it also seems likely that increasing knowledge of the physical oceanography of the eastern North Atlantic may, within a decade or so, allow forecasts to be made of the long-term movements of water masses. Recent studies (1967–1969) have led to an as yet untested hypothesis that the nutrient-rich years derive from increased activity of cyclonic domes or eddies in the open Atlantic (west of Ireland and south of Iceland) which domes displace water toward the surface from at least 1000 meters depth. In turn, these eddies may be driven by increased influx of Arctic water to the deeper parts of the North Atlantic, in the years immediately preceding. Correlations of extensive data for this, as for other problems of physical oceanography, are now more readily achieved using computer facilities. Much of the physical data for the North Atlantic gained over the last half-century or so are only recently being fully exploited because of the vast computational labor which would have been involved in establishing relationships before 1950.

In a *qualitative* sense, from our knowledge of circulation and the existence of major tropical upwellings fifty years ago, some of the most productive fisheries of today, including the burgeoning anchoveta fisheries off Peru, could have been "predicted." However, *quantitative* forecasting of, and establishment of appropriate cropping levels for, such fisheries as those of southwestern Africa and Peru are only now being attempted. Paradoxically, in the case of major upwellings, long before the details of water density and nutrient content had been elucidated, there had been much recorded biological data on the existence of local areas of greatly enhanced productivity. A classic example of this is provided by the records collated and maps prepared by C. H. Townsend of whaling captures reported in nineteenth century logbooks preserved in Nantucket, New Bedford, and elsewhere. The chart plotted by months, for the killings of over 8000 right-whales (two species of slower whalebone whales hunted almost to extinction), shows their seasonal progression through the areas of highest zoöplankton productivity in the oceans of higher latitudes. In contrast, in the charts prepared for nearly 37,000 killings of sperm whales (toothed, predatory whales), the majority of the points plotted lie in tropical and warmer temperate waters, but dense concentrations of kills accurately reflect certain regions of high productivity, including those associated with the Humboldt and Benguela currents. Other examples of historical biological data include those on annual variations in the population sizes of guano birds (fish-eating cormorants, boobies, and pelicans), and of the rates of accumulation of new guano deposits on islands off southern Peru. These were studied because of their economic significance in terms of exportable fertilizer, but might have provided a measure of annual and other variants to be expected in this new human fishery for anchoveta.

When we return to a consideration of likely developments in the next few decades, it is almost certain that great improvements can be expected in the forecasting of the movements and condition of fish stocks. Extrapolations are likely to be made from three types of data: information on the age structure of the fish population; records of water movements, particularly of nutrient-rich water masses; and *continuous* recording of zoöplankton stocks in the fishery areas. The last is required not only to give an estimate of the biomass of potential fish food but also because regular monitoring of indicator species can help detect the consequences of major water movements. From all these data there should emerge—in a herring fishery, for example—in addition to a forecast of the age and size distribution of the catch to be expected (as Hodgson's work had already made possible), an assessment of the condition of the fish (for example, their fatness in each size group) and a prediction of the likely catch returns per unit of fishing effort. One key to such forecasting will be the even more extensive deployment of continuous recorders, including Hardy's original continuous plankton recorder and recording sensors working on the Coulter counter principle such as those developed by John Kanwisher and others. Continuous plankton records for the North Sea obtained by towing recorders behind the commercial vessels on regular shipping routes already allow partial predictions to be made of the numbers and trophic state of adult fish. Regular survey work with the continuous plankton re-

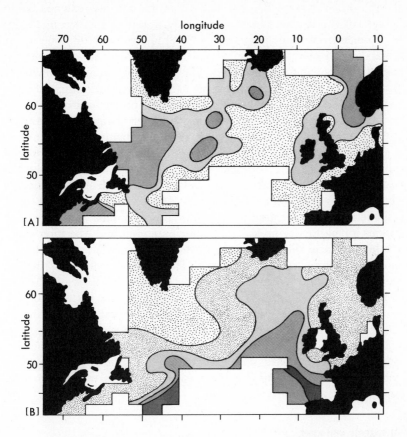

**Figure 14·5. The distribution of zoöplankton in the North Atlantic.** Maps were prepared by pooling results from the Scottish continuous plankton recorder survey from 1958 to 1965. The recorders had been towed by weather ships and by vessels on certain regular commercial routes, and the rectangular boundaries mark off the blank sea areas not sampled. **A:** Three levels of estimated total biomass of zoöplankton are shown, the contours between levels being drawn at "biomass index" values of 120 and 200. **B:** Five levels of diversity of copepod species are shown, the contours between levels being drawn at levels of 11, 16, 24, and 40 species. Some features of the hydrography of the North Atlantic are reflected by the two maps including: the warm nutrient-poor waters of the Gulf Stream with its northwestern "meander" east of Newfoundland (low biomass production and high species diversity), the waters of the continental shelves (relatively higher production and lower diversity), and the nutrient-rich waters of the Labrador current and Irminger systems (high production and low diversity). [After maps prepared by R. S. Glover, FRSE, for the *Annual Report (1967–68)* of the Scottish Marine Biological Association.]

corder is carried out from the oceanographic laboratory in Edinburgh of the Scottish Marine Biological Association, and now extends far to the west of the British Isles. Some survey results are shown in Figure 14·5, taken from maps prepared by R. S. Glover in 1968. The upper figure shows a biomass index of total zoöplankton, and the lower the diversity of copepod species found. The pattern of biomass is obviously related to the major current systems of the North Atlantic, with the diagonal band of low biomass corresponding to the warm waters of the Gulf Stream (with a characteristic meander toward the northwest off Newfoundland), and the regions of higher biomass corresponding to the continental shelves as well as the nutrient-rich waters of the Labrador current and Irminger system. It is also obvious that the pattern of diversity of species is inversely related: high species diversity corresponds to low biomass productivity. More detailed plankton maps could certainly be prepared using continuous recorders, and large-scale versions for particular areas could contribute greatly to the forecasting of fishery returns. The difficulties of this sort of prediction should not be overemphasized since, as Alister C. Hardy has pointed out, the first weather maps were poor things compared to today's forecasts used in aerial navigation. Finally, there is the possibility that within the next two decades, remote sensing of phytoplankton bloom areas in the sea will become practical, since detection of the extent of upwelling areas is already possible (see Figure 14·4). This being so, high-flying aircraft and even satellites should in future be able to contribute to productivity forecast maps for the oceans as they do to weather forecasting today.

## Trends in vessels and gear

As noted earlier, the nets and lines used in commercial fishing today are little modified from those in use seventy years ago. The vessels employing them are mostly larger and the fuel expenditure per unit fishing time—and also per unit catch—has greatly increased. A quick survey of the historical development of trawling (sometimes called dragging) will illustrate this conservative rate of evolution of gear.

There is some controversy about where in Europe trawling began, but it was certainly being carried out by both Dutch and English fishermen in the early years of the seventeenth century. Their basic gear was the beam-trawl, which continued in use, with little modification, until the last decades of the nineteenth century. The oblong mouth of a beam-trawl (Figure 14·6D), which in the later years could be 25 or even 30 feet across, was held open by a long wooden beam with the head-rope or upper edge of the trawl opening attached to it. At the ends of the beam were attached two curved metal supports arising from the runners (like sledge runners) and bearing the shackles attaching the trawl to the Y-shaped yoke of its towing warp. The weighted foot-rope forming the lower edge of the trawl opening was considerably longer than the head-rope and, in action, curved back on the sea bottom so that the fish disturbed by it were already covered by a roof of moving net extending back from the beam. The net itself tapered back from this oblong opening for perhaps 40 feet and then formed a narrow cylinder, usually of more closely woven netting termed the codend, in which the captured fish accumulated. The furthest end of the codend was tied closed before shooting the trawl, and so remained until after the fishing was completed. When the trawl beam was hauled back alongside the fishing boat, the codend could be pulled aboard and there emptied. It is important to note that a beam-trawl had to be hauled alongside the fishing craft shooting it and that the length of the beam was restricted since it had to be considerably less than the length of the vessel operating it. Of course, other limitations were imposed in the early sailing trawlers by the fact that only the muscle power of the crew was available to haul up the trawl, to bring the beam alongside, and to bring the codend inboard. (In some early inshore trawling, the codend and catch were got inboard by a process of turning the trawl-net inside out.) About the same time as steam-powered trawlers began to be built, a major and important innovation occurred with the introduction of the otter-trawl. In this, the opening of the trawl is held extended by the action of the heavy metal-bound wooden otter-boards, which are attached to a pair of towing warps so that they pull outwards like kites as they are towed along (Figure 14·6E). There is thus no limitation on the width of the trawl opening, and modern otter-trawls can be up to 100 feet wide. The head-rope, which is lifted up by a series of floats, is still shorter than the foot-rope and forms a rather flat curve if the trawl is shot correctly and being fished at an appropriate speed. The longer foot-rope may be weighted or partly made of chain and forms a deep bight well behind the line of the head-rope. Otter-trawls replaced beam-trawls in European vessels from 1880 onwards, and there was little further change until about forty years ago when the technique arose of attaching the kite-like otter-boards not directly to the ends of the trawl opening but by long lateral warps so that they can shear well out to the sides—and presumably help drive fish into the trawl from an even wider area.

Until relatively recently, otter-trawls were hauled as beam-trawls had been, finishing up *alongside* the vessel. Thus, though sail had given way to steam, and steam in turn to diesel propulsion, some characteristic features of trawlers (or draggers) remained little changed over the years. The majority of the world fleet of trawlers operating in 1969 still have—as did their nineteenth-century forerunners—sets of

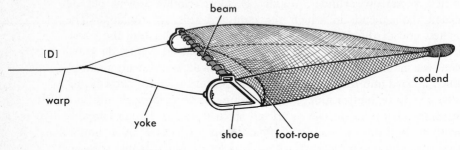

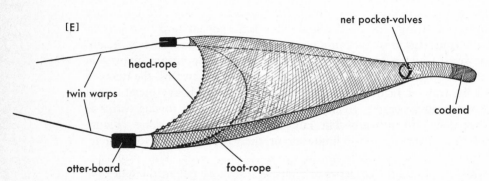

**Figure 14·6. The evolution of trawlers and of trawl nets. A:** A steam trawler (or dragger) of the early nineteenth century with sets of gallows fore and aft to which the twin warps brought the otter-boards when the trawl was hauled *alongside* the vessel after fishing. **B:** A large modern deep-sea trawler of 1955, still with gallows. **C:** A modern stern-trawler in which the trawl is hauled up a stern ramp. **D:** The beam-trawl as used from before 1600 until the 1890's. **E:** The otter-trawl with its opening extended by the use of kite-like otter-boards, as introduced in the 1880's. For further discussion, see text.

gallows fore and aft. These are immensely strong steel structures like inverted V's, inclining outwards and rising about 10 feet above deck level in a moderately large trawler (Figure 14·6A and B). The paired towing warps pass over pulley blocks on these and it is from them that the otter-boards hang before the trawl is shot and after it is hauled. In a conventional trawler there is always the stage of unpleasant wallowing (and sometimes real danger to limbs) during the last stages of hauling with the trawl coming alongside, followed by the struggle to recover and hoist aboard the codend, hopefully heavy with the catch. Only in the last twenty years have stern-trawlers become widespread. In them, first the otter-boards and then the rest of the trawl are brought to one huge gallows across the stern and the codend is hauled aboard mechanically up a stern ramp or through a stern opening (see Figures 14·6C and 14·7). Such vessels are also better suited to more modern methods of processing the catch. The advantages of modern stern-trawlers became apparent with the success and obvious efficiency of such vessels in the re-equipped West German fishing fleet in the late 1950's, and it is not without significance that the United States and Britain have been laggard in building replacement trawlers with modern stern-hauling gear. It is worth emphasizing that, in spite of the limited changes in trawling techniques which have occurred over the last century, more than 30 per cent of the fish crop gained at present from the world's oceans is taken by some form of trawling. Another major development in postwar trawling was mentioned during the discussion of echo-sounding above. Operation of midwater otter-trawls at relatively high speeds has become practicable, and returns from this technique depend on the efficiency of detection of fish shoals. A further recent development in pelagic trawling has been the use of paired vessels, moving at relatively high speeds on parallel courses, towing between them a very large, fine-meshed trawl without otter-boards. Pair-trawling of this kind will only give economic returns with closely shoaling pelagic fish, but it is so effective in operation that a real danger of over-fishing certain herring stocks by this method has arisen in recent years.

Long-lining is a fishing technique as ancient as trawling, and the only changes which have occurred are those of scale: longer lines and better mechanical methods for winding the lines inboard and storing them. (Unfortunately, so far as I am aware, no *mechanical* method has been designed for baiting the many thousands of hooks involved, which has always been a tedious and unpleasant task.) Modern long-lining is of two sorts. It is carried out in middle depths in the open ocean for such fishes as tuna and bonito. The longer-established technique of long-lining on the bottom is mainly carried out for fishes like cod and halibut where they occur on a sea bottom so irregular and rocky that a trawl cannot be used without damage. A modern Japanese deep-sea vessel long-lining for tuna can shoot more than 50 miles of line each day and recover a similar amount of line laid earlier. A bottom long-liner working in some of the rough grounds off the West of Scotland will lay in a day about 30 lines, each about ¾ mile long with about 150 lateral leaders (themselves about 10 feet long) to the baited hooks.

**Figure 14·7. Modern stern-trawlers.** Above: The *Ross Valiant* is a modern British stern-trawler, with "factory" equipment for processing and deep-freezing the catch at sea, which makes long trips to the Newfoundland banks from her home port of Grimsby. Below: This view of the stern-ramp in another British stern-trawler shows the full codend of the trawl hauled aboard; the otterboards can be seen hanging on either side of the ramp. [Upper photo © Sid Burton, Grimsby, England. Lower photo © Peter Brady, Fleetwood, England.]

The other netting techniques of commercial fisheries fall into two main classes: drift-netting, which is declining, and ring-netting, which is expanding in extent and in variety of usage. Techniques of gill- or drift-netting are now responsible for a much smaller proportion of the world's fishery returns than they were earlier this century, and it seems likely their decline will continue. When fishing, the vessel called a drifter is attached to perhaps 3 miles of drift-nets which hang vertically from about 10 feet below the surface down to about 60 feet as a continuous wall of netting like a gigantic fence. The meshes are just wide enough in these drift-nets or gill-nets for the fish's head to be caught by the opercula covering the gills on each side. Drift-nets normally make most of their catch during the hours of darkness and have been most important in herring fisheries. In the early years of this century, fleets of over 2000 drifters worked out of the English North Sea ports. The number has now declined to a few hundred vessels.

The group of commercial fishery techniques known, in their simplest forms, as ring-netting, seine-netting, or purse-netting basically consist of laying a wall of netting around a shoal of fish and then hauling the wall in so that the fish become concentrated in an ever-narrowing space. Perhaps the earliest seine-nets were those hauled onshore after a small boat had laid them in the form of a wide arc out to sea. Such longshore seining is still carried out in many parts of the world. In comparatively shallow seas over suitably smooth sand or mud seabeds, bottom-seining for such fish as the plaice can be carried out. The net used, often termed a Danish seine, is like a very wide light trawl without otter-boards or special bridles. The bottom-seiner first anchors a buoy and then lays out her gear on a triangular course: the first side being a warp laid along the bottom away from the buoy, the next side being the net laid at an acute angle to the first, and the third side being another warp laid back to the buoy. The two warps are drawn in together and the fish caught pass into a codend like that on an ordinary trawl-net. A bottom-seiner can be a relatively small vessel, with much lighter gear, a smaller crew, and less fuel expenditure than a trawler.

Much more important in the expanding fisheries of the world are methods of purse-seining and ring-netting as developed in the herring fisheries of Norway and of Scotland, respectively. Such methods can be and are being applied to the expanding fisheries for smaller plankton-feeding pelagic fish such as herring, sardines, and anchoveta. Brief reference was made above to the use of sonar in locating fish shoals for ring-netting (see Figure 14·2B). Once located, the shoal is encircled with a vertical wall of net—rather like a fine-meshed version of a drift-net. Once the circle is closed, the foot-rope of the annular wall is drawn in more rapidly so that after the circle of the head-rope has been hauled to about a sixth of its original laid diameter, the shoal of fish is concentrated effectively in a basin of net. The ring-netter or purse-seiner then uses a hoist-operated scoop-net—like a giant landing net or perforated ladle—to bale out the fish which have been encircled. In the West of Scotland, ring-netting was often carried out by pairs of vessels, one boat acting as the buoy holding the end of the circle while the other laid out the net and then closed the ring by passing the warps to the first vessel. The first vessel then hauled the ring tight while the second prepared to bale out the contents. A recent development in purse-seining has been the use of a wide, flexible suction hose-pipe instead of a scoop-net to bring the captured fish aboard. The next two decades are likely to see further development of purse-seining as well as of trawling.

Finally, there is a real possibility that future improvements in conventional fisheries need not only involve *surface* vessels. It is not often realized that many of the difficulties, including uncertainties as regards catch and the risk of damage to expensive gear, of at least two kinds of fisheries would be overcome if submarines fishing while submerged could be employed. In the case of pelagic shoaling fish, a large factory-ship type of submarine could be effective. The last stage of capture, after concentration by a ring-net technique, could employ a "hose-pipe" leading directly into factory processing without manual effort. The other kind of fishery where a submerged technique could become important is long-lining for bottom fish—characteristically in decline at present because of the labor conditions involved. If one-man or two-man submarines can become commercially available and safe within the next decades, they could, working like the traditional Grand Banks dories from a mother-ship, completely revolutionize this kind of bottom fishing. To anyone who has seen something of present-day commercial fishing, there is another aspect of possible submerged fishing vessels which is very attractive. Fishermen, like few other workers except miners in the deeper coal-mines today, are employed in conditions of more or less continuous discomfort with occasional periods of immediate danger to life and limb. Most of the human discomfort, and much of the danger, involved in traditional fishing vessels working traditional gear would be absent in a submerged vessel.

## Trends in processing

In the middle of last century, the largest fraction of the world's fish catch was preserved by salting. Smaller quantities were dried and smoked or were distributed fresh. The use of ice in the distribution of "fresh" fish became important toward the end of the century. It is significant that true fishing industries handling fresh fish first arose in countries like Japan and Britain where there were large urban concentrations close enough to landing ports to make rapid transport and distribution feasible. In the case of Britain, real industrialization of this type of fishing paralleled the growth of a railway network in the second half of the nineteenth century, with rival British railway companies contributing to the development of the docks and landing systems of such "new" ports as Lowestoft, Grimsby, Milford Haven, and Fleetwood. By the early years of this century, such planned fisheries ports were the world's largest—in terms both of the number of vessels operating out of them and of actual fish landings. Through the first decades of the twentieth century, the overnight *solid* fish trains from such ports to London were accorded all the priorities and railroad mystique of the crack passenger expresses. Over the same period, the complex wholesaling and distributing organizations of the huge fish-markets of many coastal cities such as Marseilles, Tokyo, and New York City were being developed.

It is important to realize that the small-scale industrialization of fish-curing (preserving by packing in brine, by smoking, by drying, and so on) had occurred much earlier and played a major part in world trade from at least the sixteenth century, by supplying essential protein supplementation to diets in tropical countries and in cold temperate communities in winter. In the eighteenth century, codfish, salted and dried in New England, was valued as a dietary supplement for the labor force on plantations in the West Indies, and at the same time the citizens of Prague, and even of Moscow, in winter consumed large quantities of salt herring processed in Scotland or in Holland. The history of British and Dutch imperialism is based in part on the rise of these nations as naval powers, and this in turn grew in part from their seventeenth- and eighteenth-century development of huge merchant fleets transporting pickled herring for trade around the world.

More recent trends in fish-processing are illustrated in Figure 14·8, which covers the period of great fisheries expansion (see also Figure 13·1) since the Second World War. Just under half the catch was marketed as fresh fish in 1948, and although the tonnage in this category has nearly doubled, it now represents only about 30 per cent of the landings. Similarly, in spite of a steady increase in the tonnage of fish processed by the traditional curing methods, the proportion of the world catch treated in this manner has declined from 25.5 per cent in 1948 to 13.2 per cent in 1967. The fraction of the catch going to canning has remained at about 8.5 per cent, although the tonnage involved has been increased nearly fourfold. Two types of processing have become increasingly important. Tonnage of fish frozen has increased sevenfold, and now accounts for over 12 per cent of the world catch. In 1948 shredding and drying processes resulting in fish meal or other concentrates accounted for 1.5 million tons or 7.7 per cent of the world's catch, a large part of this being accounted for by the menhaden and similar fisheries in the North Atlantic. In 1967 the tonnage processed in this way had risen to over 20 million tons (and is still rising), accounting for more than a third of the world's fish crop in that year. Roughly half the fish tonnage processed in this way comes from the fishery for anchoveta off Peru.

Thus the two methods of fish-processing which have expanded most rapidly—and which are likely to continue to do so in the next two decades—are providing for the opposite ends of the spectrum of market values. On the one hand, modern factory trawlers (see Figure 14·7) catch high-value bottom fish like cod and haddock, fillet and deep-freeze them aboard, and land them. They then require little more than external packaging before they appear as relatively expensive protein on the shelves of supermarkets in Europe and North America. On the other hand, the Peruvian crop of anchoveta is processed into fish-meal of high nutritive value but of low money price, and is sold as animal feed. Several nations now have factory ships with modern equipment for oil extraction and for dehydrating fish-meals at sea. Use

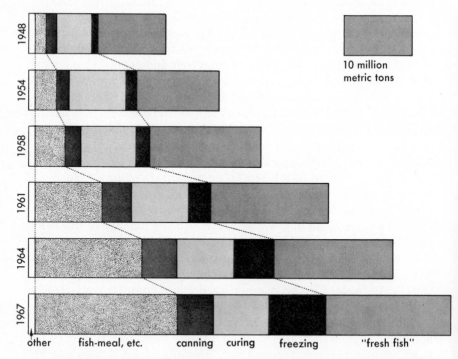

10 million metric tons

other    fish-meal, etc.    canning   curing   freezing   "fresh fish"

**Figure 14·8. Processing of the catch in world fisheries** during the recent expansion (1948–1967). For further discussion, see text. [Modified from figures in the *Yearbook of Fishery Statistics* for 1967 published by the Food and Agriculture Organization of the United Nations, Rome, 1968.]

of these, as well as of freezer-trawlers, is likely to increase in the next few years.

We can recapitulate some of the recent trends in conventional fishery techniques which are likely to continue in the expansion of the next decade or so. Use of sonar and other electronic aids to fish-finding will increase, as will biological forecasting of productivity. A great proportion of the crop will come from short-lived pelagic, shoaling species, and such techniques as open-water purse-seining and fast midwater trawling will become increasingly important. More trawlers with modern stern-hauling gear, more freezer-vessels, and more factory ships will be employed. A considerable proportion of the high-value fish caught will be processed and deep-frozen at sea, and probably about half the world catch will be converted to meals and concentrates, hopefully for *direct* human nutrition. Other processing techniques such as freeze-drying and irradiation are still little used, though technologically possible, but could become important within ten years. The two- to threefold increase in conventional fisheries which is possible would leave few species under-fished and very many stocks over-fished. This will require increased regulation of fisheries aimed at appropriate conservation of stocks to obtain the maximum sustainable catch. It is to be hoped that this regulation will involve extensive international agreements on marine resources rather than further extensions of national sovereignty to encompass much more of the productive seas.

# 15

# Future marine exploitation (B): Genesis of a "sea-farming" technology

WITH CAREFULLY CONTROLLED CROPPING, improvements in, and extensions of, existing fishing methods could perhaps triple the returns from marine fisheries in a decade or so. To provide more protein for a larger human population by further exploitation of marine productivity is possible, but would require new techniques akin to those of agriculture.

Ideally, the ultimate aim of fishery research and development should be the introduction of marine husbandry, not merely in controlled cropping of fish resources, but in supervised control of the basic marine pasture as in stock farming. Only in a few limited shellfish "industries" is this level of maritime farming likely to be reached within the next few years. In fresh waters the development of fish-ponds with dense populations of edible fish species maintained by fertilization will certainly continue. Undoubtedly, there will be further attempts at similar fish-farming in shallow, semienclosed marine waters. However, complete control and major modification of biological communities in the open sea are unlikely to be possible in the foreseeable future. Limitations in the global supply of nutrient salts may have become critical (see Chapters 8, 12, and 13). Developments which are much more likely before true maritime farming of even coastal waters include cropping protein for human food at a lower trophic level than fish and the adoption of a "herding" type of husbandry involving fish or marine mammals. There are formidable technical difficulties at present in both possible developments.

## Possible intermediate cropping

The food fishes presently cropped by man from the sea have fed themselves mostly at the third and fourth trophic levels. As we have seen, the potential crop of animal protein at the second trophic level could be expected to be greater by one or two orders of magnitude. Thus, with a ten- to hundredfold increase in protein crop theoretically possible, it is tempting to emulate the evolution of whalebone whales (see Chapter 2) and attempt to collect animal protein at the level of the zoöplankton. The principal organisms of the second trophic level in the open sea, such as calanoid copepods, could be highly nutritious and —without much preparation—are reasonably palatable. Mingling with *Calanus* and its allies, of course, there are many other planktonic forms (see Chapter 4), and these include some, like certain medusae and ctenophores, which are distasteful and which could, in quantity in human diet, prove dangerous.

Early in the Second World War, Alister C. Hardy and some associates carried out large-scale experiments off the West Coast of Scotland on the direct cropping of zoöplankton. In essence, their method was to fix large plankton nets in tidal flows so that these could swing to filter the currents in both directions. In this way it was hoped to avoid the great expenditure of fuel involved in towing such fine-meshed nets through the water. It was intended to dehydrate the plankton captured for use as a protein-rich meal for poultry and other livestock. Direct use for human nutrition was ruled out, partly because of the impossibility of excluding medusae and other forms from the meal and partly because bacterial spoilage could occur even after the drying process. The experiments were continued for about two years, but failed to collect sufficient plankton to meet even a fraction of their costs, and were eventually abandoned. Hardy concluded that such efforts would usually be defeated by the quantities of water involved. The fuel expenditure to tow sufficiently large nets of fine mesh is calculable and is impossibly high. Even the tidal-flow method with fixed nets tried in Scotland involved considerable fuel-energy expenditure, and it was made less effective by the uneven distribution—or patchiness—of the plankton. The fixed swinging gear was very expensive and extremely liable to damage in bad weather conditions. More recently, an engineering survey of the costs involved in direct cropping of zoöplankton of various sizes was made by P. Jackson who concluded that capture of calanoid copepods by any means was economically impracticable. It is of interest to note that, with mesh-sizes capable of stopping *Calanus* and similar-sized organisms, the fuel costs involved in towing a large plankton net through a given volume of water are closely similar to those expended in pumping a similar volume of water through filters. The capital expenditure on both types of plankton-collecting gear would be much higher than that for conventional fishing equipment, and the increased likelihood of damage would also add to the costs. Although Hardy began this and other work with considerable optimism, his final conclusion was that whalebone whales and basking sharks were essentially more efficient plankton collectors than any man-designed apparatus.

On theoretical grounds—given the quantities of water to be filtered—the only exploitation of this sort which could be economic would be of larger planktonic organisms such as the euphausiids or krill of polar waters and certain deep layers in temperate seas. In 1956, a group of Russian fishery biologists, including R. N. Burukovskii and V. O. Stasenko, reported on the economics of a direct fishery for krill in the Antarctic, and E. I. Osochenko of the same group evaluated the production of fish-meal from krill. It is not known if the Russians intend to begin harvesting of Antarctic krill in the near future. One existing commercial fishery perhaps illustrates the minimum size of planktonic organism which can be cropped economically. There is already a Japanese fishery which involves netting largish planktonic organisms—two species of sergestid shrimps about 2 cm long. Fuel costs are low, but considerable manual work is involved. Capture of the more abundant but smaller zoöplankton organisms such as *Calanus* would be uneconomic—even with the low labor costs of an inshore fishery in Japan. Although the calanoid copepods probably represent the largest unit of annual production of animal protein in the world, they are unlikely to be cropped directly by man within the next decades unless some entirely new technique of concentrating them from the sea is found which does not involve water filtration. Discovery of a chemical attractant or of an electromagnetic method of concentration could bring about a technological breakthrough in our exploitation of marine productivity. It is perhaps more probable that cropping at this trophic level could begin in semienclosed bodies of seawater with a contrived "flow system" for culturing and cropping a copepod like *Calanus* or a larger, but still primary-consumer, shrimp.

## Fish-herding husbandry

In general, it seems likely that a herding type of husbandry involving fish or marine mammals is more likely to be developed within the next twenty years than is complete maritime farming with local addition of fertilizers, control of the basic plant pasturage, and specific and regular cropping of definite areas. Highly successful transplantation experiments have already been carried out with stocks of bottom-dwelling fish such as the plaice. Some of the earliest experiments were organized in the North Sea by Walter Garstang around 1905. Young plaice were caught from crowded populations on banks off the coast of Holland, measured, marked, and then liberated. Half were released where they had been captured and the other half transported to areas of the Dogger Bank which have a rich supply of benthic organisms suitable as food for young fish, but no naturally occurring stocks of young plaice. Subsequent monthly samples from both areas recaptured sufficient of the marked plaice to show that growth in the fishes transplanted to the Dogger Bank was nearly three times greater than growth in those replaced in their original habitat. Similar experiments have been repeated, yielding comparable results. It is easy to calculate that such transplantation could be economically profitable: for transfers conducted on a suitable scale, the increased value of the fish yield could be much greater than the costs of live transport. Although this is a practical way of increasing marine productivity of a kind valuable to man, it is impossible to carry out in international waters unless preceded by international agreements to share costs and crops, to prevent fishing during the growth period, and to control the final cropping. Even if transplantation was carried out within national waters, there would still be difficulties in controlling the cropping of the transplanted stock. There are obviously extraordinary legal difficulties in defining ownership in a "herd" of fish at sea—even more so if the ownership were multinational. However, if these questions can be solved, it becomes significant that a few years ago Dr. J. E. Shelbourne of the Lowestoft laboratory was successful in rearing large numbers of young plaice in closed artificial tanks to an age of three months. Survivorship was remarkably high (60 per cent), and the plaice so reared were eminently suitable for planting out on congenial grounds.

Apart from the legal side, many difficulties of future fish-herding would be solved by the development of effective ways of closing off areas of the sea bottom. It is certainly possible that methods could be developed from present technology involving the use of beams of phased light, or of sound or other vibrations or radiations, which would be effective in "fencing off" particular areas of the sea to enclose fish or other animals. If such a method became practicable, its economic effect could be similar to the historical effects of the invention of barbed wire on the exploitation of the prairies. Related to this possibility is, of course, the use of similar physical methods for concentrating a fish crop before capture. The possible development of commercially economic and safe miniature submarines within the next decade is also of significance to fish-herding.

It is also worth considering that chemical methods might be employed to control fish-herds or to concentrate them finally for capture. Recent work by E. D. Hasler has re-emphasized the great importance of the olfactory sense in the reproductive migrations of stocks of salmon. It is possible that several kinds of fish are capable of detecting extremely low concentrations of organic substances, some of which may be species-specific metabolites with an action similar to that of the externally secreted hormone-like attractants of insects. Distance-reception by fish of such substances might possibly be employed in herd control and in bringing the fish to a specific place for capture.

If fish-herding becomes practicable, there will be immediate and considerable economic pressure toward selective breeding of specific stocks. Once again, there are already some demonstrations that appropriate fish-breeding can be carried out. For example, a Scottish fisheries scientist, J. H. S. Blaxter, has already carried out successful cross-fertilizations between different stocks of North Sea herring, and this has involved successful long-term storage of live sperms necessary to achieve cross-fertilization between stocks which naturally spawn in spring and those which spawn in autumn. Thus selective breeding of fish stocks could now be achieved much more rapidly than was the historical breeding of domestic livestock, and it could include selection for behavioral traits increasing ease of herding, as well as growth traits giving greater yields.

It is difficult to predict the extent to which fish-herding and the selective breeding of fish stocks will have developed by, say, 1990.

## The lessons of fish-ponds

Fish-farming in fresh waters has a long history, but the last few decades have seen an enormous expansion in this type of aquiculture. The present crop is difficult to estimate, but it probably amounts to at least 1 million tons of fish annually. Thus 1/60 of the world's fish production or the equivalent of 2 per cent of the annual catch of marine fish is gained from a tiny fraction of the fresh waters of the world. Crops amounting to 100 tons of fish per year per square mile of ponds are commonly achieved (equivalent to about 35 $g/m^2$), and with artificial feeding levels of from 400 to over 1500 tons per square mile (about 140 to over 530 $g/m^2$) per year can be reached. [In this section, crops from fish-ponds are reported in short tons or pounds (avoirdupois) per square mile or per acre, and approximate metric equivalents are computed for comparative purposes. Elsewhere in this book only metric tons are used in assessments of productivity. Note that a production of 10 metric tons per square kilometer (or its equivalent, 10 $g/m^2$) is approximately equivalent to 28.6 short tons per square mile.] The fishes used are various kinds of carps and species of the African genus *Tilapia,* and the grey mullet. The fish-ponds are usually stocked with fish fry or fingerlings which have been raised by special hatcheries and, in southeast Asia, there is an important trade by air in carp fry, transported in polyethylene bags containing highly oxygenated water.

Some freshwater fish-farming involves carnivorous species, but provision of animal food is expensive (and about as inefficient as feeding fish-meal to broiler fowls; see page 91) and generally can only supply a luxury trade. For example, farming of rainbow trout is a big business in Denmark, and the smoked product forms a high-value export to many western countries. The important species in tropical fish-ponds are herbivores, plankton-feeders, or at least omnivores which can thrive on plant material. In all but the most intensive culture, gross yields have proved larger when a mixture of two or more species is stocked.

Although some freshwater fish-farming is carried out in cold temperate climates in Europe and North America, by far the most productive ponds are those found in the tropics. Not only are the potential growth rates of fishes higher in warmer conditions but the active growing season extends throughout the year. The acute need for new sources of animal protein in certain underdeveloped tropical countries has been responsible for recent extensive research and development work in Africa and Asia. Like agriculture, fish-farming in ponds has had a long history of empirical development before any scientific investigations were carried out.

In a crude classification of fish-farming, there are three levels of intensity of cultivation: first, the desired fish species may be stocked in, and cropped from, ponds or lakes which are managed to the extent that "undesirable" species are controlled, but the overall productivity of the waters is not changed by any deliberate addition of fertilizers; secondly, stocks may be managed and other fauna controlled in ponds or lakes to which nutrient salts are regularly added to increase productivity; and thirdly, stocks may be raised, usually for only part of their life-cycle, in ponds which not only are fertilized but also receive heavy supplementary foddering with organic food materials grown elsewhere. The spectrum of intensity is thus analogous to that found in agricultural livestock raising: from free-range cattle-ranching to intensive dairy-farming. Obviously, yields from different species, in different countries, in bathymetrically differing ponds, must vary greatly, but we can compare yields for a single species under different intensities of cultivation. One series of experiments with a species of *Tilapia* in Central Africa in a series of ponds which were otherwise comparable gave values for maximum standing crop for unfertilized ponds of 256 tons per square mile (or 90 $g/m^2$), for fertilized ponds of 608 tons per square mile (213 $g/m^2$), and for ponds both fertilized and foddered of 1760 tons per square mile (616 $g/m^2$). In these cases—which do *not* represent optimal conditions for the species—the maximum standing crop corresponds roughly to two-thirds of the maximum annual yield. To provide a standard for comparison we can calculate world commercial fisheries returns for 1967 (given in Chapter 13) in a somewhat different way. The annual yield for 1967 of marine fishes and invertebrates actually cropped amounted to about 51.5 million metric tons. If this is taken as being cropped from the entire area of the oceans or 361 million square kilometers, this would be equivalent to an annual yield of only $0.14$ g/m$^2$. However, it is estimated that the coastal waters, including the continental shelves, and some regions of upwelling which make up only 8 per cent of the total ocean area yield about 80 per cent of the total catch. Thus these coastal waters show a present actual fish yield of about $1.4$ g/m$^2$. In the same year, the yield from freshwater fisheries if marine migratory species are deducted, amounted to about 7 million metric tons derived from a freshwater area of about 5 million square kilometers. This would give an average yield for fresh waters of again $1.4$ g/m$^2$. Thus it seems that fish-farming in tropical conditions can give yields from two to three orders of magnitude greater than the present average fish crop from world fresh waters. It is important to realize that such fish-farming methods could not be applied to a large proportion of the world's fresh waters. A brief survey of some of the difficulties of fish-farming will help clarify this.

If we first consider the most intensive levels of pond-culture, they always involved foddering. At present, a wide range of plant materials is used, including several by-products of agriculture such as seeds, cane-wastes, mill-sweepings, and oil cakes. The economics of foddering requires that the increased value of the finished fish be considerably higher than the cost of the fodder. In most tropical areas the price of such fodders will obviously rise with the introduction of more modern processing methods to produce a greater proportion of foodstuffs directly from the by-products. It need hardly be emphasized that all fodders result from organic synthesis by green plants elsewhere and are also part of a finite organic productivity. Foddering also involves high labor costs, and because of this and the likelihood of decreasing supplies of suitable cheap fodders, future trends in fish-farming are likely to be directed toward getting the largest possible fish crops from the use of fertilizers alone. There are some interesting difficulties in this.

In the vast majority of freshwater lakes and fish-ponds, the waters have a low calcium content and are acidic or neutral. Before ordinary chemical fertilizers can be added to such natural waters, lime or limestone has to be added to bring up the calcium content and create an alkaline reaction. The most valuable fish-pond fertilizers are phosphates, with potassium salts in addition where the natural waters tend to dystrophy. Addition of nitrogenous fertilizers is of markedly less value and does not usually increase the crop of fish protein. This had been noted empirically in German fish-ponds early in the century. Yet another instance of the unfortunate compartmentalization of science is the fact that workers in the research teams developing tropical fish culture in Africa and Malaya in the 1950's were surprised by the "paradox" that nitrogenous fertilizers did not contribute to protein yields. They had rediscovered the fixed-nitrogen relationship elucidated for agriculture by J. B. Lawes sixty years before (see Chapters 8 and 13), with its implication that protein production is promoted by *non-nitrogenous* fertilizers. In fish-ponds, blue-green algae capable of nitrogen-fixation correspond to the nodule-bacteria of agricultural legumes. If the blue-green algae receive nitrogenous salts as fertilizers, they use these for their growth and perform little or no nitrogen-fixation. If well supplied with other nutrients in the absence of inorganic nitrogenous salts, they utilize elemental nitrogen, create increased organic nitrogen compounds in the fish-pond, and add to the potential yield of fish protein. Just as in agricultural practice, increased protein yields from fish-ponds result from the addition of phosphates and other non-nitrogenous fertilizers. Work by C. F. Hickling and his associates on tropical fish-ponds at Malacca showed that the fertilizer treatment giving the highest yields was with limestone and phosphates added as agricultural triple superphosphate. At Malacca, yields as high as 648 tons per square mile (or $227 \text{ g/m}^2$) were obtained using fertilizers alone, and Hickling points out that the cost of fertilizers was markedly less than the cost of the fodders which would have been necessary to result in the same yields. Again it should be emphasized that application of superphosphate at these concentrations (60 pounds per acre, or about $7 \text{ g/m}^2$) would be economically impossible in a large lake or over a coastal area of the sea.

Other difficulties in intensive pond-culture arise from the biology of the fish. The highest yields result when the fish stock is introduced at a uniform size and subsequently cropped before the growth rate has slowed too greatly. This implies that "production" ponds are best kept entirely separate from those in which breeding is carried out and from those in which eggs are raised to fingerling size. Some of the most suitable fish for tropical pond-culture are species of the genus *Tilapia,* but they have the grave disadvantage that, under certain conditions in production ponds, they will begin to breed at a size well below the optimum size for harvesting. If such breeding occurs, the pond rapidly becomes stocked with vast numbers of tiny, undernourished fish of no commercial value. Several ingenious methods have been evolved to prevent "wasteful breeding" in production ponds. These include the stocking of some predatory fish along with the *Tilapia* so that any young fish produced by accidental breeding will be eaten by the larger carnivores and so contribute to the commercial fish crop. Another method is to stock only male fish in the production ponds. Yet another method, which has been employed in Israel and Africa as well as at Malacca, is to produce sterile hybrids by crossing two species of *Tilapia* and to stock only hybrids in the production ponds.

In some circumstances, less intensive methods of fish-culture (corresponding to open-range cattle-ranching) can give a worthwhile increase in yields. In medium-sized temperate lakes, existing populations of several species of fish can be completely eliminated by chemical or other means, and the waters then restocked with known numbers of selected fish species. This treatment has been successfully employed in lakes in northwest Russia, and subsequent controlled cropping of such "rehabilitated" lakes showed up to tenfold increases in yields. Russian workers claim that yields of about 35 tons per square mile (or 12 $g/m^2$) could result from such restocking of a lake with only two species —one of carp and one of coregonid whitefish.

Obviously, freshwater fish-farming can never produce more than a small percentage of the world protein requirement, but present productivity of this sort can be considerably expanded. One expert, S. J. Holt, now of FAO, believes that extension of fish-farming methods to the smaller bodies of fresh water throughout the world could bring about a fifteenfold increase in the world production of freshwater fish over the next few decades. This can be contrasted with the two- or threefold increase possible in conventional marine fisheries. There is considerable doubt whether the methods of freshwater fish-farming can be applied to inshore marine waters in the near future.

# True maritime farming

The prospect of the more intensive culture methods of freshwater farming ever being applied to *offshore* marine waters is remote. However, for certain areas of the open seas, including the productive banks of the continental shelves, a few technological changes could make a fish-herding husbandry important within a few decades. More intensive fish-culture is probable only in inshore and semienclosed waters (Figure 15·1).

As with freshwater fish-ponds, so in certain brackish waters in warmer climates, techniques of fish-farming have been developed empirically. Large brackish fish-farms have been successfully managed for centuries in Indonesia, India, Japan, Formosa, and the Philippines, and smaller units are to be found in several countries around the Mediterranean Sea. In most cases, the brackish ponds have been created by local impoundment of areas of shallow sea or of estuaries, and many have been reclaimed from mangrove swamps or salt marshes. Extensive—and nutritionally important—operation of brackish-water

**Figure 15·1. Tambaks, the extensive brackish-water fish-ponds** near Djakarta, Java. The oblique aerial photograph shows a few of the brackish-water tambaks created by impoundment of areas of shallow sea and of estuaries which together cover several hundred square miles. The milkfish, *Chanos chanos,* is the principal species cultured and it is allowed to graze on carefully maintained algal mats on the pond bottoms. Very high yields of fish protein are achieved, see text. [Photo courtesy of Dr. W. H. Schuster, Loosdrecht, Netherlands.]

fish-farms occurs in several parts of Indonesia; the Javanese tambaks, which total several hundred square miles, are thought to produce about 60 per cent of the fish protein consumed in Java. The species used include the grey mullet and, even more extensively, the herring-like milkfish, *Chanos chanos,* young fry of which are captured in the open sea. Organic fertilizers including sewage and grain husks are successfully used, and care is taken to maintain algal mats on the pond bottoms to provide grazing for the fish. A few attempts to utilize inorganic fertilizers have been unsuccessful, largely because these are utilized by blooms of phytoplankton which are not consumed by the fish stocks and which interfere with the growth of the algal mats on the bottom. The highest yields from "manured" Javanese tambaks are as high as those from the most intensive culture in fresh waters, but most yields are considerably lower. More scientifically based brackish-water farming in the Philippines, involving milkfish in combination with a large shrimp called sugpo, has become a multimillion dollar industry in a few decades.

The most extensive and most truly *marine* cultivation occurs in Japan, where for several centuries fish-rearing has gone on in fenced-off areas of shallow sea. Much of this is essentially fish-fattening: young fish are captured live in the open sea and held only for short periods of intensive feeding, the fodder including fish-processing wastes and small valueless fish; relatively few species are reared from the egg to market size. Cultivation of invertebrates—mainly bivalve molluscs and smaller crustaceans such as shrimps and prawns—is also widespread in Japan, and is the only important marine farming in many other parts of the world.

The problems of the use of inorganic fertilizers in marine farming are obviously different from those which arise in freshwater fish-ponds. Some features of the partial failure of the wartime experiments in fertilizing sea-lochs in Scotland are significant. In marine fertilization there is no need to supply calcium along with the nutrient salts. As noted in Chapter 12, a disadvantage in the Scottish experiments was the marked increase in alkalinity after fertilization. Another lesson is the need to eliminate fucoids and other large brown seaweeds so that the added fertilizers enhance more useful primary production. Although in the open sea, nitrogen-fixation by microörganisms is probably negligible, it is fascinating to speculate on the major advances in maritime farming which would quickly follow if controlled cultivation of a bacterial or algal species, capable of sustained nitrogen-fixation in the sea, became practicable. In the absence of this, added fertilizers have to include nitrogen salts as well as phosphates. The fact that enhanced flatfish growth was achieved in the Scottish experiments, as well as the success of earlier transplantation experiments, has encouraged the Whitefish Authority in Britain to begin a further series of cultivation experiments. Results should become available within a few years. It is obvious that along many urbanized seacoasts, attempts at control of some kinds of pollution could well be linked with the development of fish-farming. As regards sewage wastes, this is already accomplished near many large cities in Japan, and it is worth remembering that for more than sixty years the sewage-disposal plants of several inland European cities, for example, Berlin and Munich, have included managed carp-ponds giving huge yields of readily marketable fish. As noted in Chapter 7, another "pollutant" from power stations and certain other industries, consists of large volumes of heated, deoxygenated water. With certain precautions, this can be used to warm culture tanks or ponds in temperate climates and achieve higher rates of fish growth. Moderately successful experiments of this type have already been carried out with coolant discharged from several conventional power stations in Britain and from one nuclear power plant at Hunterston in Scotland. A further step can help cut down atmospheric pollution. At a power plant in Dorset, England, flue gases are washed with seawater before discharge, and the washing water, laden with carbon dioxide, then is used in diatom cultures, which in turn are fed to bivalves and shrimps.

In general, the yields obtainable from marine fish-farming have not yet approached the levels achieved with intensive culture in freshwater and brackish ponds. Further, no case has yet been reported for marine culture of a fish species where the cost of inorganic fertilizers was more than balanced by the value of increased fish yields. Both more basic research and extensive development studies are required before profitable culture of marine fishes can become widespread. In contrast, culture of marine invertebrates is already profitable and is carried out in many parts of the world.

Commercially successful farming of shrimps and prawns is carried out at present in Japan, the Philippines, India, and Pakistan; while experimental rearing of shrimps in France, Britain, and the United States has been biologically successful but too expensive on the scale attempted. Although the present contribution of shrimp-farming to world protein needs is tiny, there are good reasons to suppose a many-fold expansion is possible within a few years. Several species of warm-water shrimps grow very rapidly; they are detritus-feeders or micro-herbivores; they can be reared successfully at high population densities in relatively confined space; and, as noted earlier, they might fit readily into a contrived estuarine flow system of very high productivity. The prospects for extensive commercial shrimp-farming within the next decade are good.

The most extensive and commercially profitable marine farming already being carried out is concerned with bivalve molluscs—chiefly oysters, but including mussels as well as myid and venerid clams. There are three principal reasons why farming of bivalves can be so successful. First, they are sessile or sedentary organisms, so that property rights in them can readily be defined, and they do not require to be fenced in. Secondly, they are filter-feeders of the second trophic level, feeding directly on suspended microörganisms including most phytoplankton. Thirdly, both their commercial price and their nutritive value are high. The extensive oyster-farms of Europe, North America, and Australia are expensive to maintain but supply a luxury market with a very high-priced product. The small-scale oyster-farms of the Philippines and Indonesia and the large-scale oyster industry of Japan involve fantastic expenditure in manual labor but provide an essential protein supplement of high local value. The oyster industry is certainly the largest enterprise in marine farming today. It is capable of considerable expansion, but, since all of the culture methods employed are costly in terms of labor, we cannot predict whether oysters can make a major contribution to future food from the sea. The cultivation of mussels is somewhat easier, yields are high and nutritious, but at present they are marketable only in a few parts of Western Europe. The potentiality of many temperate sea areas for intensive mussel production is enormous. As regards the myid and venerid clams which grow in sand and mud bottoms, deliberate cultivation is practiced at present only in Japan and a few areas of the United States. In recent years about 20 per cent of the clams sold in the United States were raised on private grounds with techniques of seeding and "weeding" which can be loosely termed farming. Recent development of hydraulic dredges for harvesting clams and mechanical methods for removing unwanted predatory animals from clam grounds may allow considerable extension of clam culture in the near future.

We can summarize this brief discussion of the future of sea-farming. The possibility of intermediate cropping of normal-sized zoöplankton as human food is remote. Development of a fish-herding husbandry seems possible within the next two decades, but development of marine fish-culture at the intensities which are practicable in fresh and brackish waters seems less likely. The most immediate developments in true maritime cultivation are likely to come within invertebrate species such as mussels or shrimps. Almost any development of fish-herding or of maritime farming will create problems of national and of international law. The difficulties implicit in, for example, establishing a property right in free-swimming fish stocks or the conveyancing of a lease of a section of the sea bottom, will have to be resolved by legislation and by the evolution of case-law. Of course, even the future expansion of conventional marine fishing will require rational international regulation of many fisheries on the high seas, and a more realistic approach to the fishery problems involved in mutual recognition of territoral waters.

# Recapitulation and implications

ECOLOGICAL STUDIES involving bioenergetics are relatively new. Thus research in aspects of aquatic productivity is active, concepts are changing, and accumulations of new data from laboratory experiments and from the field continue to modify the significance of older data. Inevitably, parts of this book are now out of date. Continuance of basic research in this field is a prerequisite for the more efficient exploitation of aquatic resources and thus, possibly, for the survival of man.

Much of this short recapitulation will be concerned with this utilitarian aspect of aquatic productivity—with the expanding but finite contribution which can be made to world nutrition. However, before we discuss these economic and geopolitical aspects of applied studies in oceanography and limnology, it is worth noting that much important research in the field is not consciously directed toward helping to feed the world. The possible utilitarian value may be recognized, but in this field, as in other branches of science, many of the most productive research workers are driven merely by their personal desire to find out—by their need to explain—rather than by acceptance of a "niche" in a program of research efforts. The organization and support of research may be determined by specific community needs, by real or imagined national priorities, or by sheer human necessity, but the motivation of good research is very often a more personal intellectual curiosity. This being so, it is fortunate that a research field of such basic significance to human welfare as aquatic productivity also involves many biological problems intriguing in their own right, including some which are central to any analysis of the dynamics of organic evolution. A few of these problems of theoretical biology have been outlined in Chapter 11 and elsewhere. The mutually beneficial interactions of "pure" and "applied" aquatic studies have been presented in different contexts in several parts of this book. The remainder of this short chapter must attempt to summarize the global implications of applied studies in aquatic productivity.

## World population and food

In several ways, the next three decades will be critical for the human species. The possible catastrophe of nuclear warfare receives considerable informed discussion, and is involved in the decision-making of statesmen of most nations. The more inevitable consequences of the recent acceleration in the rates of world population growth are less discussed, and seem less considered in the decisions of geopolitics. The survival of man and the future of civilization are inseparable, and both are threatened by ignoring or minimizing the biological limitations of our environment. The facts of recent population growth are simple.

Sometime in the early 1970's (according to most computations available in 1969) the world population will reach a level of 4 billion. It will have taken less than forty-five years to double from a level of 2 billion in 1930. Earlier, the numbers of years required to double the global population had been much larger—for example, there is good evidence that the world population stood close to 1.1 billion in 1850 and had reached the half-billion mark for the first time within a year or two of 1650, so that a little under two centuries were required for that doubling. Fairly conservative extrapolation of the trends suggest that the *next* doubling, that from the 4 billion population of 1975, could occur in less than thirty years. What is more significant than population growth is this acceleration of the rate of growth in an exponential fashion. This is "the population explosion." From this acceleration stem some unpleasant consequences which are already inevitable, and several possibilities of catastrophe. The causes of the rate acceleration can be readily identified.

In general, changes in birth rates have not contributed so greatly to the acceleration as have changes in survivorship. Lowered infant mortality, a higher rate of survival of infants to maturity, and an extension of the average reproductive life of females have all contributed. The average rates of infant mortality (deaths occurring under one year of age) were probably about 170 per thousand live births in Europe and North America 100 years ago. In 1966, among those countries with reasonably complete statistics, infant mortality rates ranged from 133.6 (colored population, South Africa) and 108.2 (Chile) per thousand, to 14.7 (Netherlands) and 12.6 (Sweden) per thousand. The rate for the United States was 23.7 per thousand, being only about sixteenth lowest in the list of larger "developed" states of the world. The United States position as regards late foetal mortality was only slightly better. That the country whose technology was capable of landing the first man on the moon in 1969 had this position in important statistics of national health demonstrates something of relative priorities over the last few years.

As regards the survival of reproductive females, the figures of H. F. Dorn are often quoted. Although it seems that females are potentially capable of reproduction between the ages of thirteen and fifty-five, it is convenient to take age twenty as the average beginning of child-bearing age, and age fifty as the more usual termination of potential reproduction. Of every 100 females born in European populations in the sixteenth century, only 30 survived to our nominal beginning of child-bearing age (that is, age twenty), and about 8 to age fifty. The estimates for the United States prepared in 1962 forecast that of every 100 newborn white females, 97 will survive to age twenty, and 91 will survive through the full potential child-bearing period to age fifty. Even for a country like India, where diseases are less universally controlled and the risks of malnutrition are higher, the corresponding figures for female survivorship per hundred are 83 to age twenty and 47 to age fifty. If the effects of increased survivorship across two generations are considered, other factors being ignored, the potential acceleration of population growth becomes clear. As a hypothesis, in a preagricultural society without medical knowledge, given average female reproductive life and average survivorship of children, there would potentially be about 5 grandchildren per average female surviving in turn to reproductive age. In a developed society with health care, if the average reproductive life is doubled and the survivorship of children to reproductive age increased from 30 to 90 per cent (all other factors being ignored in this hypothesis), then the average number of grandchildren surviving could be 158 in contrast to 5. (Note that, using the same figures for one generation only, the numbers of children of the average female in each society surviving would be 2.2 and 12, respectively.) As mentioned in Chapters 9 and 11, perhaps the most important single factor which can cause an increase in the rate of population growth of any animal species is reduction of the age of first reproduction, or shortening of prereproductive life. In fact, in man, the age at first reproduction is of greater significance than the number of births per female lifetime in determining the potential rate of increase of the population. Thus, if control of an expanding human population has to become a matter of legislation, and biological advice is sought, it must be pointed out that limitation of licensing of marriage for child-bearing to females *over* 24 would be biologically more effective than any attempt legally to limit the number of offspring per marriage. Apart from being soundly based in population biology, this advice has much to commend it socially and economically, and is relatively less likely to meet sustained religious or cultural objections.

If we consider the acceleration which has already occurred in population growth rates, increased life expectancy and increased reproductive capability have resulted from the humane extension of medical science as widely as possible. The decreased mortality has only been balanced by decreased birth rates in exceptional local circumstances, hence the general acceleration. If the growth rates continue to accelerate, then an extrapolation to the year 2039 (when many of today's children *could* still be alive) would give a world population level of 32 billion, that is, *ten times* the present level. Within a single human lifetime, therefore, limited global resources of food and fuel require that rational regulation of population growth must be adopted throughout the world, if catastrophic "regulation" by famine is to be prevented. In the view of many demographers, it is already too late to prevent extensive famines in some countries in the 1970's. The example of Japan, where regulation of population growth began to be effective soon after 1949, needs to be followed by most of the world. But—the Japanese population is literate and mostly highly educated, and the executive government, the medical profession, and the *social pressures of public opinion* in Japan have all been firmly committed to population control since about 1947.

As with other problems resulting from population growth, questions about the future protein nutrition of humanity fall into two groups: those concerned with the next two or three decades, and those concerned with the more distant future. Much of the misunderstanding in present debate on the imminence of famines can be attributed to confusion of the two, but this does not excuse either the Panglossian credulousness, or the fatalistic despair of a Cassandra, which has accompanied some confused statements in recent years. Briefly, there *are* possible technological advances (including those involved in future exploitation of aquatic productivity) which can increase the protein available to man in the next few decades and, if the grosser inequalities of protein distribution are corrected, there is hope of sustaining the likely world population of at least 1990. On the other hand, organic productivity is finite and there is a trophic limit to the human population so that, in the longer term, the only final hope for the species lies in control of the rates of increase and the establishment of a stable level of world population.

Preventing catastrophe in the short term will require major efforts to increase food production within the next few years, including improvement of agricultural yields throughout the world and greatly increased basic research on, and technological development of, the

exploitation of aquatic productivity. The fuzziness of the present estimates of the potential marine harvest discussed in Chapters 9 and 13
and elsewhere is itself justification for greatly increased research efforts
in various fields of biological oceanography, both "pure" and "applied." From natural marine ecosystems must be gained both more
detailed "structural" knowledge of the changing "link proportions" in
food-webs and, as more "functional" understanding, more precise
estimates of energy transfer rates (gross ecological efficiencies), if rational exploitation of marine resources is to expand. Further data on
natural food-webs and natural transfer efficiencies are prerequisite
both for any major future extension of the crop through improvement
in conventional fishing methods and for any development of sea-
farming. Therefore, spokesmen in political circles must plead for increased spending on marine research, and justify it as most likely to
help provide the protein already needed by the expanding world population. They should not, however, suggest that marine resources are
"boundless," or that any further possibility remains of feeding the
world of the twenty-first century unless the rates of population expansion are reduced in the very near future. Ultimately, there is no alternative to population limitation, since the amount of solar energy
available and the global capacity for organic synthesis are *finite*. Other
considerations should be fundamental to any political consideration.
If the population increase *does* continue unchecked for a few more
decades, and if advances in biology and technology *do* manage (with
appropriate changes in social attitudes to food) to provide some sort
of nutrition, this could merely postpone a more catastrophic reduction
of population numbers. Long before that ultimate "carrying capacity"
of the planet is reached, the need to devote finite energy resources to
nutrition would have forced a return to a mere subsistence level of
amenities and food for all. Direct nourishment from lower trophic
levels of high population densities ("standing room only") throughout
the world would not seem likely to promote either the best conditions
for the pursuit of human happiness or the optimum conditions for the
further biological and intellectual evolution of man as a species. Both
pragmatically and intellectually, there can be no alternative to population limitation.

As was outlined in Chapter 13, increased exploitation of aquatic
productivity is already necessary to prevent widespread protein deficiencies. The need for increased agricultural yields could mean *less*
animal protein of terrestrial origin in the next decades. Hopes of extension of intensive agriculture throughout the "underdeveloped"
tropics are fallacious. Availability of chemical fertilizers and of fossil
fuels may limit certain kinds of organic production. Complete chemical
synthesis of amino acids in significant quantity for world dietary sup-

plements is unlikely, and that not only on grounds of the energy expenditure required. Microbial conversion of organic materials into protein could be developed in time to contribute to nutrition within a couple of decades, but is unlikely to supply a major fraction of protein requirements in the foreseeable future, and it too is limited by natural organic production of substrate and by considerable energy requirements. [Similar analysis of the limitations imposed by energy requirements shows the glib assumptions that space travel will somehow solve the world's population problems to be likewise fallacious. As is well known, it took the efforts of nearly a half-million men and expenditure of 3.3 per cent of the annual gross national product of the richest nation on earth ($30 billion out of $900 billion) for the Apollo program to put two men on the moon. Balancing the world's population expansion even in the 1970's would require the export of over a quarter-million humans *per day*. Even if there were some suitable planetary environment to go to, the effort of launching even a fraction of this number into space would be beyond the energy resources of the planet Earth.]

The likelihood of expansion of other sources of protein being very low, global shortages must be met increasingly from aquatic productivity during the period until the world population level can be stabilized. As we have seen, expansion of fish-farming in fresh and brackish waters is probable, and the genesis of similar marine farming possible. Considerable improvements are possible in conventional marine fishery methods, and at least a doubling of yields is possible within a decade or so. Development of a fish-herding husbandry in the sea is also possible. A greater proportion of the catch is likely to be processed into protein concentrates, which are better suited for storage and distribution in areas of dietary deficiency. No matter whether increased efficiency in the exploitation of marine protein resources comes from conservation and controlled cropping of natural stocks or from an entirely new type of marine husbandry, more extensive control of resources will be necessary. It is noteworthy that this sort of control of resources could result from an extension of international agreements, after the pattern of some whaling and fishery treaties (and from a *real* intensification of their enforcement), or it could come from an extension of national sovereignties to encompass larger areas of sea. In either case, more widespread knowledge of the biological background must precede international or national political action.

## Education and envoi

Catastrophic contraction of world population numbers will occur unless decisions to limit population growth are taken within the next decades, and unless a crash program to increase available protein to cover the interim population expansion is instituted at once. There is an urgent need for a higher level of education of the general populace on some of the fundamental aspects of biological productivity discussed above. A world able to appreciate aspects of weightless space-flights and the low gravity of the lunar surface is a world community which could understand the ultimate limits of biological productivity and could support rational debate on the relative contribution to be expected from the further development of marine resources. Application of general biological principles and of accounting methods for energy turnover can be useful in debates on human economics and political decisions, and their use must be encouraged in the discussions of secondary and early college education.

Some such questions have already been raised: Should fish-meal from anchoveta caught off Peru be used directly to combat protein deficiency in South America rather than to nourish broiler fowl in North America and Western Europe? Would there be biological as well as social advantages in legally establishing a later minimum age for licensing child-bearing marriage—perhaps as distinct from non-reproductive marriage?

Other questions, which can even less be completely resolved, are still worth discussing in relation to an accountancy of bioenergetics. What is the best population density for man? What economic and social pressures would best reduce family size in western nations, and in underdeveloped countries? After a decade, what would be the optimum level of population growth for man in terms of available nutrition? And (even more difficult to quantify) what population density would be best for the further biological and intellectual evolution of man? Would the evolutionary potentialities of the human species be enhanced, and racial strife be reduced, by economic pressures toward ethnic exogamy: for example, reduced taxation for the widest racial cross-breeding? What social and religious attitudes are responsible for local protein deficiencies, and how rapidly can they be changed? What population density might create the best conditions for the pursuit of human happiness? When should careful husbanding of the world's stocks of fossil fuels be started to ensure that the energy requirements of food production and collection can be met for a few more generations? And there are many others.

The survival of man depends in part on certain fundamental aspects of organic productivity again becoming matters of general knowledge. Although modern quantitative science had then only just begun, in the "nations of farmers" of four generations back, many empirical verities of food production were community knowlege and formed part of primary education. If any process of transmission of information by education (a function almost diagnostic of our species) is to survive in the future, then the present generation of students must learn and discuss something of man's trophic relations with his environment and their limits. Then informed discussion by a world community of the economics of human survival could follow. The aim should be that no politician (anywhere in the world) should be able to use words like "inexhaustible," "boundless," and "limitless" with regard to food supplies without being laughed to scorn. Given the educational conservatism (no matter what party label) of all politicians and "statesmen" and their general level of scientific illiteracy, this may seem an impossible task. It may be somewhat reassuring to remember that in the early years of this century, politicians (in several countries, and all reasonably representative of their constituents) could still use belief in a world created at 4004 B.C., or in a "flat Earth," as premises for their arguments. Another reason for optimism in the educability of politicians lies in their increasing reliance—as advisers and assistants—on technologically well-educated civil servants. Such men, and others concerned in the predictive analysis of global defense systems and situations, could "beat their swords into plowshares" and help produce a rational strategy on the trophic aspects of the survival of man on this planet. The future of civilization and the survival of our human species are inseparable. That this protasis needs to be emphasized again demonstrates the need for a wider general education in human ecology. It is tragic that there can be young critics today so biased in their educational experience that they propose a "happier future" for man *without* technology and science. Criticism of the detrimental side effects of some parts of today's technology is abundantly justified, particularly when that criticism is concerned with the ill-considered degradation of parts of the environment by pollution. However, nothing can justify those critics who would abolish the whole of scientific technology, or deny to all future human problems the opportunity of rational consideration in a scientific framework and the possibility of a technological solution. Conservation cannot be accompanied by irrational rejection of all science. The preservation of environment and the conservation of natural resources both *require* rationally directed technology even at today's levels of human populations. That some younger and more vocal intellectuals can adopt a totally antiscientific stance (neo-Luddite and practically nihilist) reflects tragic lapses in their education and in their understanding of man. Their denial of science is no less than a denial of human reason, but it arises from and emphasizes their overwhelming disillusionment with present technology. Only through more widespread education in certain fundamental aspects of organic productivity can we hope to create a sociopolitical climate wherein the need is recognized for *more rational control* of technology based on more scientific knowledge of the ecology of our planet, rather than for irrational rejection. A valid future education for our species must encompass considerable insight into our natural environment and clear appreciation of the finite extent of human artifacts within it.

In summary, increased exploitation of aquatic productivity must occur within the next decades in order to supply world food needs. This must involve increased basic and technological research on marine and freshwater resources, and legal changes (national or international) to allow controlled cropping, stock ownership, and conservation. The really urgent global need for the development of food from the sea to meet the expected shortages of protein could almost be treated as a matter of international public health. Many of the problems involved need to be tackled by large integrated teams of scientists and tech-nologists, as recently the problems of space-travel have been so success-fully solved. This does not alter the need, discussed above, for the differently motivated processes of some basic research. It must again be emphasized that the possible technological advances which could increase the food avaliable to man in the next few decades offer only a temporary respite from the main problem. At best they could provide palliatives for thirty years further acceleration in the rates of increase of human populations, but control of these rates represents the only complete solution to the problem. Once more, there is a real limit to the organic productivity of our planet.

# Further reading

It is obvious that there can be nothing even approaching a real bibliography of aquatic productivity in a book of this size. Several of the areas which have been briefly discussed are like that of biological oceanography in having a research literature whose growth is practically exponential. Accordingly, I have tried to provide brief annotated citations for eight major subject areas, especially noting certain books with extensive bibliographies (marked * below). In cases of multiple publication, usually the American editions or revised editions are quoted. The subject areas are: (**A**) general ecology; (**B**) biological oceanography; (**C**) limnology and freshwater ecology; (**D**) biology of aquatic invertebrates; (**E**) bioenergetics; (**F**) population dynamics and evolutionary ecology; (**G**) nutritional aspects of the human population explosion; and (**H**) fishery science.

**A** Among the best modern texts on general ecology are Eugene P. Odum's *Fundamentals of Ecology* * (Philadelphia: Saunders, second edition, 1959) and G. L. Clarke's *Elements of Ecology* * (New York: Wiley, 1954). Several recent paperbacks are also valuable and these include: *Basic Ecology* by R. and M. Buchsbaum (Pittsburgh: Boxwood Press, 1957), *Ecology* by Eugene P. Odum (New York: Holt, Rinehart and Winston, 1963), *Ecology of Populations* by A. S. Boughey (New York: Macmillan, 1968), and *Communities and Ecosystems* * by R. H. Whittaker (New York: Macmillan, 1970). Among the older books which remain significant are R. Hesse, W. C. Allee, and K .P. Schmidt, *Ecological Animal Geography* * (New York: Wiley, 1937), Charles Elton, *Animal Ecology* * (London: Sidgwick and Jackson, second edition, 1947; New York: Macmillan, third edition, 1947), and W. C. Allee, A. E. Emerson, O. Park, T. Park, and K. P.

Schmidt, *Principles of Animal Ecology* \* (Philadelphia: Saunders, 1949).

**B** Even if biological oceanography is not extended to encompass much of the rest of marine biology, the subject involves a vast and steadily increasing research literature which has resulted in a huge production of secondary material in books and review articles. Unfortunately, good introductory books for the interested nonbiologist and suitably comprehensive texts for the intermediate student are both rare. For those laymen and beginning students who wish to go beyond Rachel L. Carson's justifiably famed classic, *The Sea Around Us* (New York: Oxford University Press, revised edition, 1961), or *Life*'s picture book, *The Sea* by Leonard Engel and the editors of *Life* (New York: Time Inc., 1961), or *The Living Sea* by Jacques-Yves Cousteau with James Dugan (New York: Harper & Row, 1963), two easily read but authoritative books can be highly recommended. One is Alister C. Hardy's enthusiastic and eminently readable, *The Open Sea: Its Natural History* \* (Boston: Houghton Mifflin, 1965), earlier published in its two component volumes, *The Open Sea: The World of Plankton* \* and *The Open Sea: Fish and Fisheries* \* (London: Collins and Boston: Houghton Mifflin, 1956 and 1959, respectively). The other book, which has been a minor classic since shortly after its first appearance in 1928 and has remained through recent revision a most readable and excellent introduction to marine biology, is *The Seas* by F. S. Russell and C. M. Yonge (London and New York: Warne, revised edition, 1963).

When we turn to more comprehensive intermediate-level texts, *The Oceans* \* by H. U. Sverdrup, M. W. Johnson, and R. H. Fleming (Englewood Cliffs, N.J.: Prentice-Hall, 1942) remains outstanding, although considerable parts of it are now out of date and the biological sections are uneven. Perhaps the finest of shorter but more modern texts on techniques is Harold Barnes' *Oceanography and Marine Biology* \* (New York: Macmillan, 1959). Also at this level, *Treatise on Marine Ecology and Paleoecology* \* edited by J. W. Hedgepeth (New York: Geological Society of America, 1957), *The Chemistry and Fertility of Sea Waters* \* by H. W. Harvey (Cambridge: Cambridge University Press, second edition, 1957), *Plankton and Productivity in the Oceans* \* by J. E. G. Raymont (Oxford: Pergamon, 1963), and *The Plankton of the Sea* by R. S. Wimpenny (New York: American Elsevier, 1966) are all valuable. There are several good multi-author compilations and review series including: *The Sea; Ideas and Observation on Progress in the Study of the Seas* \* edited by M. N. Hill (London and New York: Interscience, three volumes, 1962–63), *Perspectives in Marine Biology* \* edited by A. A. Buzzati-Traverso (Berkeley: University of California Press, 1958), *Grazing in Terrestrial* *and Marine Environments* * edited by D. J. Crisp (Oxford: Blackwell, 1964), *Some Contemporary Studies in Marine Science* * edited by Harold Barnes (London: Allen and Unwin, 1966), *Primary Productivity in Aquatic Environments* * edited by C. R. Goldman (Berkeley: University of California Press, 1966), and three continuing annual reviews, *Oceanography and Marine Biology, an Annual Review* * edited by Harold Barnes (London: Allen and Unwin, volumes 1——, 1963 ——); *Advances in Marine Biology* * edited by F. S. Russell (New York and London: Academic Press, volumes 1——, 1963——); and *Progress in Oceanography* * edited by M. Sears (Oxford: Pergamon, volumes 1——, 1963——).

**C** In freshwater ecology and limnology, the finest modern comprehensive survey in English is *A Treatise on Limnology* * by G. Evelyn Hutchinson (New York: Wiley, volume I, 1957, volume II, 1967), as yet incomplete. A good, though somewhat dated, book is *Fundamentals of Limnology* by F. Ruttner (translated by D. G. Frey and F. E. J. Fry, Toronto: University of Toronto Press, 1953); while *Life in Lakes and Rivers* by T. T. Macan and E. B. Worthington (London: Collins, 1951), *The Biology of Polluted Waters* by H. B. N. Hynes (Liverpool: Liverpool University Press, 1962), *Lakes, Streams and Ponds* by R. E. Coker (Chapel Hill: University of North Carolina Press, 1954), and *Freshwater Ecology* by T. T. Macan (London: Longmans Green and New York: Wiley, 1963) are all useful.

**D** Relatively up-to-date accounts of the biology of invertebrates in general are provided by R. D. Barnes, *Invertebrate Zoology* (Philadelphia: Saunders, second edition,1968) and by W. D. Russell-Hunter, *A Biology of Lower Invertebrates* and *A Biology of Higher Invertebrates* (New York: Macmillan, 1968 and 1969, respectively). Aspects of modern comparative physiology are covered excellently in E. J. W. Barrington's *Invertebrate Structure and Function* * (Boston: Houghton Mifflin, 1967) and more ecologically in J. A. C. Nicol's *The Biology of Marine Animals* * (New York: Pitman, 1960). Two excellent and most readable accounts of functional morphology and physiological ecology in very different groups of marine animals are provided in *The Sea Shore* by C. M. Yonge (London: Collins, 1949) and in *Aspects of Deep Sea Biology* by N. B. Marshall (New York: Philosophical Library, 1954). Existing knowledge of one important aspect of the nutrition of aquatic animals has been excellently summarized in *Biology of Suspension Feeders* * by C. Barker Jørgensen (Oxford: Pergamon, 1966). Finally, dealing with the genus *Calanus* in a superbly detailed synthesis is *The Biology of a Marine Copepod* * by S. M. Marshall and A. P. Orr (Edinburgh: Oliver and Boyd, 1955).

**E** Studies on energy flow and energy balance in biological systems extend from older work on energetic aspects of whole-animal nutrition to more modern interest in bioenergetics for populations and communities on the one hand and for subcellular organization on the other. A classic and extensive survey of the earlier agriculturally oriented work is *Bioenergetics and Growth* * by Samuel Brody (New York: Reinhold, 1945; reprinted Hafner, 1964), and a more popular and less dated account is *The Fire of Life* by M. Kleiber (New York: Wiley, 1961). An excellent, modern introduction to energy transformation at the molecular and cellular levels is contained in Albert L. Lehninger's *Bioenergetics* (New York: Benjamin, 1965) and, for population energetics, L. B. Slobodkin's *Growth and Regulation of Animal Populations* (New York: Holt, Rinehart and Winston, 1962) is justly regarded as seminal. An introduction to community energetics can be found in the books by Odum, Clarke, and Whittaker listed under **A** above, and in an excellent short book, *Ecological Energetics* by John Phillipson (London: Arnold and New York: St. Martin's Press, 1966).

**F** Accounts of studies on population dynamics and evolutionary ecology are now happily tending to merge with those in bioenergetics. This was not always so. Slobodkin's book (**E**, above) is a valuable introduction to the new synthesis, while Elton's book (**A**, above) remains significant as a survey of the older studies. Other useful books include: H. G. Andrewartha and L. C. Birch, *The Distribution and Abundance of Animals* * (Chicago: University of Chicago Press, 1954); Charles Elton, *The Ecology of Invasions by Animals and Plants* * (London: Methuen, 1958); H. G. Andrewartha, *Introduction to the Study of Animal Populations* * (London: Methuen and Chicago: University of Chicago Press, 1961); E. Mayr, *Animal Species and Evolution* * (Cambridge, Mass.: Belknap-Harvard, 1963); G. F. Gause, *The Struggle for Existence* (Baltimore: Williams and Wilkins, 1934; reprinted New York: Hafner, 1964); W. E. Hazen, *Readings in Population and Community Ecology* * (Philadelphia: Saunders, 1964); and R. H. MacArthur and J. H. Connell, *The Biology of Populations* * (New York: Wiley, 1966). In a class by itself is a collection of erudite but elegant essays by G. Evelyn Hutchinson entitled *The Ecological Theater and the Evolutionary Play* (New Haven: Yale University Press, 1965).

**G** The 1960's have seen a steady increase in publications dealing with nutritional and other aspects of the human population explosion. One of the best concise summaries of man's population dynamics remains that of H. F. Dorn entitled "World Population Growth: An International Dilemma" (*Science*, **135**:1291–1295, 1962), an article deservedly much copied and reprinted. There are several useful surveys of limited world resources included in *The Year 2000: A Framework for Speculation on the Next Thirty-three Years* by Herman Kahn and

A. J. Wiener (New York: Macmillan, 1967), but in that book fundamental biological limitations are somewhat neglected. Several books by concerned scientists correct this, perhaps most notably *Science and Survival* by Barry Commoner (New York: Viking, 1963, reprinted 1967) and *The Population Bomb* by Paul R. Ehrlich (New York: Ballantine, 1968). Other surveys of present and future world nutrition —particularly the aspects of protein nutrition briefly discussed in Chapters 8 and 13 of this book—from several divergent viewpoints are to be found in: *The Numbers of Man and Animals* * edited by J. B. Cragg and N. W. Pirie (Edinburgh: Oliver and Boyd, 1955), *The Hungry Planet* by Georg Borgstrom (New York: Macmillan, 1965), *World Protein Resources* * by R. F. Gould (Washington, D.C.: American Chemical Society Publications, 1966), *The Limits of Man* by Hugh Nicol (London: Constable, 1967), *The World Food Problem* by the Panel on World Food Supply of the President's Science Advisory Committee (Washington, D.C.: U.S. Government Printing Office, Superintendent of Documents, 1967), *Famine—1975! America's Decision: Who Will Survive?* by W. and P. Paddock (Boston and Toronto: Little, Brown, 1967), *Too Many: A Study of Earth's Biological Limitations* * by Georg Borgstrom (New York: Macmillan, 1969), and *Population, Evolution, and Birth Control: A Collage of Controversial Ideas* edited by Garrett Hardin (San Francisco: Freeman, second edition, 1969).

**H** Lastly, there are a number of valuable books on aspects of fishery science which can lead the interested student to another large and rapidly increasing research literature. On the over-fishing problem, there are two classic works: E. S. Russell, *The Overfishing Problem* (Cambridge: Cambridge University Press, 1942), and Michael Graham, *The Fish Gate* (London: Faber and Faber, 1943). Increasing sophistication of models of exploited populations is reflected in three excellent publications on this topic: *Sea Fisheries: Their Investigation in the United Kingdom* * edited by Michael Graham (London: Arnold, 1956), *On the Dynamics of Exploited Fish Populations* * by R. J. H. Beverton and S. J. Holt (*Fishery Invest., London,* (2), **10**:1–533, 1957), and *Handbook of Computations for Biological Statistics of Fish Populations* * by W. E. Ricker (*Bull. Fish. Res. Bd. Canada,* **119**:1–300, 1958). An introduction to some of the difficulties in the legislative control of fisheries can be found in *The Fisheries: Problems in Resource Management* edited by J. A. Crutchfield (Seattle: University of Washington Press, 1965), and *The International Law of Fisheries* by D. M. Johnston (New Haven: Yale University Press, 1965). A survey of the present technology of the fishing industry is provided by *Modern Fishing Gear of the World* edited by Hilmar Kristjonsson (London: Fishing News (Books), 1959) and by the continuing series of books from the same publisher. As regards the future exploitation of aquatic productivity (including fish-farming) there are many books at a variety of levels and the following represent a somewhat arbitrary selection: *Tropical Inland Fisheries* * by C. F. Hickling (London: Longmans Green, 1960), *Handbook on Fish Culture in the Indo-Pacific Region* by S. L. Horn and T. V. R. Pillay (Rome: Food and Agriculture Organization of the United Nations, 1962), *The exploitation of Natural Animal Populations* * edited by E. D. LeCren and M. W. Holdgate (Oxford: Blackwell, 1962), *Fish Culture* by C. F. Hickling (London: Faber and Faber, 1962), *Effective Use of the Sea* by the Panel on Oceanography of the President's Science Advisory Committee (Washington, D.C.: U.S. Government Printing Office, Superintendent of Documents, 1966), *The Biological Basis of Freshwater Fish Production* * edited by S. D. Gerking (Oxford: Blackwell, 1967), *Harvest of the Sea* by John Bardach (New York: Harper & Row, 1968), and *The Farming of Fish* by C. F. Hickling (Oxford: Pergamon, 1968). The last two are particularly suitable for the interested nonscientist.

# Index